Auto Engine Tune-Up

by Randall K. Richard

THEODORE AUDEL & CO.
a division of
HOWARD W. SAMS & CO., INC.
4300 West 62nd Street
Indianapolis Indiana, 46206

First Edition

1968 Printing

Library of Congress Catalog Card Number: 66-28618

Foreword

The term "Tune-Up," in the minds of millions of car owners, signifies better engine performance and economy. To the mechanic it represents the results of adjustment and/or replacement of parts that have been affected by gradual wear as the car is operated over a period of time.

There may be some difference of opinion as to what operations should be included and performed in a tune-up. Generally, the three factors of ignition, compression, and carburetion are accepted as constituting a tune-up. Each factor has an important bearing on the performance of a car. It is the purpose of this book to lead you through a simplified procedure of checking these factors with the end results of better car performance.

Do not attempt to sell a tune-up job to a customer until you can do satisfactory work. Study this book through several times, and then, step by step, go through the procedure as outlined. Keep the book handy for reference until you can perform each function in systematic order.

It is the hope of the author that this book will aid both the beginning and experienced mechanic in understanding the basic operating principles and testing of the automobile engine.

Randall K. Richard

About the Author . . .

Mr. Richard is a member of the Automotive Testers of America, Inc., and the Society of Automotive Engineers (S.A.E.) He has a bachelor of science degree in electrical engineering from the University of Illinois and is the author of many service articles that have appeared in automotive magazines. In addition, he has held numerous automotive clinics and training sessions throughout the United States in the past ten years.

Contents

Contents

Contents

CHAPTER 1

The Gasoline Engine

One of the first attempts at building an internal combustion engine was made by Christian Huyghens, a Dutch physicist, in 1860. His experimental engine worked on the principle that useful work could be accomplished by exploding gunpowder in a closed vessel having a movable cover. Lenoir, a Frenchman, was the inventor of the first practical gas engine. He constructed his engine in 1860. It was a horizontal, double-acting, noncompressing, reciprocating engine with a crank and flywheel. The engine used benzine as fuel, and ignition was obtained by using a "jump-spark." Since the engine was a noncompressing type, no shock was heard from the explosion, and it ran as smoothly and as silently as a steam engine. The engine was very uneconomical, however, having a thermal efficiency of only 4% (compared to the present automotive efficiency of approximately 20%). The heat loss through the cylinder walls was so great that the piston walls had to be flooded with oil.

Another French designer, Beau de Rochas, set forth the best theoretical working conditions for an internal combustion engine in his patent of 1862. The following four conditions were included in his patent:

1. Largest cylinder volume with smallest exposed surface.

2. Maximum possible piston speed.

3. Highest possible pressure at the beginning of the expansion or working stroke.

4. Greatest possible expansion.

To obtain these results, de Rochas proposed the use of a single cylinder, and that the cycle be carried out in four strokes of a piston as follows:

1st Stroke—Admission of air and fuel

2nd Stroke—Compression

3rd Stroke—Ignition at top dead center of piston travel

4th Stroke—Exhaust

This cycle is the same as the present *Otto* cycle and is used in most of the automotive engines today.

At the Paris Exposition of 1878, two Germans, named Otto and Langen, exhibited the *de Rochas* cycle engine that revolutionized the gas-engine industry. The exhibited engine successfully employed the *de Rochas* cycle for the first time, and it was due to this exhibit that the *de Rochas* cycle became known as the *Otto* cycle. The *Otto* cycle is now used in practically all automobile, truck, tractor, and marine gasoline engines. An English engineer, Dugald Clerk, modified the *Otto* engine in 1879 in such a manner that the air-fuel mixture was compressed and burned once every revolution of the crankshaft. This method is known as the *two-stroke cycle*.

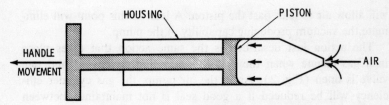

Fig. 1. Comparing the engine to an air pump, illustrating the air intake.

THE ENGINE AS A PUMP

Comparing the engine to an air pump may not seem to be logical at first glance. However, a detailed analysis will reveal many similarities. When the handle is pulled out (see Fig. 1), air is drawn into the cylindrical housing through the small opening at the end of the housing. Referring to the illustration, what would keep air from being drawn into the housing when the handle is retracted? An inspection of the diagram reveals the answer—a leak or incomplete seal of the pump piston against the housing

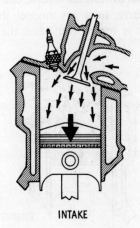

Fig. 2. Illustrating the position of the intake valve when the piston is in the downward position.

11

will allow air to leak past the piston. A leak at this point will eliminate the vacuum producing capability of the pump.

The action just described is the same action that takes place in a gas engine when the piston is traveling downward and one valve is open (Fig. 2). As in the air pump, the gas cylinder efficiency will be reduced if a good seal is not maintained between the piston and cylinder wall. In Fig. 3, the air-pump handle sec-

Fig. 3.   Comparing the engine to an air pump, illustrating the air discharge.

tion is reversed, and the air in the cylinder is forced out the small opening. Trapped air in the cylinder will be forced out under pressure only if a good seal is maintained between the piston and the cylindrical housing. A poor seal will allow air to escape past the piston toward the handle end of the pump.

Similarly, in a gas engine, the air-gas mixture trapped in the cylinder is forced out when the piston travels upwards with one

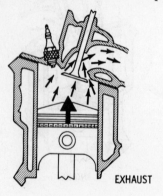

Fig. 4. Illustrating the position of the exhaust valve when the piston is in the upward position.

EXHAUST

valve open (Fig. 4). Obviously, a good piston-to-cylinder wall seal is required to ensure efficient operation.

In the previous air pump discussions, the hand supplied the power necessary to move the piston back and forth. In the gas engine, another source of power must be utilized. This source of power is an air-gas mixture that is ignited at the proper time.

POWER FOR THE PUMP

If gas, atomized oil, or any other fuel is drawn into the air pump with the air, a potentially explosive mixture exists in the pump. All that is necessary to ignite or explode the mixture is a source of energy. In the gas engine, the air drawn into the cylinder is mixed with gasoline, the mixing taking place in the car-

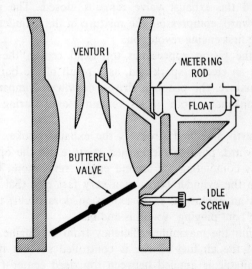

Fig. 5. Illustrating the mixing of air with gasoline in the carburetor.

buretor (Fig. 5). When the resulting mixture is ignited, power is produced by the burning mixture and is used to drive the piston (pump). Hence, we have replaced the hand-powered air pump by gas power in order to drive our larger pump or gas engine.

THE FOUR-STROKE CYCLE ENGINE

The usual type of automotive cycle is the four stroke or *Otto* cycle, delivering a power pulse to the crankshaft once every second engine revolution. Referring to Fig. 6, the first stroke is called the *intake* or suction stroke. During the time the piston travels downward, the exhaust valve is closed and the intake valve is open, allowing a charge of the air-fuel mixture to be drawn in.

At approximately the bottom of the stroke, the intake valve closes, and the exhaust valve remains closed. The piston then travels upward, compressing the mixture in the cylinder thus completing the first engine revolution.

When the piston approaches top dead center, the mixture is ignited by an electric spark and, as a result of the burning of the air-fuel mixture, the piston is driven downward, imparting power to the crankshaft. Both valves remain closed during the power stroke.

The fourth and final stroke is the exhaust stroke. The piston travels upward, pushing the burned mixture out the open exhaust valve, thus completing the second engine revolution. The air-fuel mixture in the cylinder burns at a very fast rate that approaches but is not an explosion. If an explosion does occur, the familiar "knocking" or "pinging" sound is audible.

To obtain the maximum efficiency from an engine, the initial ignition of the air-fuel charge is controlled so that most of the power available is applied between top dead center (TDC) and bottom dead center (BDC) of the power stroke. During low en-

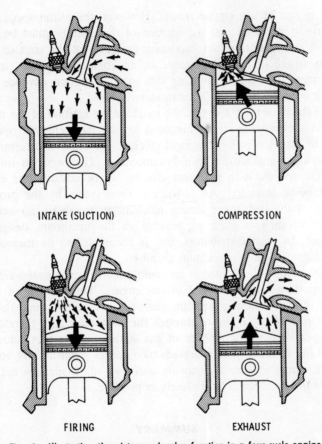

INTAKE (SUCTION)   COMPRESSION

FIRING   EXHAUST

Fig. 6. Illustrating the piston and valve function in a four-cycle engine.

gine speeds, ignition will frequently occur either at top dead center or a few degrees of crankshaft rotation before the piston reaches top dead center (ignition advanced). At high engine speeds, the rate of burning of the air-fuel mixture is approximately the same as that at low engine speeds. However, the piston speed has materially increased and the ignition of the mixture must be advanced in order to obtain maximum pressures at the start of the power stroke. When the throttle of an engine is opened, more fuel enters the cylinder, making still another ignition advance desirable because there is a richer mixture to burn.

For the reasons just stated, the spark or the ignition of the mixture in a cylinder must be advanced for the most efficient operation. In actual practice, the most efficient operation is determined by the car manufacturer on a dynamometer. The engine is run at different speeds, with the most efficient spark advance for each speed being recorded. An attempt is then made, by the proper design of the distributor timing mechanism, to obtain an actual engine advance as close as possible to the maximum designed advance. In most distributors, this is accomplished by means of centrifugal weights and vacuum chambers.

The amount of advance in an engine due to centrifugal weights is proportional to the speed of the engine. The amount of advance obtained from a vacuum chamber is directly proportional to the amount of air drawn through the carburetor and, therefore, is proportional to the amount of gas in the mixture that actually enters the cylinder. The spark-advance curves published by automobile manufacturers are actually *optimum* spark-advance curves and should be adhered to as closely as possible.

SUMMARY

The modern automotive engine is in reality more complicated than the description given in the preceding pages. However, the principles involved are simple and easy to understand. The purpose of the engine is to deliver the maximum power available throughout the entire speed range, at any load, and with maximum economy. In order to accomplish this objective all working parts must be performing at peak efficiency. The piston rings must fit tightly, the valves must close completely, and there can be no air leaks in the entire carburetor and fuel-intake system. The correct air-fuel mixture is required at all times, and the mixture must be ignited at the proper instant. Improper cooling and lubrication will remove power from the engine and cause rapid wear of the moving parts.

The proper functioning and testing of the above components will be treated in detail in later chapters, but the pump-engine concept will be referred to throughout the book. Before any skilled individual can utilize his skills, he must have first-hand knowledge of the tools of the trade. For the automotive mechanic, basic electricity is one of these tools, and is covered briefly in Chapter 2. Other tools of the trade is a complete understanding of the carburetor and fuel systems, ignition systems, charging and starting circuits, and cooling systems.

REVIEW QUESTIONS

1. What is the difference between an Otto-cycle engine and a 2-cycle engine?

2. What is the source of power used in a gasoline engine to move the piston?

3. What is the purpose of the carburetor?

4. What device in a gasoline engine is used to ignite the gas-air mixture in the cylinder?

5. What is the purpose of the intake and exhaust valves in a 4-stroke cycle engine?

6. What is the position of the piston at the time the gas-air mixture is ignited?

7. The spark advance in a gasoline engine is accomplished by what two methods?

CHAPTER 2

Basic Electricity

There is a very close similarity between the discharge or flow of electricity from one point to another, and the discharge or flow of water from one tank to another.

ELECTRIC PRESSURE OR POTENTIAL

Suppose we have two tanks of water (#1 and #2 in Fig. 1) connected by a water conducting tube T. Tank #1 is at a higher

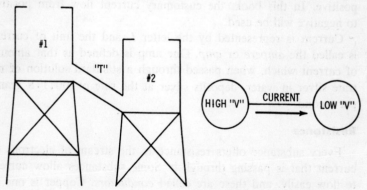

Fif. 1. Analogy between hydrostatic pressure and electric potential.

level than #2; therefore, the water pressure (hydrostatic pressure) in tank #1 is greater than in tank #2. Since the pressures are unequal, water will flow from the tank having the higher pressure to the tank having the lower pressure.

In a similar manner, electric current flows from a high potential to a low potential (pressure) when the two potentials are connected by means of a conducting tube or conductor. The amount of electric potential or pressure is measured in terms of *volts* and designated by the letters V or E. How potential is obtained will be discussed in a later chapter. One volt is the unit of electrical pressure required to force one ampere through one ohm of resistance.

Current

Ever since electrical currents have been known to exist, it has been the custom to assume that the current flows from positive to negative. In an automotive system, the current is assumed to flow from the positive terminal of the battery, through the electrical components in the automobile, and back to the negative terminal of the battery. Actual electron flow, however, is from negative to positive. In this book, the customary current flow from positive to negative will be used.

Current is represented by the letter I, and the unit of current is called the *ampere* or *amp*. One amp is defined as that amount of current which, when passed through a standard solution of nitrate silver in water, deposits silver at the rate of .001118 grams per second.

Resistance

Every substance offers resistance to the stream of electrons or current that is passing through it. Some substances allow current to flow easily, and these are called *conductors*. Copper is one of the common metals that offers very little resistance to current flow.

Another common metal is silver, which offers less resistance to current flow, but is too expensive to use for normal wiring purposes. Other metals that can be used are aluminum, steel, gold, tungsten, etc. All of these metals offer more resistance to current flow than copper. It is sometimes desirable to have an electrical component that does not pass current as readily as copper. Among these components are the coil resistor and heating units.

Materials that do not easily pass current but offer high resistance to current flow are called *insulators*. Common insulating materials are rubber, cork, wood, and plastics. The unit of resistance is called the *ohm*. One ohm is equal to the resistance of a column of pure mercury 106.3 centimeters in length and 14.45 grams in mass at a temperature of 32° F. at sea level. Resistance is represented by the letter *R*.

Ohm's Law

In a DC circuit, Ohm's law enables us to determine an unknown factor when two factors are known. The factors represented are *E* for volts, *I* for amperes, and *R* for ohms. To find amperes (current) when the voltage and resistance are known, divide the voltage by the resistance:

$$I = \frac{E}{R}$$

To find the voltage required to pass a desired amount of current through a known resistance, multiply the current by the resistance:

$$E = I \times R \text{ (or IR)}$$

The product *IR* is commonly referred to as the *voltage drop* or *IR drop* of a circuit.

21

To find the resistance in ohms when the voltage and current are known, divide the voltage by the current:

$$R = \frac{E}{I}$$

The *IR* referred to can be used to determine the amount of heat developed in *watts* by any given device. Here, the formula is changed slightly to:

$$I \times I \times R \text{ or } I^2R$$

This means that the current is multiplied by the current and then by the resistance of the unit being studied. The answer obtained is in watts. As an example, a 5-ohm resistor that has ten amperes flowing through it will produce $10 \times 10 \times 5$, or 500 watts of heat.

ELECTRICAL CIRCUITS

In an automatic lawn-sprinkling system, water flows through underground pipes to the sprinklers. The amount of water that flows depends upon the water pressure, the roughness of the inside pipe surface (which tends to retard the water flow), and the energy lost in driving the sprinkler. Simply stated, the amount of water flow depends upon the water pressure and the resistance of the system.

Current, usually expressed in amperes, can be thought of as water flow and is measured on a flow gauge called an *ammeter*. Current will not flow unless electrical pressure or voltage is available to force the current through the system. It should be kept in mind that electricity exists in any conductor, such as a wire. Just

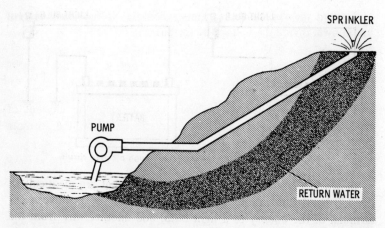

Fig. 2. A water sprinkling system illustrating the flow of current through a conductor.

as a water pump or a storage tank does not make water, a generator or a battery does not make electricity. They do make or create an electrical pressure called voltage which moves the electricity, and this movement we measure as current.

The resistance of an electrical circuit acts much like the resistance of the pipe and the sprinklers in the previously mentioned lawn-sprinkling system. Electrical resistance is present in all wires, light bulbs, and other electrical parts. Some of the water used to sprinkle a lawn is soaked up by the ground and eventually returns to the pump via a well, lake, etc., to be used again, as shown in Fig. 2. Water, therefore, can be spoken of as flowing through a closed circuit.

The same is true of an electrical circuit (any electrical circuit). Current cannot flow unless the electrical system is a closed circuit and contains a source of electrical pressure or voltage, such as a generator or battery.

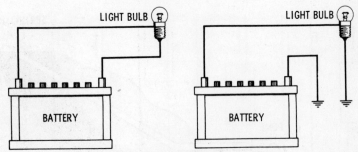

Fig. 3. Illustrating the current flow through a closed circuit.

Shown in Fig. 3 are two electrical systems that are identical. In the left-hand illustration, the wire leads from the positive (+) terminal of the battery to a light bulb, and another wire from the light bulb back to the negative (—) terminal of the battery, completing the circuit.

In the right-hand illustration, the identical circuit exists, only symbols are used instead of drawing in the wire from the bulb to the negative terminal of the battery. The ground symbols are used by the electrical designer as a secretary uses shorthand, and it means that there is a connection between the points shown. In automotive practice, one terminal of the battery and one side of the lights may be connected to the frame of the car, in which case the frame serves the purpose of the return wire.

The system shown is referred to as a *negative-ground system*. In a *positive-ground system*, the positive terminal of the battery would be shown connected to the ground symbols and the negative terminal would be connected to the light bulb.

PARALLEL CIRCUITS

When two or more resistances are connected as shown in Fig. 4, they are said to be in *parallel*. When two or more resistances

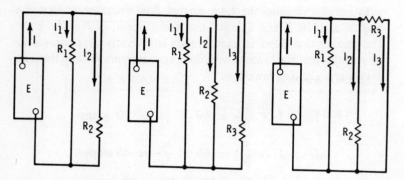

Fig. 4. Illustrating parallel circuits.

are connected in parallel, it is necessary to find the total resistance of the circuit in order to use Ohm's law. Resistances in parallel can be computed by using the following formula:

$$R_t = \frac{1}{\frac{1}{R_1} + \frac{1}{R_2} + \frac{1}{R_3} + \dots}$$

Example: In Fig. 4A, assume that R_1 is equal to ½ ohm, R_2 is equal to ¼ ohm, and the battery voltage is equal to 10 volts. The total resistance then is:

$$R_1 = \frac{1}{\frac{1}{\frac{1}{2}} + \frac{1}{\frac{1}{4}}} = \frac{1}{2 + 4} = \frac{1}{6} \text{ ohm}$$

The current that would flow from the battery can now be calculated using Ohm's law:

$$I = \frac{E}{R} = \frac{10}{\frac{1}{6}} = 60 \text{ amps}$$

25

In parallel circuits, the total current flow branches so that the branch currents I_1 and I_2 equal the total current, or $I = I_1 + I_2$. The current that flows in each branch is inversely proportional to the resistance of the branch, with the larger currents flowing through the lower resistance branches.

$$I_1 = I \times \frac{R_t}{R_1} = 60 \times \frac{\frac{1}{6}}{\frac{1}{2}} = 20 \text{ amps}$$

$$I_2 = I \times \frac{R_t}{R_2} = 60 \times \frac{\frac{1}{6}}{\frac{1}{4}} = 40 \text{ amps}$$

$$I = I_1 + I_2 = 20 + 40 = 60 \text{ amps}$$

In a parallel circuit, the total supply voltage E (V) is impressed across each branch in the circuit. The total voltage drop (IR drop) in each branch must therefore equal the supply voltage; in the example, 10 volts. Using Ohm's law and the above concept, the branch currents may be easily calculated.

$$I_1 = \frac{V}{R_1} = \frac{10}{\frac{1}{2}} = 20 \text{ amps}$$

$$I_2 = \frac{V}{R_2} = \frac{10}{\frac{1}{4}} = 40 \text{ amps}$$

$$I = I_1 + I_2 = 20 + 40 = 60 \text{ amps}$$

SERIES CIRCUITS

When two or more conductors are connected as shown in Fig. 5, they are said to be in *series*. To find the total resistance of a series circuit, it is merely necessary to add the resistance together:

$$R_t = R_1 + R_2 + R_3 + \ldots$$

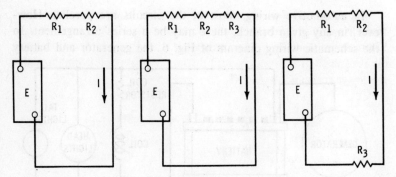

Fig. 5. Illustrating series circuits.

Example: In Fig. 5A, assume that R_1 is equal to $\frac{1}{2}$ ohm, R_2 is equal to $\frac{1}{4}$ ohm, and the battery voltage is 10 volts. The total resistance is:

$$R_t = R_1 + R_2 = \frac{1}{2} + \frac{1}{4} = \frac{3}{4} \text{ ohm}$$

According to Ohm's law, the current is:

$$I = \frac{E}{R} = \frac{10}{\frac{3}{4}} = 13\frac{1}{3} \text{ amps}$$

Since there are no branches in a series circuit, one specific value of current flows through all circuit components. In a series circuit, the voltage drops across each of the resistors must add up to the total supply voltage, which in the case of the above example is 10 volts.

IR drop across $R_1 = I \times R_1 = 13\frac{1}{3} \times \frac{1}{2} = 6\frac{2}{3}$ volts

IR drop across $R_2 = I \times R_2 = 13\frac{1}{3} \times \frac{1}{4} = 3\frac{1}{3}$ volts

or $V = IR_1 + IR_2 = 6\frac{2}{3} + 3\frac{1}{3} = 10$ volts

27

In automotive wiring, most of the circuits are parallel. However, in any given branch, there may be a series arrangement. In the schematic wiring diagram of Fig. 6, the generator and battery

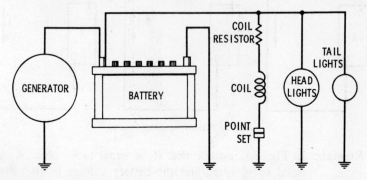

Fig. 6. Illustrating a series parallel automotive circuit.

are shown as the source voltage connected across three parallel branches. One of the branches is the primary ignition circuit showing the coil resistor *CR*, the coil *C*, and a set of points. The remaining branches are lighting circuits.

MAGNETISM

Most of us have seen common horseshoe magnets and know that a nail or any other steel object held close to the end of the magnet will be drawn to it and retained by some force. The force that draws steel to the magnet and retains it, is known as *magnetic force*. The magnetic force emanates from one end of the magnet and travels through the air to the other end of the magnet. The end of the magnet from which the magnetic force emanates is normally called the *north pole* of the magnet. The end of the magnet that receives the magnetic force is referred to as the *south pole*.

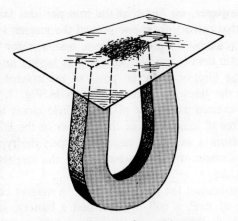

Fig. 7. Illustrating lines of force.

To prove that a magnetic force can exist in air, we need a horseshoe magnet, a piece of paper, and some iron filings. By placing the paper over the magnet and sprinkling the iron filings

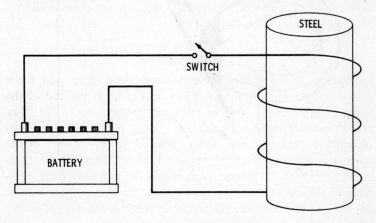

STEEL

SWITCH

BATTERY

Fig. 8. Illustrating an electromagnet.

29

on top of the paper, we find that the iron particles fall in a definite pattern that extends from one pole of the magnet to the other. The pattern resembles a group of lines, and it is for this reason that a magnetic field is usually described as having *lines of force*. The closer the filings are to the poles of the magnet, the closer together are the lines of force, as shown in Fig. 7. Therefore, more pull is exerted as a piece of steel is held closer to the magnet. The degree of magnetism or the number of the lines of force that emerge from a magnet is dependent upon the type of metal the magnet is made of and to what degree the magnet was originally magnetized.

All magnets are not the permanent type. A magnet can be made from a piece of steel, a coil of wire, and a battery, all wired as shown in Fig. 8. When the switch is closed, the circuit is completed and the battery voltage pushes current through the wire

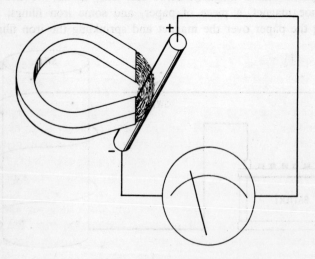

Fig. 9. Illustrating a method of generating electricity.

wound around the steel. When current flows, magnetic lines of force are produced in the steel. The number of magnetic lines of force produced is dependent on the type and volume of the steel, the number of turns in the coil, and the amount of current flowing through the coil.

When the switch is opened, current ceases to flow, and the lines of magnetic force disappear. To what degree the lines of force disappear depends primarily upon the type of steel used. In soft steel, for instance, only a light magnetic field will be retained. The magnetism left is referred to as *residual magnetism*, and the resulting magnet is a weak permanent magnet.

POWER GENERATION

To generate electrical energy in any given conductor, it is only necessary to move the conductor through a magnetic field. The amount of electrical energy produced in the conductor will depend upon:

1. The *number* of magnetic lines of force *cut* by the conductor.
2. The *speed* with which the magnetic lines of force are cut.

If the conductor in Fig. 9 is moved through the magnetic field fast enough, a very small voltage can be detected across the conductor by a sensitive voltmeter. If the conductor movement as shown produces the polarity indicated (positive on top), then reversing the conductor movement would produce the opposite polarity (positive on the bottom).

Since it is the relative motion between the conductor and the magnetic lines of force that produces electrical energy, the conductor could remain stationary and the magnet moved. This could be considered the simplest of generators. To make a simple ro-

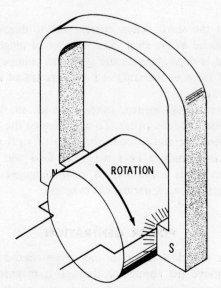

Fig. 10. Illustrating a simple generator.

tating generator, it is necessary to reshape the magnet and place the conductor on a rotating cylinder (Fig. 10). As the cylinder rotates, the conductor is forced through the magnetic field (lines of force) and electrical energy is produced in the conductor. By adding slip rings (Fig. 11), the electrical energy can be collected and put to useful work.

The amount of voltage produced in the conductor varies as the conductor rotates through the magnetic lines of force. Near BDC and TDC, the conductor is traveling a path nearly parallel to the lines of magnetic force, and no *cutting* of lines is accomplished. Midway between BDC and TDC, the conductor is cutting the maximum number of lines of force, thus producing a maximum voltage. Referring to the end view of the simple generator in Fig. 12, this action can be easily seen.

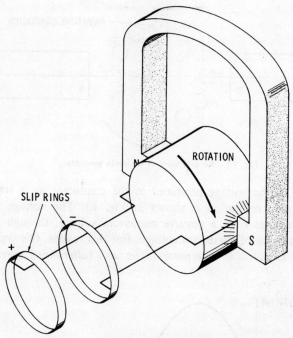

Fig. 11. A simple generator with slip rings added to produce useful work.

Considering the bottom conductor only, as the conductor leaves BDC and begins to rotate clockwise, it cuts an increasing number of lines of force until it reaches the 90° point, which is opposite the north pole of the magnet. From the 90° point to TDC, the conductor cuts a decreasing number of lines of force until zero energy is produced at TDC. This cycle repeats from TDC through 180° to BDC. During this time, the lines of force are being cut in the opposite direction, changing the polarity of the energy produced in the conductor.

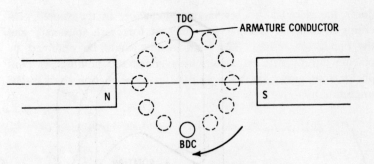

Fig. 12. An end view of a simple generator.

A plot of the voltage produced in the conductor as it travels one complete revolution is shown in Fig. 13. The voltage produced alternates from a positive maximum voltage, through zero volts, to a negative maximum voltage. For this reason, this type of generator is called an *alternator* or an *AC* (*alternating current*) *generator*.

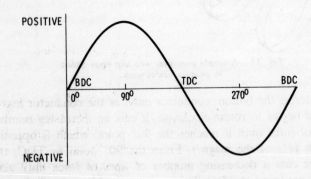

Fig. 13. Alternating voltage wave form.

Previously, it was pointed out that it is the relative movement between a conductor and the magnetic lines of force that produces the electrical energy in the conductor. In the simple generator in Fig. 12, the magnetic lines of force are stationary and the conductor rotates. The same results could be obtained by placing the magnets on a rotating cylinder and holding the conductor stationary. The latter is the type construction used in the present automotive alternator.

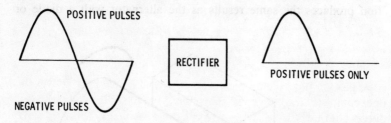

Fig. 14. Illustrating the principle operation of a rectifier.

Of course, automotive equipment is direct-current (DC) equipment and some method must be used to convert the alternating current (AC) produced by the generator or alternator. Two methods used to accomplish this conversion are:

1. The use of rectifiers or diodes.
2. The use of commutating segments.

RECTIFIERS

Rectifiers or diodes are electrical components that have the ability to allow positive voltage pulses to pass through, but do not allow negative pulses to pass, as shown in Fig. 14. Diodes and rectifiers are used to convert the AC voltage generated to DC voltage, and in recent automotive systems are incorporated in the alternator housing.

COMMUTATORS

In the discussion of the one-conductor generator, slip rings were shown as collection devices for the energy produced. The slip rings can be cut, and all positive voltage pulses are then collected on one segment of the slip ring and all negative voltage pulses on the other, as shown in Fig. 15. This type of construction produces the same results as the alternator with a diode or

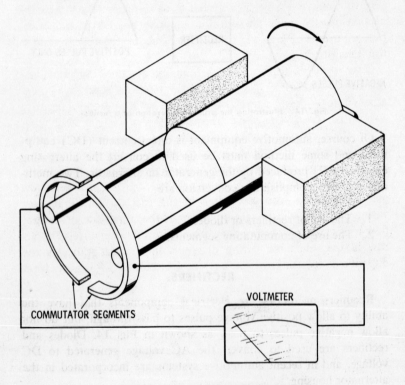

COMMUTATOR SEGMENTS

VOLTMETER

Fig. 15. Illustrating the split slip ring.

rectifier. Attaching the split slip rings to carbon brushes and attaching the conductor to a suitable copper contact, such as a commutator segment, transforms the alternator into the conventional DC generator still found on many present-day automobiles.

TRANSISTORS

A transistor consists of two diodes assembled back to back on very thin material which is referred to as the *base*. The base connection may be made through the mounting ring of the transistor, but, regardless of how the connection is made, the base serves as the transistor trigger.

Two types of transistors are found in common practice and are known as PNP or NPN. The PNP refers to a positive—negative (base)—positive transistor, and the NPN refers to a negative—positive (base)—negative transistor. When using a PNP transistor, the input and output leads must be connected to the positive potential of the circuit. In using an NPN, the input and output leads must connect to the negative potential of the circuit.

The input and output leads are called *emitter* and *collector*, and can lead to some confusion in the user's mind. Transistor wiring diagrams will be less confusing if the usual rule of current flow is applied: *Electricity flows from positive to negative.* The arrow in the schematic wiring diagrams in Fig. 16 indicates the direction of current flow. The current flow in the PNP is away from

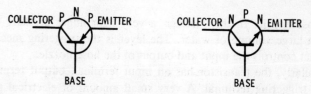

Fig. 16. Illustrating the two types of transistors.

the emitter and in the NPN is toward the emitter, but in each transistor the current flow is from positive to negative.

In operation, the transistor reacts in very much the same manner as a lever-type hose nozzle on a garden hose. When the lever is depressed, a large quantity of water is allowed to flow out of

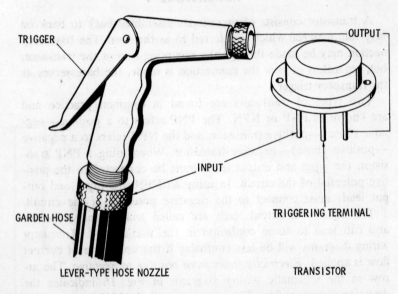

TRIGGER

OUTPUT

INPUT

GARDEN HOSE

TRIGGERING TERMINAL

LEVER-TYPE HOSE NOZZLE

TRANSISTOR

Fig. 17. Illustrating the similarity action between a garden hose and a transistor.

the hose nozzle. In this manner, a very light finger pressure controls a large volume of water. The lever is the triggering mechanism that controls the input and output of the hose nozzle.

Similarly, the transistor has an input terminal, output terminal, and a triggering terminal. A very small amount of electrical pressure applied to the trigger terminal of the transistor will control a comparatively large current flow through the transistor. The transistor acts in the electrical circuit just as the nozzle acts on a garden hose, as shown in Fig. 17.

In the automotive system, the transistor can be used to advantage in the ignition and charging system circuits. For instance, in the ignition system, much higher currents can flow through the coil while the ignition points handle a minimum current. This is illustrated in Fig. 18. When the point set is closed, a small current (usually 1 ampere)flows, triggering the transistor. With the transistor conducting, large values of current (typically 8-10 amperes) will flow through the transistor and ignition coil, greatly increasing the energy input and output of the coil.

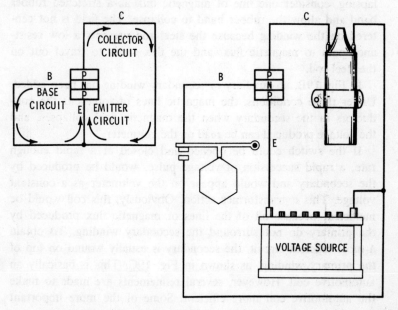

Fig. 18.   Illustrating the use of a transistor circuit in an ignition system.

INDUCED VOLTAGE COILS

In the discussion of a magnetic field, a brief discussion of an electromagnet and the statement that "Electricity can be produced in a conductor by cutting the conductor with a moving magnetic field" was made. This statement describes *transformer* action and is the principle used in the automotive ignition coil.

In Fig. 19A, a long piece of steel rod is shown with a winding connected to a battery and a switch. When the switch is closed, current flows through the winding, producing the magnetic field shown. When the switch is opened, the current ceases to flow and the magnetic field collapses. To visualize the magnetic field collapsing, consider one line of magnetic flux as a stretched rubber band and allow the rubber band to collapse. The field is not centered on the winding because the steel rod presents a low resistance path to magnetic flux, and the flux tends to travel out on the steel rod.

In Fig. 19B, an auxiliary or secondary winding has been added. Under these conditions, the magnetic lines of force *cut* the conductors in the secondary when the magnetic field collapses, and the voltage produced can be read on the voltmeter.

If the switch could be opened and closed at a rapid enough rate, a rapid succession of voltage pulses would be produced by the secondary and would appear on the voltmeter as a constant voltage. This is transformer action. Obviously, this coil would be inefficient because all of the lines of magnetic flux produced by the primary do not surround the secondary winding. To obtain a more efficient circuit, the secondary is usually wound on top of the primary winding, as shown in Fig. 19C. This is basically an automotive coil. However, several refinements are made to make the automotive coil more efficient. Some of the more important are as follows:

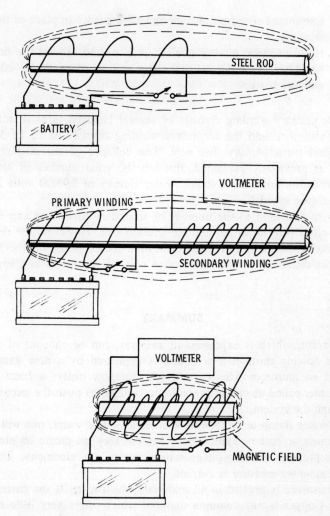

Fig. 19.   The development of an automotive coil.

1. Laminated core iron of high magnetic quality in place of the steel rod.
2. High magnetic quality steel sheet is wound around the finished coil in order to make the coil as magnetically efficient as possible.

The primary winding consists of several hundred turns of medium size wire and the secondary winding consists of 15 to 35 thousand turns of very fine wire. The collapse of the magnetic field, as previously explained, through the great number of secondary turns produces voltages in the vicinity of 20,000 volts at slow engine speeds.

There is a limit to the number of secondary turns that can be used effectively in an automotive ignition coil. However, the discussion of the factors involved is beyond the scope of this book. Further discussion of the automotive coil will be found in Chapter 9.

SUMMARY

Current, which is expressed in amperes, can be thought of as water flowing through a pipe and is measured by a flow gauge called an ammeter. This current will not flow unless a force is available, called electrical pressure or voltage, to push the current through the system.

A water pump or storage tank does not make water, nor will a generator or battery make electricity, but they do create an electrical pressure called voltage which moves the electricity. This movement we measure as current.

Resistance is present in all materials which restricts the current flow. Copper is one common material which offers very little resistance to current flow. At times it is desirable to have an electrical component that does not pass the current as readily as copper, so coil resistors and heating elements are used to slow the flow of current. Materials that do not easily pass current but offer high resistance to current flow are called insulators.

REVIEW QUESTIONS

1. What letter is used to represent current?

2. What is the formula for finding the current in a circuit when the voltage and resistance are known?

3. How is current usually expressed?

4. What is meant by the *lines of force?*

5. What is meant by the *residual magnetism?*

CHAPTER 3

Batteries

Most automotive users realize that there is a battery installed under the hood. They also know that the battery has two terminals, and that water must be added occasionally. Mechanics know that the terminals that extend from the battery are made of lead, and that the liquid contained in the battery is sulfuric acid. However, there are many types of battery construction wherein the terminal material and the liquid between the terminals (called the *electrolyte*) are different from those found in the conventional automotive battery.

Suppose we put a weak solution of diluted sulfuric acid in a tank and immerse a piece of zinc and copper, keeping the two metals separated. The metal pieces are referred to as *electrodes*. Attaching a sensitive voltmeter to the electrodes, we will read a small voltage. We will find the copper to be positive and the zinc negative. Immersing a copper and carbon electrode, we will find a different amount of voltage is produced and that the carbon is positive and the copper is negative. The amount of voltage produced depends only upon the electrolyte and electrode material.

This experiment can be conducted with any pair of elements. A listing of some of the more common elements are:

Zinc

Iron

Copper

Silver

Platinum

Lead

Carbon

If all of the above elements were placed in a container of sulfuric acid, a voltage would be produced between the copper and platinum, a larger voltage between iron and lead and the largest

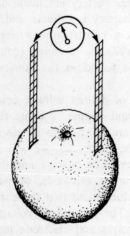

Fig. 1. Illustrating the potential difference between electrodes of an orange.

value of voltage between zinc and carbon. Most commercial dry cells (flashlight batteries) use zinc and carbon for electrodes.

It is not necessary to use sulfuric acid as an electrolyte. Any solution, if it is acid, base, or salt, can be used as an electrolyte if it will act chemically more readily on one electrode than it will on the other. For example, if electrodes are placed into an orange (Fig. 1), a potential difference will appear between the electrodes. Of course some electrolytes are better suited for battery purposes than others. The potential (or voltage) produced by any battery cell is determined by three factors:

1. The kind of material used for electrodes.

2. The type of electrolyte used.

3. The temperature at which the cell operates.

NOTE: The potential (or voltage) developed does not depend upon the size of the plate.

Electrodes consisting of a lead plate and a lead-oxide plate immersed in a thimbleful or a gallon of dilute sulfuric acid will produce a voltage of 2.1 volts per cell. While the potential of any cell is independent of plate size, a large cell is preferable to a small cell because of its greater current capacity and longer life. Lead and lead-oxide plates are used in automotive batteries because of their ruggedness and recharging characteristics.

AUTOMOTIVE BATTERIES

Any battery can be thought of as a chemical energy storage tank. When charged, electrical energy supplied to the electrodes

47

is converted to chemical energy in the plates and electrolyte. Here, it is stored until external battery connections are made, then the chemical energy is reconverted to electrical energy and delivered to the circuit. The essential features of the operation of an automotive battery can be illustrated with the aid of Fig. 2, showing two pieces of metallic lead immersed in a dilute solution of sulfuric acid.

Charging the Cell

Positive voltage is applied to one electrode and the other electrode is grounded. Current passes through the electrolyte (as shown by the dotted arrow), liberating hydrogen gas on the negative electrode and oxygen at the positive electrode. The hydrogen reacts chemically with the negative plate, leaving a plate of pure lead. The oxygen reacts chemically with the positive plate, leaving a plate of lead oxide. The electrolyte is now more acidic and the cell is charged.

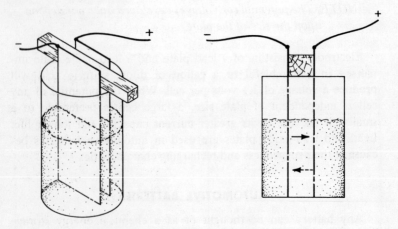

Fig. 2. The essential features of the operation of an automotive battery.

Discharging the Cell

As the battery is used, the cell converts chemical energy to electrical energy and the current flow in the cell is reversed. Both plates are changed to metallic lead with a coating of lead sulfate, and the sulfuric-acid electrolyte contains more and more water until it is a very weak acid solution. The lead sulfate that is formed on the plate usually is broken up chemically when the cell is re-charged. Sometimes, however, this decomposition does not take place. The sulfate coating remains on the plate, and the cell is said to be sulfated. The formation of lead sulfate seriously re-duces the efficiency of the battery. Permanent sulfating is usually caused by over-discharge.

ELECTROLYTE

The amount of sulfuric acid in the electrolyte is an indication of the state of charge of the battery. The more sulfuric acid in the electrolyte, the higher the specific gravity of the solution. The specific gravity of the electrolyte is measured with a hydrometer. Sulfuric acid has a specific gravity of 1.835, while water has a

Chart 1. Battery Condition for Different Specific Gravities

Specific Gravity	Amount of Charge
1.265 - 1.290	Full
1.235 - 1.260	Three-fourths
1.205 - 1.230	One-half
1.170 - 1.200	One-fourth
1.140 - 1.165	Barely Operative
1.110 - 1.135	Completely Discharged

specific gravity of 1.000. Initially, the electrolyte is composed of part sulfuric acid and part water, so that in a new, initially charged battery, the specific gravity of the electrolyte is very close to 1.300. Assuming no loss of electrolyte, Chart 1 can be used to determine the state of charge of a battery cell.

The specific gravity of an electrolyte varies not only with the amount of acid in the liquid but also with temperature. When the temperature drops, the electrolyte becomes thicker and the spe-

Chart 2. Specific Gravity Reading Correction Chart

Electrolyte Temperature	Add To or Subtract From Hydrometer Reading	Electrolyte Temperature	Add To or Subtract From Hydrometer Reading
120	+16	55	—10
115	+14	50	—12
110	+12	45	—14
105	+10	40	—16
100	+ 8	35	—18
95	+ 6	30	—20
90	+ 4	25	—22
85	+ 2	20	—24
80	0	15	—26
75	— 2	10	—28
70	— 4	5	—30
65	— 6	0	—32
60	— 8		

Example: A gravity reading of 1.230 is obtained and the electrolyte temperature is 40° F. The correct reading then is 1.230 — .016 or 1.214.

cific gravity increases. To determine accurately the state of charge of a battery, the temperature effect must be added or subtracted from the hydrometer reading. Chart 2 can be used for this purpose.

TEMPERATURE VERSUS BATTERY EFFICIENCY

The efficiency of a battery is directly dependent upon the temperature of the electrolyte, as previously discussed in relation to specific gravity. A cold battery will discharge faster under use than a warm one, and the temperature usually used for compari-

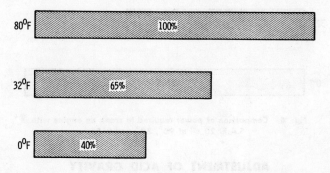

Fig. 3. Comparison of cranking power available from fully charged battery at 80°, 32° and 0°F.

son purposes is 80° F. A fully charged battery with an electrolyte temperature of 80° F. is considered to be 100% efficient. When the electrolyte temperature is lowered to 32° F., the battery is 65% efficient in cranking power, and when the electrolyte temperature is lowered to 0° F., the battery is only 40% efficient, as illustrated in Fig. 3.

In cold weather, the cranking problem is compounded, as the power requirements of an engine increase rapidly when the temperature drops. The increased cranking requirements of an engine lubricated with S.A.E. 20 oil as the temperature decreases is shown in Fig. 4. Comparing the decreased battery efficiency with the increased power requirements when the temperature decreases makes it apparent that the battery must be maintained in a fully charged condition if it is to perform its duties satisfactorily.

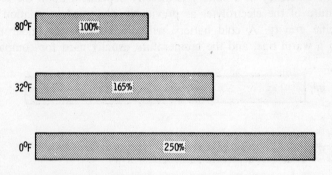

Fig. 4. Comparison of power required to crank an engine with S.A.E. 20 oil at 90°, 32° and 0°F.

ADJUSTMENT OF ACID GRAVITY

Hydrometer floats are not usually calibrated below 1.160 specific gravity and, therefore, cannot indicate the condition of a battery in a very low state of charge. It may be necessary to charge the battery for several hours before a hydrometer reading will indicate that the battery is taking a charge.

If the specific gravity of all cells is not within 5 points of the desired value (corrected to 80° F.) at the end of a full charge, remove some of the electrolyte with the hydrometer and add water to reduce the gravity (if too high) or add 1.400 Sp. Gr. acid to raise the gravity if too low. Continue charging to give the electrolyte time to mix, and recheck the gravity after another hour. Continue this adjusting procedure until the gravity is brought to the desired value by charging for one hour after each adjustment has been made.

Never adjust the gravity of any cell which does not gas freely on charge. Unless the electrolyte has been lost through spilling or leaking, it should not be necessary to add acid to a battery during its life. Acid should never be added unless it is certain that the cell will not come up to normal gravity by continued charging. Remember to make the temperature correction for hydrometer readings, as warm electrolyte will read low and this might be mistaken for failure of the battery gravity to rise normally. It might also be mistakenly concluded that the battery would not take a full charge.

SELF-DISCHARGE OF BATTERY

The grid framework of the battery plates is cast from an alloy of antimony and lead, containing from 6% to 12% antimony. During the charging of a battery, a small amount of antimony dissolves from the positive plate grids and deposits on the sponge lead of the negative plates. This antimony sets up a local electrochemical action with the sponge lead, slowly discharging the negative plates. Small quantities of other impurities may also affect either the positive or negative plates.

All automotive batteries will slowly discharge when not in use, and will discharge faster when warm than when cold. They will also discharge faster when fully charged than when only partially charged. To minimize the extent of battery self-discharge, store wet batteries in cool place, away from hot air ducts or radiators in winter, and shielded from direct sunlight in summer. Wet batteries used for display purposes or stored in unused cars must not be forgotten and neglected. They should receive a boosting charge whenever the specific gravity falls .05 below the specific gravity figure for a fully charged battery.

If a battery remains at less than full charge (below a 75% discharged condition) for any length of time, the chemicals on the plates in the form of lead sulfate will crystallize and harden. This is the sulfation referred to earlier, and the battery may not accept a charge. A battery that becomes sulfated should be charged at a slow rate to protect the positive plates from damage that can result from a fast charge. The maximum temperature should not be allowed to exceed 110° F. on a sulfated battery.

OPEN CIRCUIT VOLTAGE

The open circuit voltage of a fully charged lead-acid cell, regardless of physical size, is 2.10 volts at a specific gravity of 1.260, and 2.12 volts at a specific gravity of 1.280. Open circuit voltage is measured when the battery is not operating on a charge or discharge. A sensitive voltmeter can be used to indicate specific gravity or state of battery cell charge.

No temperature correction factor has to be applied to the gravities indicated by open circuit voltmeters. The voltmeter cannot be used to check cells which have just come off charge. The gases held on the plates will cause the instrument to give a false (high) reading. Voltmeters are useful for testing batteries in stock, but must be used with *caution* on batteries already in use which are subject to charge and discharge. Cranking the engine briefly with the ignition turned off before testing the battery, will remove the gas effect from the readings. Letting batteries stand on open circuit for several hours after charging will also dissipate the gases from the plates and enable correct readings to be obtained on the voltmeter.

DISCHARGE VOLTAGE FACTORS

The discharge voltage of a battery cell will depend largely upon these factors:

1. Design and condition of the battery.

2. State of charge at the beginning of discharge.

3. The temperature of the electrolyte.

4. The rate of discharge.

The discharge or cranking voltage is never as high as the open circuit voltage of the cell.

CAPACITY

The number of plates used per cell, their size and thickness, and the amount of electrolyte determines the battery capacity. A 10- or 20-plate battery will have the same open circuit voltage, but the 20-plate battery will have greater capacity and a higher voltage on discharge with any given load. The starting capacity is roughly proportional to the plate area. Automotive batteries are built with thin plates to provide a large plate area in order that acid may have quick access to as much active material as possible.

Standard Capacity Ratings for Battery Industries

The battery industry has arrived at several accepted standards of battery performance which have been incorporated in the standards of the Association of American Battery Manufacturers, the Society of Automotive Engineers, and the U. S. Government. The battery standards are as follows:

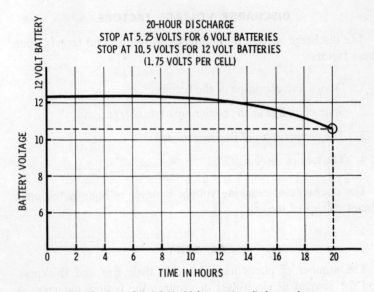

Fig. 5. Typical A.A.B.M. 20-hour rating discharge chart.

20-Hour Rating in Ampere-Hours—This indicates the lighting ability of the battery. The fully charged battery is brought to a temperature of 80° F., and is discharged at a rate equal to 1/20 of the published 20-hour capacity in ampere hours. For example, a 6-volt battery rated at 100 AH capacity would be discharged at 1/20 of 100 (or at 5 amperes) until the terminal voltage falls to 5.25 volts. The number of hours required for the discharge, multiplied by the rate of 5 amperes, is the ampere-hour capacity of the battery and its 20-hour rating. See charts shown in Figs. 5 and 6.

All 6- and 12-volt batteries of 80 ampere-hours capacity and more are discharged at 300 amperes. All 12-volt batteries of less than 80 ampere-hours capacity are discharged at 150 amperes at

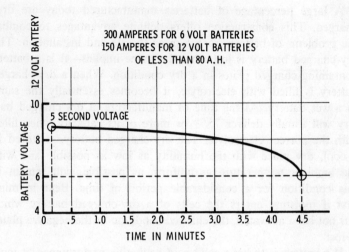

Fig. 6. Typical A.A.B.M cold rating discharge chart at 0°F.

a temperature of 0° F. These ratings indicate the cranking ability of a fully charged battery at low temperatures, and are expressed in the following two ways:

1. By the terminal voltage of a fully charged battery taken 5 seconds after the start of a discharge and at the rate indicated for the ampere-hour capacity of the battery being tested. The initial electrolyte temperature is set at 0° F.

2. By the number of minutes required for the battery to reach a terminal voltage equivalent to 1.0 volt per cell, when discharged at the rate specified, with an electrolyte temperature of 0° F. at the start.

DRY-CHARGED BATTERIES

A large percentage of batteries manufactured today are dry-charged. This construction offers definite advantages to combat the problems of battery storage prior to sale and installation. The dry-charged battery is just what the name implies—it is a battery containing charged plates in a dry condition. When a dry-charged battery is filled with electrolyte, it becomes essentially the same as a wet battery. At the time of manufacture, a dry-charged battery will usually deliver 75% or more of its capacity when filled with the correct electrolyte. The dry-charged battery, if stored in a cool, dry place with the humidity as low as possible and with the ambient temperature as uniform as possible, will remain in this condition for a considerable period of time. Bear in mind that if moisture enters the cells of a dry-charged battery which has not been activated, the charged condition of the negative plates is lost.

If a battery is to have good cold activation performance, it must first have good shelf life. Rapid activation characteristics are necessary in a dry-charged battery, since the battery is ordinarily filled and installed while the customer is waiting. Only the recommended electrolyte should be used to fill the battery cells. If the electrolyte is mixed from a concentrated acid, the acid should always be poured into the water in order to reduce the generation of heat.

BATTERY TESTS

Tests are made on a battery to determine the state of charge and condition. The electrical system should be checked if the battery has failed, is low in charge, or frequently requires water.

Some battery test equipment combines the necessary instruments and controls in one single unit. Be sure to follow the directions of the manufacturer when using such combined equipment.

Hydrogen and oxygen gases are produced in the course of normal battery operation. Flames or sparks can cause this gas mixture to explode if they are brought near the vent openings of the battery. The sulfuric acid in the battery electrolyte can cause a serious burn if spilled on the skin or spattered in the eyes. It should be flushed away immediately with large quantities of clear water.

Before-Charge Tests

A high-rate discharge tester in conjunction with a voltmeter is used for this test. If the battery solution is not within 60° to 100° F., let the battery stand until it warms up before making the test. Add water if necessary to bring the battery solution to the proper level. Fill only to the narrow ring near the bottom of each vent well.

1. Connect the high-rate discharge tester and the appropriate voltmeter to the battery terminals.

2. Adjust the discharge tester to draw three times the ampere-hour rating of the battery. After 15 seconds, and with the battery still under load, read the battery terminal voltage. The voltmeter clips must contact the battery posts and not the high-rate discharge tester clips. Unless this is done, the actual battery terminal voltage will not be indicated. (See Fig. 7)

3. If the terminal voltage is 9.5 volts or more for a 12-volt battery, or 4.75 volts or more for a 6-volt battery, the battery has good output capacity and will accept a normal charge. Test the specific gravity if water has not been added recently, and recharge if necessary.

59

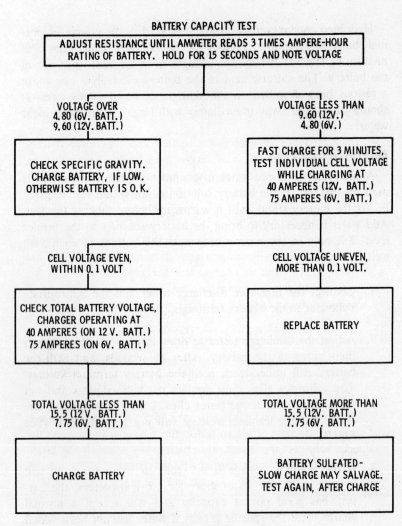

Fig. 7. Battery capacity test diagram.

4. If the terminal voltage is below 9.5 volts for a 12-volt battery, or below 4.75 volts for a 6-volt battery, make a test charge on the battery.

The condition of a discharged battery may be tested by passing current through it.

1. Connect a fast charger to the battery and charge the battery for 3 minutes at a rate of 40 amperes for a 12-volt battery, and at a rate of 75 amperes for a 6-volt battery.

2. After 3 minutes of fast charge, and with the fast charger still operating, test the individual cell voltages of the battery.

3. If the cell voltages vary more than 0.1 volt, replace the battery. If the cell voltages are all within 0.1 volt, test the total battery voltage (charger still operating). *NOTE: If the external battery construction does not permit a cell test to be performed, place the battery on a continued slow charge.*

4. If the total battery voltage is now under 15.5 volts for a 12-volt battery, or 7.75 volts for a 6-volt battery, the battery is satisfactory and may be safely fast charged. Always follow the fast charge with sufficient slow charge to bring the battery to a full charge.

5. If the total battery voltage is over 15.5 volts for the 12-volt battery, or over 7.75 volts for the 6-volt battery, and the cell voltages are equal, the battery is probably sulfated. Place the battery on a continued slow charge.

After-Charge Tests

When the battery is fully charged (check with a hydrometer or battery charge tester), make a capacity test. If the terminal voltage is 9.5 volts or above for a 12-volt battery, or 4.75 volts or above for a 6-volt battery, place the battery back in service. If the terminal voltage is below 9.5 volts (12-volt battery), or below 4.75 volts (6-volt battery), replace the battery.

SUMMARY

The battery provides the stored power to operate the starter, the ignition system, and the electrical accessories. When the engine has been started and has reached sufficient speed for the generator to produce voltage, the battery and generator work together to provide electricity according to the need of the automobile. This is called *load demand*. The battery also helps to stabilize the voltage in the charging circuit.

The battery has positive and negative plates; the positive plates consist of lead peroxide and the negative plates consist of spongy lead, assembled with suitable separators and immersed in a solution of sulfuric acid. The plates are formed in groups which are called *cells*, each cell producing approximately 2-volts potential.

Whenever the battery terminals are connected to a closed circuit, a chemical reaction takes place in the battery. For example, when the starter switch is turned *on,* the lead and lead peroxide plates are gradually changed to lead sulfate and sulfuric acid is changed to water. At the same time, current flows through the closed circuit. This process is called an *electro-chemical* reaction.

Fortunately, for the service life of the automobile battery, the reaction is reversible. When a generator or battery charger is connected to the battery terminals, the positive and negative plates return to their original condition, sulfuric acid is reformed and the battery becomes recharged. The specific gravity of an electrolyte varies not only with the amount of acid in the liquid but also with temperature.

REVIEW QUESTIONS

1. What kind of acid forms on the battery plates to reduce the efficiency of the battery?

2. What happens to a battery if stored at less than full charge?

3. What is the specific gravity of a fully charged battery?

4. Why are most battery manufacturers developing a dry-charge battery?

5. How does temperature change affect a battery?

CHAPTER 4

Relays and Regulators

From the discussion in Chapter 2 it is probably evident that a generator can have almost any output desired. In the automotive system, all the accessories and the battery are designed to operate at a nominal voltage of 6 or 12 volts. The battery in particular needs a constant voltage from which it can obtain electrical energy and store it until needed in the system.

The automotive generator is controlled and its output limited by controlling the field current. To accomplish this control, an electromagnetic switch is used that falls under the general classification of a relay. Therefore, the general operating principles of relays will be discussed before the individual components that make up the regulator are presented.

As previously described, an electromagnet consists of an iron or steel core with turns of wire wound around the core. The wires are connected by means of a switch to some source of voltage, such as a battery.

In Fig. 1, when the switch is closed, the voltage source pushes current through the winding. Current flowing through the winding induces a magnetic field in the iron core; thus an electromagnet is produced and is capable of pulling steel objects to it. When the

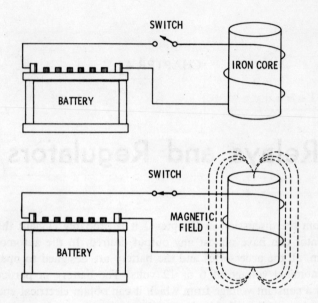

Fig. 1. Illustrating an electromagnet.

switch is opened, current ceases to flow and all but a very small amount of magnetism disappears. The magnetism that remains in the iron core is called *residual magnetism*, and is usually very weak compared to the full strength of the magnetic field when current is flowing. If a flat steel bar is placed above the electromagnet, and supported by a spring on each end, we have most of the essential parts of a relay.

When we close the switch on the circuit (Fig. 2), the magnetic lines of force produced will tend to pull down the steel bar until it reaches the iron core of the electromagnet. It is the electrical designer's job to balance the strength of the magnetic field against the strength of the springs. The magnetic field must be strong enough to overcome the spring pressure and pull the bar down.

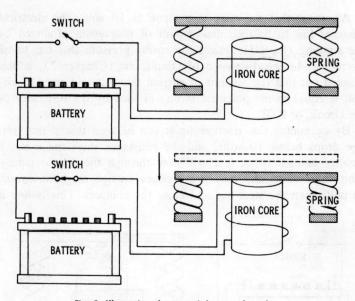

Fig. 2. Illustrating the essential parts of a relay.

Yet, the spring must be strong enough to overcome the residual magnetic field and enable the steel bar to move upward.

The push (or pull) exerted by any spring can be measured with a scale. The strength of the pull exerted by a magnetic field can also be measured by a scale, and is directly proportional to the ampere turns of the winding. The strength of any magnetic winding is determined by the amount of current that flows through the winding and the number of turns in the winding or, amps × number of turns. This is frequently written as: NI (N is the number of turns and I is the amperes). If we take the relay winding shown in Fig. 2 and add a set of contacts (see Fig. 3) we have an electrical relay or an electromagnetic switch. An analysis of both relays will reveal that they are electrically identical.

Assuming that the relay is to open at 10 volts, the electrical designer has to balance the amount of magnetism produced by the winding (the NI) against the spring pressure that has to be overcome. In the discussion of Ohm's law (Chapter 2), it was pointed out that the amount of current that flows in any DC circuit is equal to the potential (volts) divided by the resistance of the circuit, or E/R.

By examining this relationship it can be seen that if the voltage drops below 10 volts, and the resistance stays the same, a smaller amount of current will flow through the relay winding. This value of current may not produce enough magnetic energy to pull down the steel bar and close the contacts. This is fine if

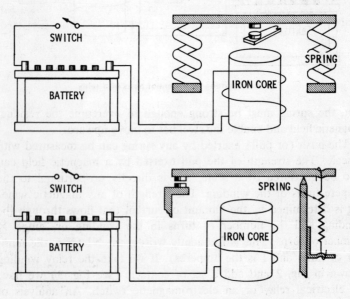

Fig. 3. Illustrating a relay with an electromagnetic switch.

the relay is to operate as originally designed at 10 volts. However, if it is desired to have the contacts close at 8 volts, then the spring pressure must be reduced. Here, we have a relay that can be made sensitive to the voltage of the circuit.

There are times when it is desirable to have a relay sensitive to the current flowing through it rather than the voltage of the circuit. In the preceding example where 10 volts is impressed on the relay, a fairly large size wire is used, and if the wire size is doubled or made twice the diameter, then the current that flows through the relay at 10 volts will increase by four. The increase in current is due to the lower resistance of the wire. Obviously, when the current is increased four times for the same voltage, then the magnetic strength would increase a like amount. We can increase or decrease the sensitivity of a relay by changing spring tension and varying the amount of turns in the winding. In the automotive regulator used with the conventional DC generator, three electromagnetic switches or relays are used. One of the relays is a voltage sensitive relay. The second relay is a current sensitive relay and the third relay contains both a current and voltage sensitive winding and is called a cutout. In the alternator type system, only the voltage sensitive relay is used as a regulator.

VOLTAGE RELAYS

The voltage relay (also referred to as voltage sensitive) of a regulator performs the function of opening the generator field circuit when the generated voltage reaches a designed value. When the voltage drops to a lower value, the relay must again close the generator field circuit. This action governs the amount of energy produced by the generator (see Chapter 2). The operation of the relay is controlled by the voltage produced at the armature terminal of the generator.

Voltage Regulating Relays

Voltage produced at the armature terminal (A) of the generator forces current to flow through the electromagnetic winding to ground. When current flows through the winding (Fig. 4), a magnetic field surrounds the metal contact support and draws it downward toward the magnet. This action opens the contacts, breaking the field circuit. Field current must now flow from the field terminal of the generator through the resistance to ground. By inserting the resistor into the field circuit, less current is allowed to flow

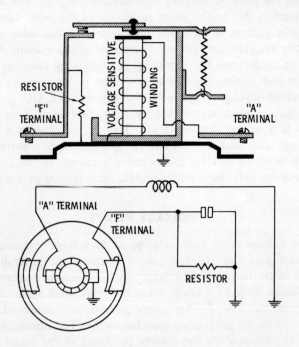

Fig. 4. Illustrating the function of a voltage relay section of a voltage regulator.

through the generator field windings. The magnetism produced by the field windings decreases and, therefore, the armature voltage decreases.

When the armature voltage decreases, less current can flow through the magnetic winding of the relay. The tension spring overcomes the weakened magnetic field of the relay, closing the contacts, and full generator field current is allowed to flow through the generator field circuit. Again, the magnetic field in the generator is strengthened and the armature voltage increases. This operation is repeated continuously when the output of the generator is at its normal operating voltage.

In a 6-volt system, the proper voltage setting is approximately 7.0 to 7.5 volts. In a 12-volt system, the proper voltage setting is approximately 14.0 to 15.0 volts. In a 24-volt system, the proper voltage setting is 28.0 to 30.0 volts.

If we could watch the actual voltage produced in a 12-volt automotive system where the voltage regulator is set at 14.5 volts, it would appear very similar to the sketch shown in Fig. 5. The left-hand margin of the graph shows the generated voltage that is

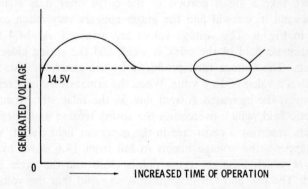

Fig. 5. A graph showing the voltage and time action.

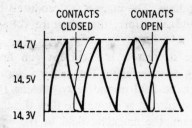

CONTACTS CLOSED CONTACTS OPEN

14.7V

14.5V

14.3V

Fig. 6. Actual generated voltage waveform.

measured from the armature terminal to ground. The bottom portion of the graph shows the time of operation. The armature voltage starts at zero and rises almost instantaneously to the regulator setting. When it reaches its value, the voltage continues to rise to a maximum and then steadily decreases until it goes back to the setting of the regulator (14.5 volts). The instantaneous voltage rise is due to the generator starting from zero speed to a point at which the output of the generator is governed by the regulator. The small rise and fall of voltage above and back to the setting of the regulator is due to a bimetallic hinge. The action of the bimetallic hinge is described later in this chapter.

If we take a small portion of the curve after it is stabilized and expand it, we will find the graph appears very much as pictured in Fig. 6. The voltage values are assumed. At 14.4 volts, the magnetic field of the relay is weak and the spring closes the contacts. The voltage then produced by the generator rises until it reaches a value of 14.6 volts. When the armature voltage reaches 14.6 volts, the increased current flow in the relay strengthens the magnetic field, which overcomes the spring tension and opens the contacts, inserting a resistance in the generator field circuit. When this happens, the voltage begins to fall from 14.6 down to 14.4 volts, at which time the relay points close and the cycle is repeated. The rise and fall of voltage is so rapid that the voltmeter reads the average value. A voltmeter connected to the above system would read 14.5 volts. In actual operation, the values may be different than shown—the preceding values were chosen for illustration purposes only.

To summarize, the voltage unit of a regulator is sensitive to the voltage output of the generator. It controls the output voltage by varying the amount of field current that can flow through the generator field windings. It is constantly in use when the generated voltage reaches the designed value of the regulator. The voltage relay portion (of the regulator) receives the most wear, since it is the only relay that is constantly vibrating in a normal charging system.

Current Limiting Relay

The current limiter unit is a relay almost identical in construction to that of the voltage relay unit. The main difference between the two units is that the current limiter is sensitive to load current; that is, the actual output current of the generator. This unit consists of a few turns of very heavy wire while the voltage sensitive unit consists of several thousand turns of fine wire, as shown in Fig. 7.

It can be seen from the schematic wiring diagram in Fig. 7 that, although the relay is sensitive to load current, it regulates the field current flow of the generator in exactly the same manner as the voltage sensitive relay. If the generator output current reaches the designed value of the current limiter relay, then the contacts are opened and the generator field current is reduced. Decreasing the field current decreases the magnetism produced by the generator field—consequently, the armature voltage is reduced. Reducing the armature voltage automatically reduces the generator load current. *From this it should be evident that the output current of a generator is controlled by controlling the voltage produced by the generator.*

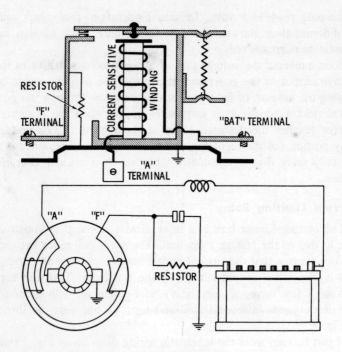

Fig. 7. Illustrating the function of the current relay section of a voltage regulator.

Too often the action of this relay is misunderstood. Many mechanics believe that, if excessive current is flowing in a circuit, they can limit the current by adjusting the current limiter units of a regulator. In some cases the current flow is reduced; however, it is reduced because the armature voltage is reduced. The only way the current flow in the automotive circuit can be reduced is by lowering the voltage or raising the resistance of the circuit. Current flow is an effect, not a cause.

The purpose of the current limiter relay is to protect the generator from being overloaded. This could occur when the battery is low in gravity (low resistance) and demands a high current, or when an excessive current load due to low resistance (such as a grounded battery wire) is presented to the generator.

Cutout Relay

The cutout is a relay similar to the previous types of relays discussed; however, its contacts are normally open. The contacts

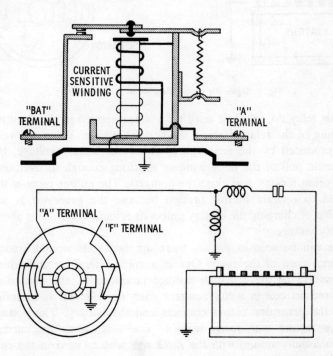

Fig. 8. Illustrating the function of the cutout relay section of a voltage regulator.

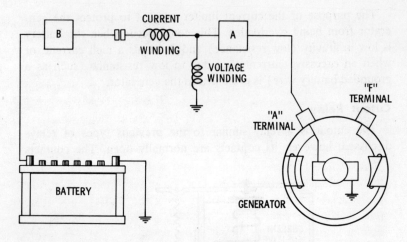

Fig. 9. Schematic wiring diagram of a cutout relay.

of this relay do not close until the voltage applied to the sensitive winding of the relay is above the battery voltage. When the voltage produced by the generator is above the battery voltage, the magnetic pull of the relay winding is strong enough to overcome the spring tension and close the contacts. The cutout relay is designed to operate in this fashion because the generator is not capable of charging the battery unless its armature voltage is above battery voltage.

As can be seen in Fig. 8, there are two coils wound around the iron core of the relay. One is a voltage sensitive coil which is sensitive to the armature voltage produced by the generator. The second coil is a load current carrying coil and is in series with the generator cutout contacts and the battery. The voltage coil is wound with many turns of fine wire, while the current coil is usually wound with the same size wire as used in the current limiter coil, but has fewer turns.

When the cutout contacts are closed, due to the voltage sensitive winding, load current is allowed to flow through the current winding, through the cutout contacts, and into the battery. This may be better seen on the simplified cutout wiring diagram Fig. 9. When the engine stops, the output voltage of the generator falls below the battery voltage. If the cutout contacts were to remain closed under this condition, current flow would reverse itself and run from the battery through the cutout points, through the coil windings, and through the generator field windings to ground. This would not only drain the battery, but would possibly destroy the generator. It is imperative that the cutout points open when the generator is not capable of charging the battery, and this is one reason the load current winding is wound along with the voltage sensitive winding on the cutout relay.

When the generated voltage falls below battery voltage, the magnetism produced by the voltage sensitive winding does not disappear. In the event that the cutout spring does not open the contacts immediately, current begins to flow in the reverse direction through the current carrying coil. The reversal of current flow in the current carrying coil weakens the remaining magnetic field so that the spring can easily open the contacts. This reversal of current flow is insurance that the cutout contacts will open.

As previously stated, the strength of the magnetic field is proportional to the number of turns in the winding and the amount of current that flows through these turns, or NI. As an example, when the cutout relay closes, the NI of the voltage sensitive winding might be:

$$1200 \text{ turns} \times .1 \text{ amperes} = 120 \text{ NI}$$

When the contacts close, current begins to flow through the current carrying winding and an additional magnetic field is added to the above. Assuming a load current of 10 amps, the magnetic field would be:

$$14 \text{ turns} \times 10 \text{ amperes} = 140 \text{ NI}$$

The total closed force therefore would be:

$$120 \text{ NI} + 140 \text{ NI} = 260 \text{ NI}$$

When the generated voltage falls below battery voltage, it is applied to the voltage sensitive and current windings of the relay, forcing current from the battery through the generator. The reversal of current causes a reversal of the magnetic field in the current winding, not in the voltage sensitive winding. Typical reverse current through the current winding is from 3 to 5 amps. Therefore the reverse magnetic field strength is:

$$1200 \text{ turns} \times .1 \text{ amps.} = 120 \text{ NI}$$

$$\text{Minus } 14 \text{ turns} \times 5 \text{ amps.} = 70 \text{ NI}$$

$$\text{Net magnetic effect} = 50 \text{ NI}$$

This is the demagnetization force, leaving a magnetic force of only 50 NI that the spring must overcome to open the contacts.

Combined Operation

The regulator used with the conventional DC generator consists of three of the previously described relays—a voltage regulating relay, a current limiting relay, and a cutout relay. A simplified wiring diagram of the externally grounded generator and regulator is shown in Figs. 10 and 11.

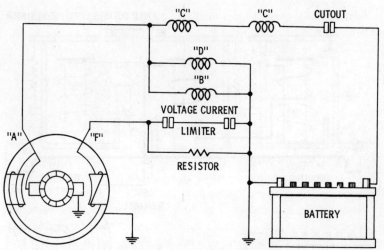

Fig. 10. The three unit regulator schematic.

It may be helpful to trace the actual circuits involved through the generator and regulator. When the engine starts, the armature windings cut the residual magnetic field produced by the pole shoes, generating a voltage at the armature terminal of the generator. This small amount of voltage forces a small current through the voltage sensitive winding D of the voltage relay, and through the voltage sensitive winding B of the cutout relay. As previously mentioned, the generator action keeps building up the voltage present at the armature terminal. For the purpose of illustration, assume that the regulator has the following voltage and current settings:

Cutout voltage   = 13   volts

Voltage setting   = 14.5 volts

Current limiter setting = 25 amps

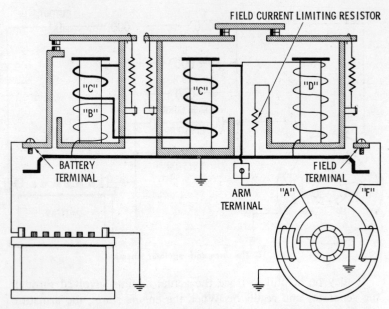

Fig. 11. Illustrating the voltage regulator and generator hook-up.

As the generator speed increases, the amount of voltage produced at the armature terminal increases. When this voltage reaches the cutout setting of the regulator (13 volts), the voltage sensitive winding *B* of the cutout produces enough magnetic strength to close the cutout relay. With the cutout relay closed, current now flows through the current limiter and cutout windings *C*, through the cutout contacts, and to the battery.

As the generator voltage continues to rise, it reaches the voltage regulator setting of 14.5 volts. When this value is reached, the magnetic field produced by the voltage sensitive winding *D* is strong enough to overcome the spring tension and open the contacts. With the contacts open, the generator field current is reduced. Tracing this condition through on the diagram, it will be found that the current follows a path from the armature brush of the generator, through the field winding of the generator, through the field terminal of the regulator, through the resistance in the regulator to ground, and back to the armature, completing the electrical circuit. The reduced field current that flows will drop the armature voltage slightly, which will weaken the voltage relay and allow the points to close. This cycle is the normal running cycle of the charging system.

When an automotive engine is started, a great deal of energy is taken from the battery. Therefore, the energy taken from the generator is very high in the first few minutes of engine operation. A regulator having a current limiter setting of 25 amperes may operate on the current limiter for a few minutes. With the battery in a discharged state, high current may flow if a low voltage is impressed across the battery. As an example, with only 13.8 volts being produced by the generator under a given set of circumstances, as much as 40 amperes could flow to the battery. If this were to happen in our example, the current limiter would reduce the generated voltage to a value of approximately 12.8 volts, or that voltage which will force no more than 25 amperes into the battery.

As the battery becomes charged, it takes a higher value of voltage to continue the charging rate of 25 amperes. The current limiter then allows the voltage to rise until the charging rate falls below 25 amperes, at which point the voltage regulating relay takes over and continues to regulate the output voltage and current of the generator. Analyzing the circuit, it can be seen that when the current limiting unit is in operation, the same resistance is inserted into the field circuit as when the voltage regulating relay is in operation. It is well to keep in mind that under normal driving conditions the voltage regulating relay is constantly in use, but usually the current limiting relay does not operate for a long period of time.

When the engine is stopped, the generated voltage falls rapidly and both the current limiting and voltage regulating relays remain closed. The voltage sensitive winding of the cutout relay is now energized by the battery and not the generator. The current winding of the cutout has reverse current flowing through it as long as the cutout contacts are closed. The reverse current flow in the current winding creates a reverse magnetic field that "bucks" or opposes the magnetic field of the voltage sensitive winding. The net effect is a weakening of the magnetic pull on the cutout contacts, allowing the spring to positively open the cutout relay.

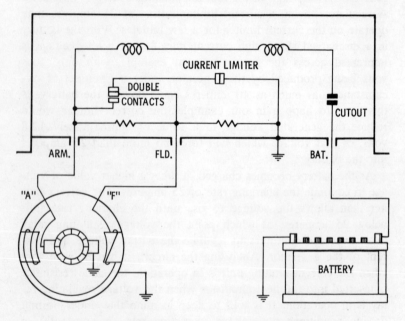

Fig. 12.   A schematic diagram illustrating the double-contact regulator.

Double-Contact Regulators

This type of regulator has been used by European car manufacturers for a number of years and is not new in theory, but has only recently appeared on American-made vehicles. In the schematic diagram shown in Fig. 12, it can be seen that the regulator performs exactly the same function as the conventional automotive regulator. The only difference between the two circuits is that the voltage regulating relay has four contacts instead of two in the field circuit.

The conventional DC regulator and generator does not have a very high charging rate at idle or low engine speeds. With the conventional DC generator and regulator, if higher voltages and higher charging rates are generated at low engine speeds, it is very difficult to control the output voltage at high engine speeds. The double-contact type regulator permits the use of a higher field current which allows higher charging rates at low engine speeds. However, this type of unit retains a satisfactory control over the generator at high engine speeds.

With the double-contact regulator there are two voltage settings. For instance, the conventional type regulator may have a voltage setting of 14.5 volts, while the double-contact type will have a low-speed, high-load setting of 14.4 volts, and a high-speed, low-load setting of 14.7 volts.

By analyzing the previous diagram (Fig. 12), it can be seen that when the engine starts, and at low engine speeds, the generator field is connected directly to ground, allowing maximum current to flow through the field winding. At some intermediate engine speed, the center contacts open and "float" between the upper and lower contacts of the regulator. Under this operating condition, a resistance is inserted into the generator field circuit, reducing the amount of field current that flows. At higher engine speeds, the center contact is pulled downward and makes contact with the lower contact of the relay. Under this condition, the generator field is closed, effectively opening the generator field circuit and no field current can flow.

This type of system tends to lengthen contact life, but presents a service problem not experienced with the standard externally grounded generator and regulator system. One of the tests frequently made on the standard system is to ground the field terminal—a connection that bypasses the current limiter and voltage regulating contacts, electrically removing the regulator from the circuit. With this connection the engine speed can be increased and the maximum voltage capabilities of the generator determined. *If the ground connection is made on a double-contact regulator, the regulator may be permanently damaged.*

Referring to the diagram shown in Fig. 13, it can be seen that with an incorrect ground connection, high voltages can be produced by the generator, forcing an abnormally high current through the lower contacts, which will burn the contacts and make them inoperative in a very few minutes. To test this type of generator-regulator system, remove the wire attached to the field terminal of the regulator and *ground the wire only. Do not ground the "F" terminal of the regulator.*

REGULATOR ADJUSTMENTS

On *Delco-Remy* single-contact units, turn the adjusting screw clockwise to increase the closing voltage, or counterclockwise to decrease it.

On *Autolite* regulators, bend the spring support on the cutout relay down to increase the closing voltage, or up to decrease it.

On *Bosch* and *Ford* regulators, bend the tang on the cutout relay up to increase the closing voltage, or bend the tang down to decrease the closing voltage.

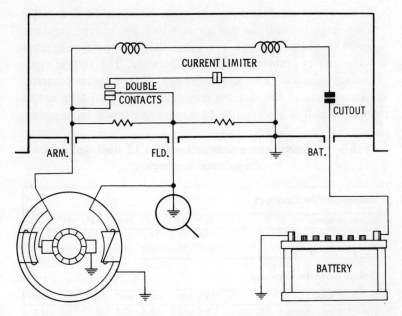

Fig. 13.   Illustrating the incorrect ground on a double-contact regulator.

The contact-opening current determines if the cutout relay opens at or below the specified maximum value. This specified value may vary from 2 to 9 amperes, depending on the make of regulator. If the value is outside the specified limits, the air gap of the cutout relay must be adjusted. Refer to the manufacturer's recommended procedure to make this adjustment.

Voltage Regulator Relay Test—Adjustment of the voltage regulator relay is seldom necessary if the battery remains charged and does not need more than the normal amount of water added, and lights or radio tubes do not have to be replaced at frequent intervals.

85

If the above conditions do not exist, however, or if a major tune-up is performed, the voltage at which the voltage regulator operates should be checked. The cover should be on the regulator and the unit at normal operating temperature. The voltage regulator relay operation and adjustment are affected by temperature. The manufacturer specifies the temperature at which tests are to be made and lists a correction factor to compensate for tempera-

Table 1. Temperature Corrections for 12-volt Voltage Regulator Settings

Delco Single Contact

Regulator temp.	45°	65°	85°	105°	125°	145°	165°
Min. Voltage Setting	14.5	14.4	14.2	14.0	13.8	13.5	13.1
Max. Voltage Setting	15.6	15.4	15.2	14.9	14.7	14.3	13.9

Delco Double Contact

Regulator temp.	85°	105°	125°	145°	165°	185°	205°
Min. Voltage Setting	14.1	14.0	13.8	13.7	13.5	13.4	13.3
Max. Voltage Setting	14.9	14.8	14.6	14.5	14.4	14.2	14.1

Autolite

Air temp.	50°	60°	70°	80°	90°	100°	120°
*Voltage	14.68	14.62	14.58	14.51	14.44	14.37	14.23

*operating voltage after 15 min. operation at 10 amps., permissible variation .4 volt + or − at given temperature.

Voltage Regulator Used With Chrysler Alternator

Air temp.	0°	20°	40°	60°	80°	100°	120°	140°
*Min. Voltage Setting	14.0	13.9	13.8	13.7	13.6	13.5	13.5	13.4
*Max. Voltage Setting	14.6	14.5	14.4	14.3	14.2	14.1	14.0	14.0

*Voltage setting for upper contacts. Lower contacts should not exceed above specs more than .7 volts at 2200 engine rpm.

ture variation when making adjustments. Table 1 lists the temperature corrections to make on 12-volt regulators.

The voltage regulator relay may be checked with a suitable volt-ampere tester or by use of the many battery-starter-regulator testers on the market. Special fixed and variable resistors, as well as carbon piles, may be used in various hook-ups. Detailed instructions are furnished by the test-equipment manufacturers for the use of their equipment. These instructions should be carefully followed.

Test Procedure

1. Start the engine and turn on a combination of lights and/or accessories to obtain a generator output (as read on the test ammeter) of 10 to 15 amperes.

2. Slowly increase the engine speed from idle to 1600 rpm for a *Delco-Remy, Ford* or *Bosch* regulator, or 2000 rpm for an *Autolite* unit.

3. The voltmeter reading should increase as the engine speed increases until the voltage regulator starts operating, after which the voltage should remain constant and within specifications.

4. Momentarily increase the engine speed. The voltage reading should remain constant.

5. If the voltage reading is not within the specified limit, or does not remain constant, the regulator needs adjustment or replacement.

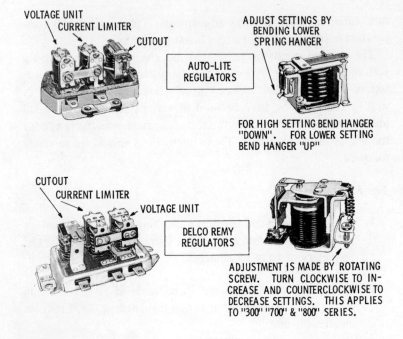

VOLTAGE UNIT
CURRENT LIMITER
CUTOUT

AUTO-LITE
REGULATORS

ADJUST SETTINGS BY
BENDING LOWER
SPRING HANGER

FOR HIGH SETTING BEND HANGER
"DOWN".   FOR LOWER SETTING
BEND HANGER "UP"

CUTOUT
CURRENT LIMITER
VOLTAGE UNIT

DELCO REMY
REGULATORS

ADJUSTMENT IS MADE BY ROTATING
SCREW.   TURN CLOCKWISE TO IN-
CREASE AND COUNTERCLOCKWISE TO
DECREASE SETTINGS.   THIS APPLIES
TO "300" "700" & "800" SERIES.

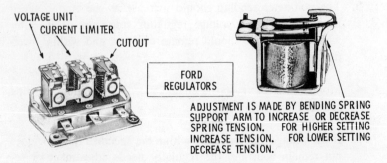

VOLTAGE UNIT
CURRENT LIMITER
CUTOUT

FORD
REGULATORS

ADJUSTMENT IS MADE BY BENDING SPRING
SUPPORT ARM TO INCREASE OR DECREASE
SPRING TENSION.   FOR HIGHER SETTING
INCREASE TENSION.   FOR LOWER SETTING
DECREASE TENSION.

Fig. 14. Typical regulator construction.

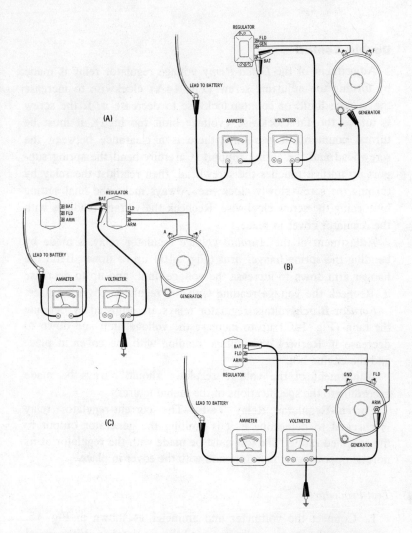

Fig. 15. Voltage-regulator relay test connections; (A) *Delco-Remy;* **(B)** *Autolite;* **(C)** *Ford or Bosch.*

Double Contact

Adjustment of the *Delco-Remy* voltage regulator relay is made by turning the adjusting screw (Fig. 14A) clockwise to increase the voltage limit, or counterclockwise to decrease it. If the screw is turned too far clockwise (voltage limit too high), it must be turned counterclockwise until there is a clearance between the screwhead and the spring support. Carefully bend the spring support up until it touches the screwhead, then readjust the relay by turning the screw slowly clockwise. Always make the final setting by turning the screw clockwise. Recheck the voltage readings with the regulator cover in place.

Adjustment of the *Autolite* voltage regulator relay is made by bending the spring hanger arm (Fig. 14B) up or down. Bend the hanger arm down to increase the voltage limit, and up to decrease it. Recheck the voltage reading with the regulator cover in place.

Ford or *Bosch* voltage-regulator relays are adjusted by bending the tang (Fig. 14C) up to increase the voltage limit and down to decrease it. Recheck the voltage reading with the cover in place and the engine hot.

Adjustment of the voltage regulator should always be made according to the specifications of the manufacturer.

Current-Regulator Relay Tests—The current-regulator relay is checked to determine if it is limiting the generator output to the specified rating. The test must be made with the regulator at its normal operating temperature and with the cover in place.

Test Procedure

1. Connect the voltmeter and ammeter as shown in Fig. 15. Start the engine and run it until the regulator is at its normal operating temperature.

2. Turn on the headlights, all accessories and, if necessary, connect an additional load (carbon pile or bank of lights) across the battery to bring the system voltage to at least 1 volt below the voltage regulator setting.

3. Stop the engine. Restart and increase the engine speed to 1600 rpm for *Ford, Bosch,* and *Delco-Remy* regulators, or 2000 rpm for *Autolite* units.

4. Note the ammeter reading. The current output of the generator should be within the specified limits.

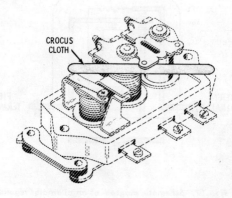

Fig. 16. Regulator contacts can be cleaned and polished with crocus cloth.

If the current output of the generator is not within specifications, adjustment of the current-regulator relay is made in exactly the same manner as the adjustment on the voltage-regulator relay described and illustrated previously (Fig. 14).

ALTERNATOR REGULATORS

The alternator is an *AC* generator used instead of a *DC* generator in the charging system of some automobiles. The alternator, unlike the DC generator, will deliver an output voltage at a low idle speed and considerably more output current at low operating speeds. Thus, an alternator meets the demand of stop-and-go city driving and increased accessory load much better than the conventional DC generator.

The output of an alternator is alternating current (AC), which

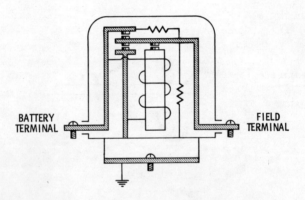

Fig. 17. Schematic diagram of an alternator regulator.

means that half the total output current flows in one direction and the other half flows in the opposite direction. The electrical circuits of the automobile, however, can use only current flowing in a single direction, which means the alternator output must be changed to direct current (DC). This is done by passing the alternating current through diode rectifiers which allow the current to flow in only one direction. Fig. 17 illustrates an alternator regulator.

DASH INDICATING LIGHTS

In recent years the automotive manufacturers have used an indicating light on the dashboard in place of the conventional ammeter. This lamp is shown in Fig. 18. The ammeter measures

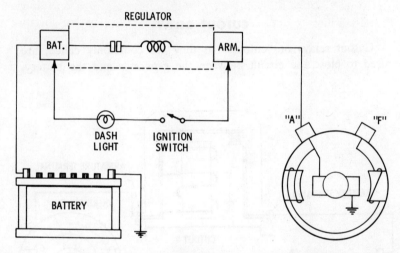

Fig. 18.   Schematic diagram illustrating the dashboard
indicating light.

the current flowing to the battery and gives an indication of battery and charging circuit conditions. The indicating light operates whenever a difference of approximately 3 volts exists between the voltage being produced by the generator and the battery voltage. Normally, a 6- or 12-volt bulb is used, which will begin to glow at approximately 3 volts, becoming brighter as the voltage difference increases.

A switch is provided to open the light circuit when the ignition key is turned off, so that the light will not continue to operate when the car is not in use. No indication of potential battery or generator trouble can be obtained using an indicating light. A voltmeter should always be used to check the generated voltage whenever possible.

CUTOUT RELAY

Cutout relays or "cutouts" as they are commonly called, are used to close the circuit between the generator and the battery.

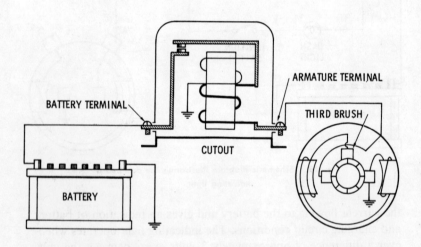

Fig. 19. A cutout relay illustrating the third brush system.

This unit is used by itself on a "third brush" generator system (Fig. 19), or in combination with other relays in the conventional generator system. The operation of a cutout relay has been described previously in this chapter.

HORN RELAY

The horn relay is connected between the horn and the battery. The horn is a fairly high-current device and will shorten switch life if the horn is directly connected through the switch to the battery. It is for this reason the horn relay is used. The horn relay contacts are capable of carrying the high current, while the horn relay switch carries smaller values of winding current.

In the diagram (Fig. 20), the conventional horn relay is shown; closing the horn switch or horn button allows current to flow

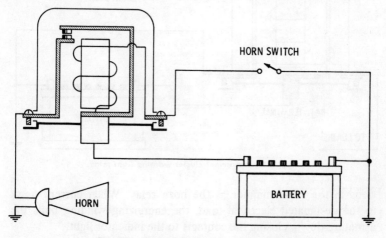

Fig. 20. Illustrating the typical horn relay.

through the energizing coil. When the coil is energized, the magnetic pull exerted closes the contacts connecting the horn directly to the battery. In order to eliminate the "4 a.m. stuck horn," some manufacturers insert the ignition switch in series with the energizing coil and horn button. In this type of system, the horn can not be operated unless the ignition is turned on.

INSTRUMENT CLUSTER WARNING LIGHTS

A relay is used in connection with an indicator light to provide a visual indication of the proper functioning of a given electrical circuit. For example, relays are used on some buses and trucks, with a small indicator light on the dash to tell whether or not the brake lights or taillights are burning. The relay (Fig. 21) func-

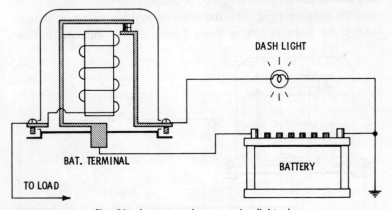

Fig. 21. Instrument cluster warning light relay.

tions in the same manner as the horn relay. When current flows to the designated electrical load, the energizing winding pulls the armature down, closing the contacts to the indicator light.

REGULATOR CONTACT SERVICE

Whenever a problem arises with a regulator, it is most commonly caused by oxides on the voltage regulating and current limiting contacts. Many types of contact materials are used in regulator construction. Each material has its particular advantages and disadvantages, such as low contact resistance, resistance to transfer or pitting, and resistance to welding or sticking. Some of the more common contact materials are tungsten, platinum, silver alloy, and gold alloy. All contact materials are subject to pitting and/or oxide formations, and have a definite life span. Silver alloy has an oxide which is conductive and is usually used on the cut-out contacts. Tungsten, platinum, gold alloy, and silver alloy contact materials are usually found on the current limiting and voltage regulating units.

Of all the contact materials mentioned, only tungsten has an insulating oxide. In operation, if a set of contacts should weld, maximum current would pass through the contact material. Tungsten has an advantage in that it is very resistant to welding, which can be an asset in a regulator or current limiting relay. If the contacts of these relays weld and do not block the flow of field current, high voltages can be produced by the generator which may damage the generator and regulator. Tungsten will "fail safe." That is, insulating oxides will form, but the contacts will not weld and no current can flow.

The rate of formation of tungsten oxide depends upon several variables:

1. Temperature.

2. Humidity.

3. Current interrupted by the contacts.

4. Frequency of contact opening.

Because of the above number of variables, the life of a tungsten contact is very difficult to predict. Other types of contact materials are not as sensitive to temperature and humidity; however, they may be more sensitive to the current interrupted by the contacts and the frequency of opening. Considering the job that a set

97

of regulator contacts has to perform, it is amazing that they stand up as well as they do. The average voltage regulator contacts may operate 1200 times per minute or 72,000 times per hour. As you can see, the number of times the contacts open and close in a voltage regulating unit is many millions of times in the life of the relay. Obviously, some wear must occur and some oxide must form. Usually, the contacts can be restored to good operating condition if they are cleaned with trichlorethylene and a piece of crocus cloth.

SUMMARY

The generator regulator has several functions. First, it protects the generator from excessive output which could burn up the generator; it protects the electrical circuits from possible damage by excessive voltage; and it controls the generator output to keep the battery in a state of full charge. It also regulates the generator output to match the car's electrical requirements.

There are three major components in a generator regulator:

1. A cutout relay.

2. A voltage regulator.

3. A current regulator.

These parts are basically electromagnetic relays or switches which are mounted on a single base plate with a cover over the complete unit.

The cutout relay opens the circuit from the battery to the generator when the engine is not running, otherwise the battery would discharge and damage the generator.

The voltage regulator limits the voltage output of the generator to a safe limit to protect the battery, ignition points, lights and all electrical components when the battery demands are at a minimum.

The current regulator protects the generator by preventing it from exceeding its rated output at times of maximum electrical demands. The current regulator operates in the same manner as the voltage regulator.

REVIEW QUESTIONS

1. What is the purpose of the current regulator?

2. What is the purpose of the voltage regulator?

3. What are the advantages of the alternator system?

4. What type of metal is used on regulator contact points?

5. What is the purpose of the cutout relay?

CHAPTER 5

Carburetor Fundamentals

Only the basic fundamentals of carburetor action will be discussed in this chapter. For a more detailed description, see Chapter 8.

CARBURETION

The basic purpose of a carburetor is to mix fuel and air for burning in the cylinders. To achieve the basic premises of a carburetor, an ordinary tin can with a small hole in the bottom could be used. In fact, the first motorized bicycle or motorcycle used a carburetor of this description. In the modern automotive engine, merely mixing the gasoline and air in the carburetor is insufficient; the correct mixture must be delivered to the cylinders in order to realize top efficiency and obtain maximum power under all speed and load conditions. These requirements are met in the modern carburetor by utilizing the *venturi* principle.

Venturi

Frequently we notice that the wind seems to increase in speed between houses, or that water seems to flow faster in the narrow stretches of a river. In a fashion, these are venturis, as shown in

101

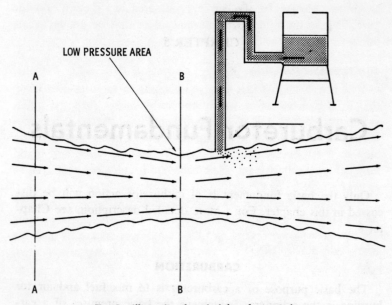

Fig. 1. Illustrating the principles of a venturi.

Fig. 1. As can be seen in Fig. 1, an observer standing at point *AA* would see a specific amount of water flow by in any given amount of time (gals. per min.). An observer standing at point *BB* would have to account for the same amount of water in the same time. Obviously, the water must flow faster at *BB* than at *AA*.

A quantity of water suddenly forced through a constricted area has to accelerate in order to maintain a constant volume of flow. The acceleration achieved in Fig. 1 creates a low-pressure area at the pipe opening near point *BB*, and atmospheric pressure exists at the top of the tank. The difference of pressure forces the water through the pipe into the stream. The greater the speed of the water, the greater the low pressure-area or "suction" on the pipe. This is the same principle and effect that occurs in a carburetor in forcing fuel into the air stream.

Atmospheric Pressure

It is a well known fact that water tends to seek its own level; that is, if two bodies of water, one being higher than the other, are connected they will eventually become level. In the same manner, bodies of air will also tend to "flow" from a high-pressure area to a low-pressure area. In this respect, air flow and liquid flow behave similarly, and their behavior is commonly referred to as *fluid flow*.

Atmospheric pressure is a constant force that tends to equalize itself in any given area. It is the weight of the atmosphere pushing downward, which amounts to 14.7 pounds per square inch at sea level. Air moves from a high-pressure to a low-pressure area,

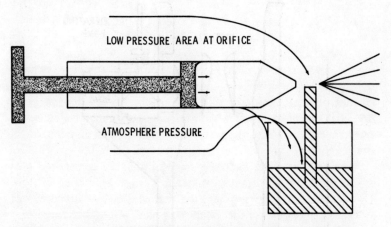

LOW PRESSURE AREA AT ORIFICE

ATMOSPHERE PRESSURE

Fig. 2. Comparing the venturi section of the carburetor to an air pump, illustrating the atmospheric pressure.

and the greater the difference in pressure, the greater the rate of air movement or its velocity.

If Fig. 2, a cross-section of an ordinary insecticide sprayer is shown. The bowl of the sprayer has an opening to the atmosphere, and has another opening immediately in front of the barrel from which air is forced. With no plunger movement, air pressure at the orifice and at the vent hole is equal and there is no movement of air. When the plunger is pushed down the barrel, a stream of air is forced over the orifice at a very high rate (or velocity). This action causes a low-pressure area to exist at the top of the orifice. Under these conditions, the atmospheric pressure acts through the vent hole, pushing down on the fluid and forcing the fluid through the orifice and into the air stream. The low air pressure that exists at the orifice is due to the *venturi effect* that exists in this area. The above described action is the same action that occurs in a carburetor.

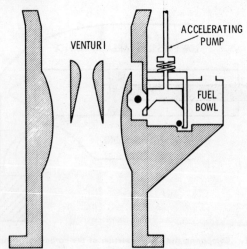

Fig. 3. Illustrating the venturi tube application.

Throttle System

As can be seen in Fig. 3, a venturi exists in the air horn and immediately adjacent to the venturi in a jet or orifice that leads back to the fuel bowl. Below the venturi, the butterfly valve is shown. As air rushes through the carburetor (downdraft carburetor), it reaches the "necked down" section called the venturi, and the velocity of the air is greatly increased. This increase in velocity causes a low-pressure area at the orifice and, as in the insecticide gun, the atmospheric pressure pushes fuel from the bowl out the orifice and into the air stream. This charge is delivered to the cylinder as a vaporized gas and air mixture.

High-Speed Circuit

In order to ensure economical and smooth running engines, some control of the amount of gas present in the gas-air mixture is

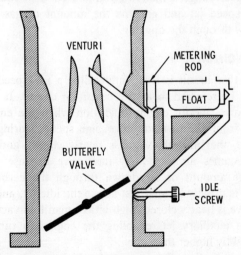

Fig. 4.   Illustrating the function of the butterfly in a typical carburetor.

necessary. Obviously, more gas must be used under high-speed and high-power conditions. As the engine speed increases, so does the piston speed, thereby causing a greater volume of air at higher speeds to pass through the carburetor. The increased velocity of the air through the venturi allows more gas to enter the mixture.

In order to control this, the butterfly valve shown in Fig. 4 is allowed to open and close, controlling the speed of the air that passes the venturi. By carefully designing the operation of the butterfly valve and jet, the most economical operation is attained throughout the entire speed range. The functioning of the high-speed jet can be tested easily using a tachometer.

The desired gas-air mixture resulting from the air flowing through the venturi does not remain balanced over the entire range of engine speeds. In an effort to balance the mixture throughout the engine speed range, a *metering* rod is used. This rod is inserted in the high-speed jet and governs the amount of gas that is allowed to flow through the opening.

Low-Speed Circuit

Although this circuit is frequently called a low-speed circuit, it might better be referred to as the *transition* circuit. It is this circuit that allows smooth engine operation when the engine speed is increased from idle to medium or high speed. During this transition period, the butterfly valve is nearly closed, and the high-speed jet becomes almost totally ineffective because of the decrease in the amount of air drawn through the carburetor. An auxiliary jet is usually located just above the idle jet, and when the butterfly valve is nearly closed, high intake-manifold vacuum draws air from the auxiliary jet, enabling the engine to run smoothly at speeds slightly higher than idle.

When the butterfly valve is open for high-speed operation, the low-speed or transition jet and the idle jet are dry. No fuel is available to the engine from these jets. To summarize this action, with the butterfly valve closed, only the idle jet is allowing gas to enter the carburetor throat. As the butterfly valve travels from its fully closed to its fully wide-open position, the transition jet allows fuel to enter the carburetor, and as the valve continues to open, the venturi becomes increasingly effective. When the valve is wide open, the transition jet and idle jet are dry, and all the gas entering the engine comes from the high-speed jet due to the action of the venturi.

Idle Circuit

Because of the variations in performance of identical engines, some external method of varying the amount of gas entering the air stream is necessary. As the idle adjustment screw is moved in (Fig. 4), less gas is allowed into the air stream, resulting in a leaner mixture. As the idle adjustment screw is moved outward, more gas is allowed into the air stream, resulting in a richer mixture.

At some point between the mixture being too rich and too lean, perfect balance occurs. When this point is reached, maximum efficiency from the air-fuel mixture is obtained and the engine will run at the highest rpm attainable. A tachometer is frequently used for setting the idle adjustment jets. By hooking up the tachometer according to the manufacturer's specifications, and screwing the idle adjustment jet in and out until the maximum engine rpm is obtained, the most efficient idle-jet setting will be assured.

Accelerating Pump Circuit

When the throttle of an automobile is suddenly opened, the butterfly valve in the carburetor is fully opened, allowing a greater volume of the air and fuel mixture to enter the carburetor chamber. However, since the air is considerably lighter than the fuel, it

107

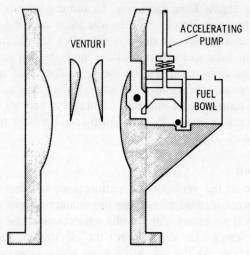

Fig. 5. Illustrating the accelerating pump.

gets into motion faster and would present a very lean mixture to the engine. To overcome this difficulty, an accelerator pump is used, as can be seen in Fig. 5. The pump is directly connected through a spring to the throttle linkage, and whenever the throttle is opened, the pump is actuated, forcing a small amount of fuel into the carburetor air horn. This small amount of fuel provides a better burning mixture than would otherwise be present under these conditions. By the time this fuel is used, the high-speed circuit is operating efficiently.

SUMMARY

The automobile engine will not run on gasoline alone. In order to produce usable power, gasoline must first be atomized and vaporized in air to produce a highly combustible air-fuel mixture.

This mixture is then burned in the cylinder under controlled conditions of temperature, pressure, and time.

The device which mixes the gasoline and air is called the carburetor. The carburetor also automatically varies the air-fuel mixture, which provides a *richer mixture* for starting, idle, and acceleration, and a *leaner mixture* for part-throttle operation. The carburetor also regulates the engine speed and power by controlling the flow of air-fuel mixture to the cylinders.

While the carburetor is rather complex, its operation relies simply on differences in pressure. The carburetor has various fixed and adjustable passageways, such as jets, ports, and pumps arranged in what are called systems or circuits. An understanding of how these pressure differences are applied to make the carburetor operate, will assist in making adjustments and in diagnosing carburetor troubles.

REVIEW QUESTIONS

1. What must be mixed with gasoline for the carburetor to function properly?

2. What is the function of the venturi?

3. What is the function of the float valve?

4. Why does atmospheric pressure play an important part in carburetion?

5. What is the purpose of the throttle valve?

CHAPTER 6

Compression

In a gasoline engine, the air-fuel mixture must be highly compressed in each cylinder before it is ignited. The upward movement of the piston will squeeze the fuel mixture into about 1/10 of its original volume, assuming a 10:1 compression ratio. This compression increases the pressure in the combustion chamber to 150 pounds per square inch or higher. When the air-fuel mixture is ignited, the pressure in the combustion chamber is increased 4

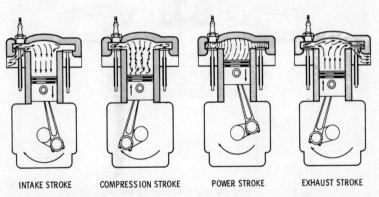

| INTAKE STROKE | COMPRESSION STROKE | POWER STROKE | EXHAUST STROKE |

Fig. 1. Illustrating the compression on all four cycles of an automotive engine.

to 5 times this value. The piston rings, intake and exhaust valves. and cylinder head gasket must effectively seal both the compression and combustion pressures if the engine is to perform properly.

A compression test will indicate low compression due to the loss of sealing protection in these parts. Since no amount of ignition system or carburetor adjustments can compensate for such mechanical engine defects, a compression test will determine if the engine will respond to a tune-up. Any mechanical defect that is disclosed by the compression test will have to be corrected before a successful tune-up can be performed.

PISTON RINGS

The piston rings provide the seal between the pistons and the cylinder wall throughout all four strokes of the conventional auto-

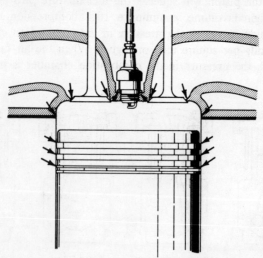

Fig. 2. Illustrating the seal produced by the rings, gaskets, and valve seats.

motive engine, as shown in Fig. 1. On the intake stroke, the piston draws air and fuel into the cylinder, creating a vacuum throughout the intake manifold system. A good seal is required between the piston ring and the cylinder wall to ensure the maximum amount of mixture to enter the cylinder, as shown in Fig. 2. During the compression stroke, any leakage past the rings will decrease the ability of the piston to retain and fully compress the mixture drawn in during the intake stroke.

When the piston is at BDC (bottom dead center) the maximum volume is available, and as the piston travels upward, the volume decreases until the minimum volume is reached at TDC (top dead center). With the 6.5:1 compression ratio engines, the ring-to-cylinder wall sealing ability was not as critical as it is in today's modern 10:1 or higher compression ratio engines. When the mixture is ignited by the spark plug, it expands and forces the piston downward. The power generated by the burning mixture is transmitted through the piston, connecting rod, and crankshaft to the power train of the vehicle. Any piston-ring leak or "blow-by" during the compression stroke subtracts from the total power available to move the vehicle. If all of the exhaust gases are not removed during the exhaust stroke, there will not be sufficient vacant piston volume to receive the maximum fuel mixture during the intake stroke. To determine if the piston rings are sealing, a compression test can be made. Since the valves are tested at the same time as the rings, the compression tester will not be discussed until later in the chapter.

VALVES

The intake and exhaust valves of an engine must fit properly and seat securely, or the engine will lose power in a similar manner to that of improper piston-ring sealing. The high pressures

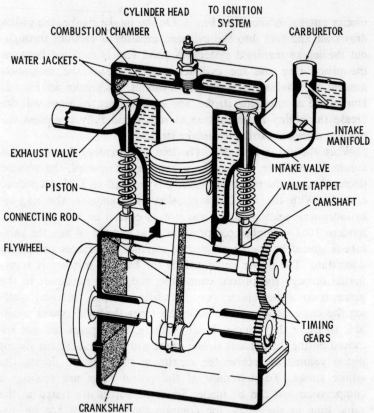

CYLINDER HEAD
TO IGNITION SYSTEM
COMBUSTION CHAMBER
CARBURETOR
WATER JACKETS
INTAKE MANIFOLD
EXHAUST VALVE
INTAKE VALVE
PISTON
VALVE TAPPET
CAMSHAFT
CONNECTING ROD
FLYWHEEL
TIMING GEARS
CRANKSHAFT

Fig. 3.   Illustrating a single-cylinder engine, showing the piston and valves.

and heat imposed on the piston and piston rings also affect the valves. A single-cylinder engine is shown in Fig. 3, illustrating the piston and valves. *At 40 miles per hour the valves in an eight-cylinder engine will open and close approximately 840,000 times per hour.*

Exhaust valves and seats momentarily operate at temperatures as high as 3800° Fahrenheit, running cherry red while maintaining the proper seat. *Each valve, weighing only a few ounces, must maintain a good seal against pressures as high as 1200 pounds per square inch.* Considering the environment in which valves operate, it is a tribute to modern metallurgy that they operate as long as they do. Since valves fall into the realm of automotive tune-up to a greater degree than piston rings, a few specific valve problems will be discussed.

Corrosion and Wear

Warpage, burning, pitting, and out-of-round wear will attack the exhaust valve since it is exposed to the high temperatures of the exhaust gases. By comparison, the intake valve has a relatively light job to perform. Burning and pitting are caused by the valve failing to seat tightly, permitting exhaust blow-by. This condition is often traced to hard carbon particles on the seat. It may also be due to weak valve springs, insufficient tappet clearance, warpage, and misalignment.

Warpage occurs chiefly in the upper valve stem due to its exposure to intense heat. Out-of-round wear follows when the seat is pounded by a valve whose head is not in line with the stem and guide. Oil and air are sucked past the worn intake valve, stem, and guide and into the combustion chamber (Fig. 4), causing excessive oil consumption, forming carbon, and diluting carburized fuel.

Misalignment

Misalignment is a product of wear, warpage, and distortion. Wear, perhaps hastened by insufficient or improper lubrication, will eventually create excessive clearances and consequent misalignment. Warpage of the entire engine block is not uncommon,

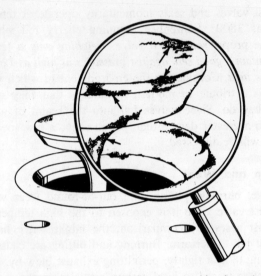

**Fig. 4. Illustrating a burned valve due to a blow-by action
around the valve seat.**

usually due to excessive heat caused by a clogged cooling system.
More frequently, the valve guide warps because of the variation in
temperature along its length. The top of the guide is near com-
bustion-chamber heat, while the bottom of the guide is cooled
by water jackets. If the guide wear is excessive, the guide should
be reamed for a valve with an oversize stem. Some engines have
guide inserts which can be replaced.

Distortion, caused by unequal tightening of cylinder-head bolts,
often upsets alignments and clearances. Any wear, warpage, or distortion affecting the valve guide destroys its function as an accurate bearing to keep the valve head concentric with its seat,
and thus prevents a leak-proof seating. A good illustration of a
misaligned valve is shown in Fig. 5.

116

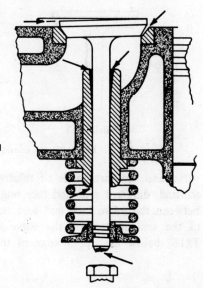

Fig. 5.   Illustrating a misaligned
valve due to wear.

Valve-Head Margin

Scrap and replace any valve that cannot be entirely refaced
with a definite margin maintained. The amount of grinding necessary to true a valve face is an indication of the head warpage
from the axis or centerline of its stem. With excessive warpage, a
knife edge will be ground on part or all of the valve head due to
the considerable amount of metal that must be removed to completely reface. Heavy valve heads are required for strength and to
dissipate heat. Knife edges lead to breakage and burning, and to
pre-ignition due to heat localizing on the edge of the valve. A
correct and incorrect valve face is illustrated in Fig. 6.

Interference Angle

The *interference angle* method of reconditioning is advantageous
where face deposits have been troublesome, and where both the

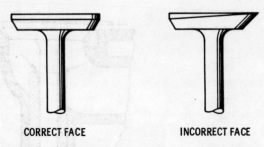

CORRECT FACE   INCORRECT FACE

Fig. 6. Illustrating the correct and incorrect valve face.

valve and seat are made of relatively hard materials. With this method, different seat and face angles are used, and line contact between the valve face and seat occurs. In general, the position of the seat contact on the valve face should be approximately 1/16″ below the upper edge of the valve face. The valve face

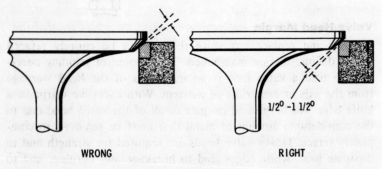

WRONG   RIGHT

Fig. 7. Relation of valve-face and valve-seat angle which is known as an interference fit.

and seat in most engines are ground at the same angle. When this is the case, the final grinding operation can be accomplished by means of valve-grinding compound. It is becoming more prevalent, however, to reface the valve at a slightly different angle than the valve seat to provide what is known as an *interference fit*. An example of this is shown in Fig. 7. In this particular operation, both the intake and exhaust valve have an interference fit with their seats. Some other engines may have this type of fit only on the exhaust valve.

It is obvious that with the different angles between the valve face and seat, grinding compound cannot be used to finish the surface. Instead, refacing equipment must be utilized. When refacing the valve seats, it is important to use the correct size valve-guide pilot for the refacing stones. This will ensure a true and complete surface.

Locating Valve Contact Area

Maximum valve life is greatly dependent upon proper location of the area of contact between the valve and valve seat. Fig. 8 shows the correct and incorrect positions. The overall contact of the valve face with the seat can be checked by lightly coating the valve seat with Prussian blue. Set the valve in place and rotate while applying a light downward pressure. If the blue is transferred to the center or upper half of the valve face (nearest the top of the head), the fit is satisfactory. If the blue is transferred to the extreme top edge, lower the valve seat with a stone of the proper angle (usually 30°). If the blue is transferred to the bottom edge of the valve face, raise the seat by using a stone of the recommended angle (usually 60°). When the seat is properly positioned, its width must be within the recommended specifications (usually from 3/64 to 3/32 inch).

Valve Guides

Valve guides allow the valves to move up and down and provide accurate positioning of the valve face on the valve seat. The

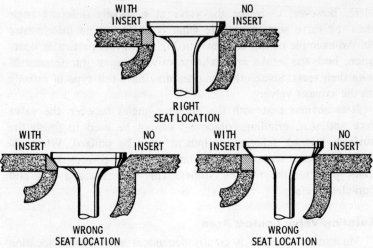

Fig. 8. Illustrating the correct and incorrect valve-face and valve-seat contact.

guides may be an integral part of the engine block or head, or may be in the form of inserts. For those engines in which the guides are an integral part, valves with oversize stems are available when the guides (or valve stems) become excessively worn. For those engines with valve-guide inserts, wear can be corrected by replacement of the guides and/or valves.

When wear of either the valve stem or the guide is suspected, both should be checked. The valve-stem diameter can be measured with a micrometer. If the wear exceeds the specifications (usually 0.002 inch), the valve should be replaced. The valve guide can be checked for wear by means of a gauge. The gauge is fastened to the cylinder head and at right angles to the valve stem being measured. Move the valve to and from the indicator. The total reading should not exceed specifications (usually 0.010 to 0.015 inch).

If the valve-guide wear is excessive, the guide should be reamed for a valve with an oversize stem. Select the correct size reamer and slowly turn it by hand in the valve-guide bore. Clean the guide thoroughly before installing the new valve. *Never attempt to ream a valve guide from a standard size directly to the maximum oversize. Instead, ream in steps, using successively larger reamers so the guide will be reamed true in relation to the valve seat.*

Valve-guide insert replacement (in cars so equippd) is necessary when the old insert is worn beyond specifications. The insert can be removed and a new one installed by means of special tools and an arbor press, or by special tools and a hammer. After a new guide has been installed, it must be hand reamed to the correct size.

Valve Springs

Whenever the valves have been removed for inspection, reconditioning, or replacement, the valve springs should be tested. This is often overlooked, but the valve springs play a very important part in proper engine operation. A weak valve spring may cause unsatisfactory seating of the valve, resulting in rough engine idling and possible damage to the valve. A distorted spring or one with too much tension may cause excessive wear of the camshaft lobes. Therefore, testing the valve springs for correct pressure and squareness should be a part of every valve reconditioning operation.

Valve-Spring Pressure—Each valve has only one spring on most cars. There are a few exceptions to this, however, one being certain Buick models that have two—one inside the other. The spring pressure is different for each car, ranging from as low as 70 pounds to as high as 280 pounds. The usual pressure, however, is from 100 to 150 pounds. Special tools are available for checking the valve-spring pressure. To measure the pressure, the spring is compressed to a specified length, and the force necessary to hold it at this length is the valve-spring pressure. A reading that varies more than 10 pounds from the specifications indicates the spring should be replaced.

Squareness—The valve spring should also be tested for distortion by using the method shown in Fig. 9. An ordinary machinist's or carpenter's square is placed on a flat surface with the valve spring positioned as shown. The length is measured as the spring is rotated. If the measurements vary by more than 1/16 inch, in-

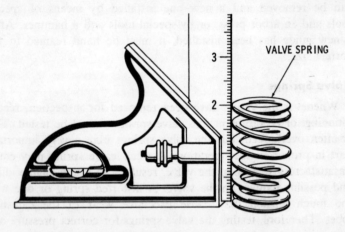

Fig. 9. Checking valve spring squareness.

stall a new spring. The overall length of the spring can also be measured with this setup and should agree with the specifications of the manufacturer.

Installation—Installation (or removal) of the valve spring requires the use of a compressor tool. These are available in different designs, many of them being made specifically for a particular make and model of engine. The valve springs can be installed in or removed from most engines with the cylinder head in place. To do this, the spark plug is removed from the cylinder that requires valve-spring service and a threaded compressed-air adapter is inserted.

Connect an air hose to the adapter and maintain at least 90 lbs. of air pressure in the cylinder while the valve spring is being removed. The air pressure will hold the valve against its seat so the valve lock and upper retainer can be removed. A plier-type tool is usually the handiest to use in this case. New oil seals should always be installed on the valve stems when the valve springs have been removed. In addition, replace any damaged spring shields (if used) or retainers.

Valve Spring Installed Height—The installed height of the valve spring should be checked, especially if the valves or seats have been reground. This measurement is made from the top of the spring seat (or shim, if used) to the bottom of the spring retainer. If the installed height is greater than the specifications, add the necessary number of spacers between the spring and its seat only to bring the assembly to the recommended height specified by the automobile manufacturer.

GASKETS

Gaskets provide a seal between two metal surfaces, compensating for any slight difference that may exist between the surface of each part. To be effective, gaskets must be leakproof against air, water, oil, and fuel. Gaskets used on heads and manifolds must also resist extreme heat and pressure. Assemble a valve reconditioning job with new gaskets and install carefully according to instructions. Lost compression and resulting troubles are frequently traceable to leaking gaskets.

BOLTING HEAD TO BLOCK

Use a torque wrench to uniformly tighten cylinder head studs to a pre-determined tension. It is dangerous guesswork to depend on the feel of an ordinary wrench. The tightening of any one stud nut by less than one half turn will distort the head and block to a measurable degree. This distortion will seriously affect alignments and clearances, resulting in lost compression and fast wear, with oil and fuel wasted. Engine or torque-wrench manufacturers will furnish the recommended order or sequence for tightening down the cylinder head studs, with the proper amount of tension to be used.

TAPPET CLEARANCE

Some of today's engines have hydraulic valve lifters for tappets, which do not require adjustment. Others have tappets which should be adjusted according to engine manufacturer's specifications. On the latter type of tappet, the correct clearance contributes to quiet engine operation and long valve and seat wear. Insufficient clearance causes the valve to ride open, resulting in lost compression and burning. Too much clearance upsets timing and shortens intake and exhaust valve life. Check the clearance between the tappet and guide, and replace if the clearance exceeds .006". A sloppy fit between the tappet and guide permits the tappet to strike the valve-stem end off center, causing a side thrust on the valve stem that results in excessive wear and improper seating.

COMPRESSION TESTING

Before making any tests, *warm the engine thoroughly*, and make all tests with the throttle *open*. Remove all the spark plugs from the motor. On cars equipped with automatic starters, ground the high-tension wire from the coil. Use extreme care in removing the spark plugs by first removing all dirt or foreign substance which may have collected on the cylinder head around the base of the spark plug. On occasion, in removing a spark plug, particles of heavy carbon will become loosened and lodge under the valve when making the test. When this condition exists, turn the motor over several times, which should dislodge the carbon from the valve seat. Insert the compression tester.

With the ignition switch off, spin the engine with the starter until the piston has pumped five times. Be sure and have the throttle wide open in making all compression tests. Make a note of this reading and open the valve on the gauge to release the pressure. Test all the cylinders and note all of the readings. Not more than 10% variation between cylinders should exist for maximum performance. Refer to specifications for normal pressure.

There is no material advantage in operating more than five compression strokes per cylinder when testing, since the battery voltage will have dropped sufficiently to decrease the revolutions per minute, thereby giving a false compression reading. A low reading in one or more cylinders is interpreted as a condition due to one of the following:

1. Faulty valves.

2. Faulty rings.

3. Faulty headgasket.

4. Faulty piston or wall condition.

To determine if a compression loss is due to bad valves or a bad ring condition, inject a small amount of light engine oil on the top of each piston, taking four complete strokes for the second reading. The light engine oil will temporarily seal the piston rings, and if the compression readings are now considerably higher (20 lbs. or more), it is a definite indication that the rings are leaking. If no increase is noted, it is an indication that the valves are not seating properly.

When the compression is low and even between two adjacent cylinders, it is an indication of gasket leakage between the cylinders. Before condemning a low compression reading, and to eliminate all possibility of doubt, run the motor for a few minutes and allow a small amount of any good grade tune-up oil to pass through the motor through the air inlet of the carburetor. After the motor has run for 5 or 10 minutes, recheck for compression, and if the reading is more nearly normal, you will find gummy or sticky valves.

SUMMARY

Every cylinder of any 4-stroke cycle engine must have at least one intake valve to permit the mixture to enter the cylinder, and one exhaust valve to allow the burned gases to escape. The type of valve usually used in automotive engines is called a *poppet, mushroom,* or *tulip* valve. The word *poppet* is derived from the popping action of the valve, and the word *mushroom* and *tulip* from the general shape of the valve.

A valve usually is made in one piece from a special alloy steel. The intake valves ordinarily are made of chromium-nickel alloy and the exhaust valves of silichrome alloy because of the extremely high temperatures that they must withstand. In some engines, especially the air-cooled types, the exhaust valve contains sodium in a sealed cavity extending from the head through the stem. The sodium conducts heat away from the head to the stem, from where it is conducted to the valve guide, thus aiding in cooling.

Valve stems are ground to fit the guides in which they operate. The reamed hole in the guide must be aligned and square with the valve seat to ensure proper seating of the valve. The guide may be an integral part of the cylinder block or cylinder head, depending on the manufacturer, or they may be removable sleeves which can be replaced it worn. Removable valve guides are usually made of cast iron.

REVIEW QUESTIONS

1. What is the purpose of the intake and exhaust valves?

2. What part provides the seal between the piston and the cylinder wall?

3. What will happen to the valve if there is to much tappet clearance?

4. What will a leaky head gasket indicate?

5. What type of metal are exhaust valves made of?

CHAPTER 7

Cooling System

Most automobiles are equipped with a liquid-type cooling system. The principle of operation is the same for all automobiles and the actual construction features differ only slightly. The cooling system is necessary because of the high temperatures generated during engine operation. High temperatures are developed in efficient combustion engines, and it is not possible to use all of the heat generated without harming the engine. The temperature within the combustion chambers rises to about twice the amount needed to melt iron, so it can be seen that something must be done to remove some of this heat to prevent damage. If the engine is not cooled during operation, valves will burn and warp, lubricating oil will break down, pistons and bearings will overheat, and pistons will seize in the cylinder.

COOLANTS

Water is normally used as the coolant in domestic automobiles; and only soft water should be used. Hard water contains minerals which form a scale on the inside surface of the cooling system, reducing its efficiency. Inhibitors are available to reduce or prevent the formation of scale and rust, and should always be used when only water is used as a coolant.

Automobiles in most sections of the country will be operating in temperatures below 32° at some time during the year, making the use of water alone impractical. Besides the inhibitors used to prevent scale and rust, the most well-known additive is antifreeze. The most common antifreeze solutions are methyl alcohol, ethyl alcohol, and ethylene glycol. The first two are subject to evaporation caused by boiling at temperatures at which the engine operates most efficiently. Ethylene glycol, however, has a boiling point of 330°, which is well above normal operating temperatures, and so is well suited for engine cooling purposes. It is noncorrosive, has no appreciable odor, and offers complete protection from freezing when used in the proper amounts. The maximum protection from freezing is obtained with a mixture of approximately 40% water and 60% ethylene glycol.

This mixture offers protection from freezing at temperatures down to —65° F. A higher concentration of ethylene glycol will only raise the freezing point of the mixture. In fact, pure ethylene glycol has a freezing point that is not much below that of water alone. Methyl alcohol has a freezing point of —144° F, while ethyl alcohol will freeze at —174°. Most antifreeze solutions now available contain an inhibitor. This is not permanent protection against scale and rust formation, however, and the antifreeze solution should be drained and discarded each spring. The system should be flushed and cleaned, and fresh soft water added when all danger of freezing is over. An inhibitor should be added to the water at this time for the summer and fall driving seasons.

Coolant Flow

The basic automobile cooling system consists of a radiator, water pump, thermostat, flexible hose, and a system of passages and

Fig. 1. A complete automobile engine illustrating some of the cooling passages.

water jackets in the cylinder head and cylinder block through which the coolant circulates. This is shown in Fig. 1. The cooling of the engine parts is accomplished by keeping the coolant circulating and in constant contact with all of the metal surfaces to be cooled.

The pump draws the coolant from the bottom of the radiator, forcing it through the passages and water jackets in the engine, and ejects it into the tank at the top of the radiator. From here, the coolant passes through tubes to the bottom of the radiator and is again circulated through the engine by the water pump. A fan draws air over the outside surfaces of the radiator tubes and cools the liquid as it travels through them.

131

WATER JACKETS

The water passages in the cylinder block and head form the engine water jackets. In the cylinder block, the water jacket completely surrounds all the cylinders along their full length. In ad-

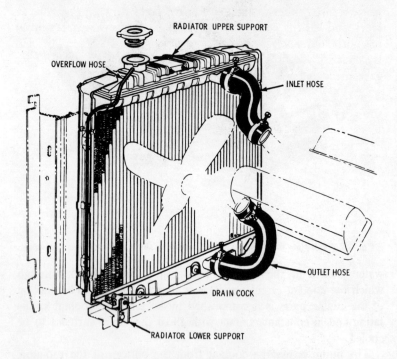

RADIATOR UPPER SUPPORT

OVERFLOW HOSE

INLET HOSE

OUTLET HOSE

DRAIN COCK

RADIATOR LOWER SUPPORT

Fig. 2. A typical vertical-flow radiator.

dition, narrow passages are provided between the cylinders for coolant circulation. In L-head engines, still other passages are provided in the cylinder block around the valve seats and any other hot parts that might be present.

In the cylinder head, water passages surround the combustion chambers. If the engine is of the overhead-valve type, passages around the valve seats will also be provided. The coolant flows from the cylinder block up into the head through openings called water transfer ports. A tight seal at the ports between the cylinder block and head is very important. This seal must be watertight at the ports and gas tight at the combustion chamber openings, and is generally obtained by using a single large metal and asbestos gasket, called the head gasket.

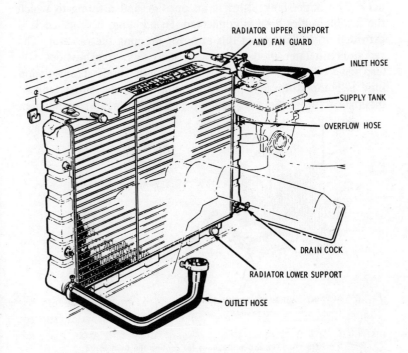

Fig. 3. A cross-flow radiator with a separate supply tank.

RADIATORS

Automobile radiators consist of two general types—the vertical-flow (Fig. 2) and cross-flow (Fig. 3). Both types contain two tanks with cores between them to form the radiating portion. The inlet tank contains an opening with a fitting to which is attached a flexible inlet hose. This tank is at the top of the radiator (on vertical-flow types) and usually contains a baffle located above the inlet opening. Most radiators of this type also have a filler neck located on the inlet tank. An overflow pipe is generally a part of the filler neck. The outlet tank also has an opening and a fitting to which the flexible outlet hose is connected. In addition, a drain cock is provided in the bottom of this tank for draining the radiator. The radiators on later model cars with automatic transmissions will also have oil-cooler connections in the outlet tank. Transmission fluid is pumped through pipes to a coil inside the outlet tank to dissipate some of the heat built up in the automatic transmission.

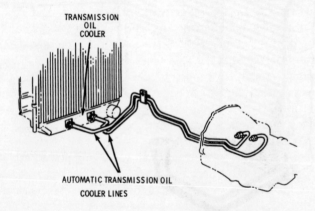

TRANSMISSION
OIL
COOLER

AUTOMATIC TRANSMISSION OIL
COOLER LINES

Fig. 4. Typical connections for cooling the fluid in an automatic transmission.

The radiator connections for cooling the transmission fluid which are typical of many cars so equipped, are shown in Fig. 4. The inlet tank collects the incoming coolant and distributes it across the top of the radiator cores (or along the side in cross-flow radiators). The baffle helps distribute the coolant and also prevents the coolant from being forced up into the filler neck and out the overflow pipe. The overflow pipe provides an opening for the escape of coolant or steam that might otherwise cause excessive pressure which could rupture the thin metal walls of the radiator.

The radiating portion of the radiator consists of many water tubes to which are attached air fins. The passage in the tubes is divided into many very thin columns. This exposes a larger radiating surface to the cooler air passing through the radiator than a single large passage would provide.

WATER PUMPS

The water pumps on all domestic cars are very similar in operating principles and construction. The pump is usually located at the front of the engine block and powered by the same shaft as the fan. Coolant from the lower part of the radiator is drawn into the pump through the lower radiator hose, and is forced through the water jacket into the upper part of the radiator. The pump is a centrifugal type, having an impeller with blades which force the coolant outward as the impeller rotates. The impeller may be made of metal or plastic.

A cross-sectional view of a typical water pump is shown in Fig. 5. The bearings shown are ball bearings and are permanently lubricated. Some water pumps on older-model cars have sleeve bearings that require periodic lubrication with a special water-pump grease. A seal assembly around the shaft prevents the coolant from leaking out around the shaft. Should any liquid escape, however,

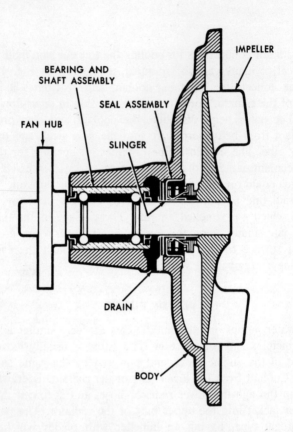

IMPELLER

BEARING AND
SHAFT ASSEMBLY

SEAL ASSEMBLY

FAN HUB

SLINGER

DRAIN

BODY

Courtesy Pontiac Motor Div., General Motors Corp.

**Fig. 5. The construction features of this water pump are
similar to those of all late model pumps.**

a slinger rotating with the shaft throws the leakage away from the
shaft by centrifugal force and it drains out of the pump body
through a hole provided for this purpose. Thus, any coolant leaking past the seal assembly is prevented from entering the bearings

where it could cause damage. Excessive leakage indicates the need for a new seal assembly.

FANS

The fan circulates a large amount of air through the radiator core to rapidly dissipate the heat carried by the coolant. In addition to removing heat from the radiator, this flow of air also provides some direct air cooling of the engine. Fans may have from four to eight blades, the number depending somewhat on the size of the motor and whether or not the car has factory installed air conditioning.

A rather recent development is a fan driven by a torque- and/or temperature-sensitive clutch. This clutch is a fluid coupling containing silicone oil. The fan speed is regulated by the amount of the silicone oil in the coupling—the more oil, the greater the fan speed. The amount of oil entering the coupling is regulated by some form of thermostatic device. As the air passing through the radiator becomes hotter, the thermostatic element opens a valve which admits more silicone oil into the coupling. Thus, the fan is driven at a faster speed to draw more air through the radiator to lower the temperature. As the temperature drops, the thermostatic valve closes, and the silicone oil in the coupling returns to a reserve chamber through bleed holes provided for that purpose. Radiating fins are an integral part of the assembly to dissipate the heat generated by the shearing action of the silicone oil. The top speed of this type of fan is somewhat lower than the top speed of the engine, since at high speeds enough air is passing through the radiators due to the forward motion of the car to provide adequate cooling without the benefit of the fan. At high speed more horsepower is available because the fan is then rotating at a much slower speed.

THERMOSTATS

Without a thermostat, the water pump would start circulating the coolant through the system as soon as the engine is started, no matter how low the temperature. Thus, a thermostat is included in the cooling system of an automobile to insure rapid warmup and to prevent overcooling in cold weather. The thermostat regulates the engine temperature by automatically controlling the amount of coolant flowing from the engine block to the radiator core. With the thermostat closed, water circulates through the engine block and head, but not through the radiator. This is possible because of a bypass through which the coolant returns directly to the water pump for recirculation when the thermostat valve has the circulation blocked through the radiator.

Two general types of thermostats are in use today—the bellows type and the pellet type. The bellows type may be found in some older-model cars and consists of a flexible-metal bellows attached to a valve. The sealed bellows, which is expandable, is filled with a highly volatile liquid, such as ether. When this liquid is cold, the bellows chamber is contracted and the valve is closed. When heated, the liquid vaporizes and expands the chamber, opening the valve. The pellet-type thermostat is found in nearly all late-model cars. This type of thermostat uses a pellet containing a paste. As the temperature rises, the paste turns to a liquid, expanding the pellet and opening the valve against the tension of a spring.

Thermostats are available to maintain the engine at various operating temperatures. When nonpermanent antifreeze is used, a low-temperature thermostat should be installed. This type of thermostat usually starts to open in the range of 150°-160°F. For more efficient operation of the engine and heater, permanent antifreeze should be used and a high-temperature thermostat installed. This type of thermostat opens in the range from 180°-190°F.

A thermostat may fail either in the closed position (most unlikely) or the open position (most likely). When it fails closed, engine overheating, loss of coolant, and eventual engine damage will result. When it fails open, slow engine warmup, low engine efficiency, and poor heater operation will result. *A defective thermostat cannot be repaired. Always replace with a new unit.*

RADIATOR CAPS

The cooling system on all late-model cars is pressurized and requires a pressure radiator cap similar to the one in Fig. 6. A pressure of from 12 to 15 lbs. is maintained in the cooling system during the time the engine is operating normally. This pressure is maintained in order to raise the boiling point of the coolant, allowing the engine to operate at a higher temperature without overflow and loss of coolant.

The cap contains two valves, which are normally closed, sealing the system. The pressure or blowoff valve is the larger of the two, and acts as a safety valve to relieve the pressure in the system if it should increase above the safe level. The smaller valve opens only when the pressure in the system becomes less than the atmospheric pressure as the system cools off. When this vacuum valve opens, air is drawn into the system through the overflow pipe.

Care should be taken when removing the cap from a pressurized system while the coolant is still hot. If the cap is removed too rapidly, the coolant may suddenly start boiling and gush out the filler neck, resulting in serious burns to the individual. To properly remove this type of cap, either wait until the engine has cooled, or rotate the cap counterclockwise to the stop, wait until the pressure has been relieved through the overflow pipe, then again turn counterclockwise until the cap is released.

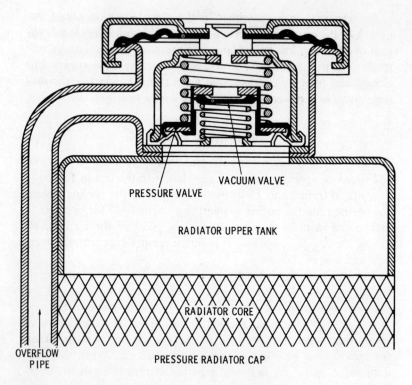

VACUUM VALVE

PRESSURE VALVE

RADIATOR UPPER TANK

RADIATOR CORE

OVERFLOW PIPE

PRESSURE RADIATOR CAP

Fig. 6.   Illustrating a typical pressure radiator cap.

DRAINING THE SYSTEM

If it is found necessary to completely drain the cooling system of coolant to prevent damage by freezing, special precautions must be taken. The drain cock located at the bottom of the radiator does not completely drain the entire system in most cars. Drain plugs are provided on the side of the engine block to completely drain the water jackets in the engine. Most four- and six-cylinder in-line engines will have one drain plug, while V-type engines usually have two—one on each side of the engine.

If the car is equipped with a heater, it will be necessary to disconnect the heater hose on some cars to drain the coolant that remains even after the rest of the system has been completely drained.

SUMMARY

All internal combustion engines are equipped with some type of cooling system because of the high temperatures they develop during operations. High temperatures are the result of the high gas pressures which act on the head of the piston. Without high temperatures, power cannot be produced efficiently.

However, it is not possible to use all of the heat of combustion without producing harmful results. There is no accurate method of measuring the temperature in the combustion chamber during the burning of fuel, but it has been determined to be twice the temperature at which iron melts. Therefore, if nothing is done to cool the engine during operation, valves will burn and warp, lubricating oil will break down, pistons and bearings will overheat, and pistons will seize in the cylinder walls.

REVIEW QUESTIONS

1. What is the main ingredient in permanent-type antifreeze?

2. What two types of radiators are used in automobiles?

3. What is the purpose of the water pump?

4. What is the purpose of the thermostat?

5. What is the boiling point for nonpermanent antifreeze?

CHAPTER 8

Carburetors and Fuel Systems

Various types of carburetors are used on modern automobile engines. The types most commonly used are the single-barrel, two-barrel and the four-barrel downdraft type. The prime purpose of any automotive carburetor is to mix air with gasoline for burning within the cylinders. Automobile engines will not run on raw, liquid gasoline. Instead, the gasoline must be broken up into tiny drops, then vaporized to produce a highly combustible air-fuel mixture. This mixture is then sent to the cylinders under controlled conditions of temperature, pressure, and time. The device which mixes the gasoline and air is called the carburetor. It not only mixes the gasoline and air, but it automatically varies the proportion. It provides a richer mixture for starting, idling, and acceleration, and a leaner mixture for part-throttle operation.

In addition, the carburetor regulates the engine speed and power by controlling the amount of fuel mixture that reaches the cylinders. In order to accomplish all of these tasks, a carburetor has a variety of jets, ports, and pump arrangements. Although a carburetor is relatively complicated, its basic operation depends simply on differences in pressure. An understanding of how these pressure differences are put to work in a carburetor will help in making adjustments and diagnosing carburetor troubles.

BASIC OPERATING PRINCIPLES

A carburetor consists of six basic circuits. They are as follows:

1. The idle circuit.

2. The main circuit.

3. The power circuit.

4. The float circuit.

5. The choke circuit.

6. The accelerating circuit.

The circuits are designed to supply the correct quantity of fuel under a given type of operation.

Idle Circuit

The idle circuit (Fig. 1) is used only when the engine is idling. The air-fuel mixture for this circuit can be regulated by turning the idle-mixture adjusting screw. When the engine is idling at a speed from 350 *rpm* to 550 *rpm*, the air-fuel mixture is discharged out of the hole(s) below the throttle plate. As the throttle plate is opened to increase engine speed, operation of the idle circuit slowly gives way to the operation of the carburetor's main circuit. The idle circuit supplies the fuel-air mixture to keep the engine running when the throttle valve is completely closed. At idle *there is very little air flowing through the venturi because the* throttle valve is closed, blocking most of the air flow.

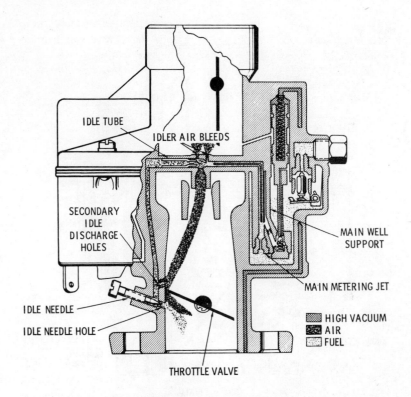

IDLE TUBE

IDLER AIR BLEEDS

SECONDARY
IDLE
DISCHARGE
HOLES

MAIN WELL
SUPPORT

MAIN METERING JET

IDLE NEEDLE

IDLE NEEDLE HOLE

HIGH VACUUM
AIR
FUEL

THROTTLE VALVE

Fig. 1. A pictorial view of the idle system.

To allow the engine to operate under this condition, an idle discharge hole is placed just below the throttle valve. Since the intake vacuum is high at idling speeds, the pressure differential between the air in the fuel bowl and the vacuum below the throttle valve forces fuel through the idle discharge holes. Gasoline flows from the fuel bowl through the idle tube on its way to the idle discharge hole. Air bleed holes opening into the idle tube intro-

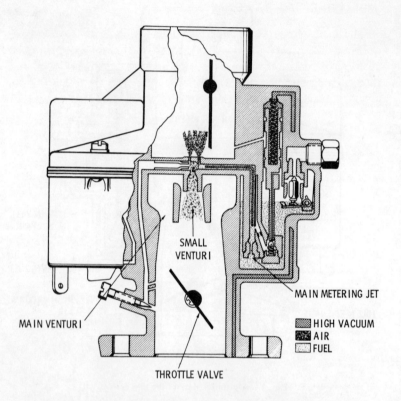

SMALL VENTURI

MAIN METERING JET

MAIN VENTURI

THROTTLE VALVE

HIGH VACUUM
AIR
FUEL

Fig. 2. A pictorial view of the throttle system.

duce a metered amount of air into the gasoline in the idle system, and also act as vents to prevent siphoning of gasoline from the fuel bowl above idle, at high speeds, or when the engine is stopped. The adjustable needle valve controls the richness of the idle fuel mixture by regulating the amount that passes through the idle discharge hole into the engine.

Main Circuit

The main circuit (Fig. 2) comes into action as the idle circuit becomes less effective and the main jets start to deliver fuel. The main circuit is in effect at all engine speeds above idle. With increased air speed through the venturi, increased air bleeding into the main nozzle takes place, preventing overrichness.

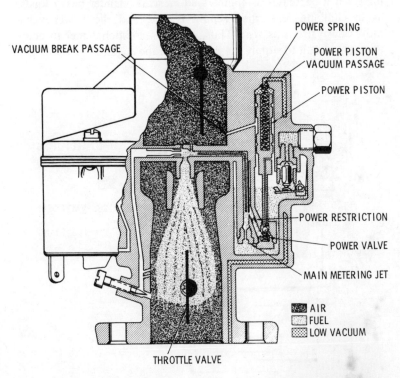

POWER SPRING

POWER PISTON VACUUM PASSAGE

VACUUM BREAK PASSAGE

POWER PISTON

POWER RESTRICTION

POWER VALVE

MAIN METERING JET

AIR
FUEL
LOW VACUUM

THROTTLE VALVE

Fig 3. A pictorial view of the full throttle system.

Power Circuit

The power circuit on most carburetors is mainly a control to meter the amount of fuel entering the main circuit. The power circuit is usually controlled by a piston-type valve, or a diaphragm-type valve. Both types of valves are controlled by engine vacuum. During normal engine operation, the engine vacuum holds the power valve against its seat (Fig. 3). At idle speed, vacuum is high, but it decreases as engine load *increases*. Under heavy loads, as in climbing hills, the vacuum is low, and the power valve moves away from its seat. Thus, it allows additional fuel to enter the main circuit to supply the demands of the engine.

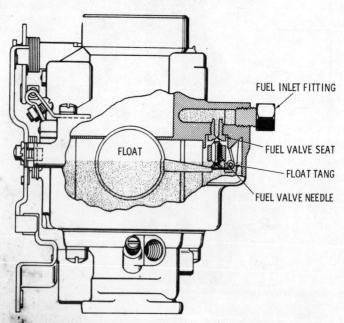

FUEL INLET FITTING

FLOAT

FUEL VALVE SEAT

FLOAT TANG

FUEL VALVE NEEDLE

Fig. 4.   The float system which regulates gasoline flow in the carburetor.

Float Circuit

The float circuit (Fig. 4) is incorporated to maintain an exact level of gasoline in the carburetor fuel bowl. The float rides on top of the fluid and rises and falls in direct relation to the amount of gasoline in the bowl.

The float is hinged to a needle valve which, in turn, operates against a "seat" located in the fuel inlet. A rising float seats the needle valve, cutting off fluid flow from the fuel pump into the carburetor. As the engine uses fuel, the float falls and moves the needle valve away from its seat. This, again, allows fuel to enter the carburetor. Exact fuel level in the bowl is vital for proper engine operation. A tab on the float hinge assembly (where it contacts the needle valve) can be bent as required to obtain correct float level and drop adjustments.

Choke Circuit

The choke circuit (Fig. 5) is used as a means of enriching the fuel-air mixture temporarily to provide satisfactory "cold weather" starting. A closed, or partially closed, choke valve in the carburetor air horn restricts air flow into the engine. Consequently, a greater proportion of fuel is drawn into the engine than is normally required for "warm engine" fuel-air mixture.

Choke valves are either manually controlled (through a flexible cable from the instrument panel to the choke valve shaft), or automatically controlled. An automatic choke uses a thermostatic spring (coiled around the choke valve shaft) and a small piston (exposed to engine manifold vacuum). In operation, the thermostatic spring contracts when the engine is "cold." The contracting spring rotates the shaft and closes the choke. This automatically provides the rich mixture for cold-weather starting. The choke valve is fully closed at a temperature of approximately 70°F

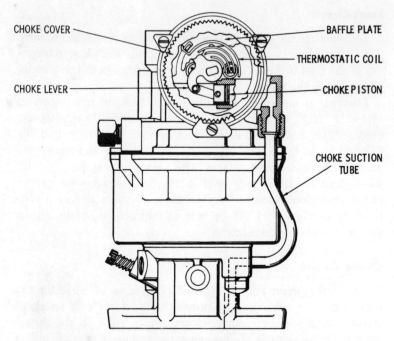

CHOKE COVER

BAFFLE PLATE

THERMOSTATIC COIL

CHOKE LEVER

CHOKE PISTON

CHOKE SUCTION TUBE

Fig. 5. Illustrating the automatic choke circuit.

After the engine is started, exhaust gases are piped into the choke housing via a "heat tube." The hot gases cause the spring to expand and rotate the choke valve shaft in the opposite direction. This opens the choke valve slowly as the engine warms to operating temperature and requires a "leaner" fuel-air mixture. The choke piston assists in opening the choke valve. It is connected to the thermostatic spring and exposed to engine manifold vacuum. The piston operates in a close-tolerance cylinder.

It can be seen, therefore, that a contracting thermostatic spring closes the choke valve, while a combination of an expanding thermostatic spring and engine vacuum opens the choke valve for "normal temperature" operation. An automatic choke is adjusted by aligning a factory-placed scribe mark on the choke cover with a raised indicator on the choke housing.

Acceleration Circuit

The accelerating circuit (Fig. 6) is connected to the throttle linkage. Its function is to enrich the fuel mixture temporarily for rapid acceleration. Fuel is drawn into the pump circuit, through a ball

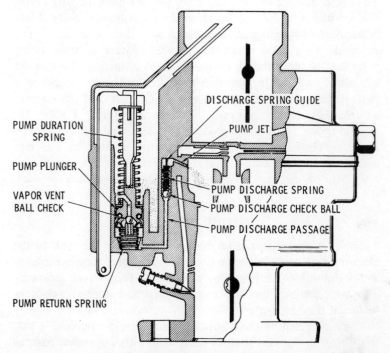

PUMP DURATION SPRING

PUMP PLUNGER

VAPOR VENT BALL CHECK

PUMP RETURN SPRING

DISCHARGE SPRING GUIDE

PUMP JET

PUMP DISCHARGE SPRING

PUMP DISCHARGE CHECK BALL

PUMP DISCHARGE PASSAGE

Fig. 6. Illustrating the acceleration pump circuit.

check valve, on the up stroke of the accelerator pump plunger. When the plunger moves downward, the ball check valve closes, forcing fuel through the pump discharge jet.

AIR CLEANER

The air cleaner is mounted on the carburetor to remove dust and other harmful particles from the air. Dust and similar material entering through the carburetor could cause rapid wear in the engine. The air cleaner may be of the "oil-bath" or "dry" type. The oil-bath type should be cleaned approximately every 2,000 miles. A partially clogged, dirty air cleaner can reduce the engine air intake to a point where the air-fuel mixture is made richer regardless of the carburetor adjustment. A reduction of air intake will also cause loss in power. Always service the air cleaner as a part of the engine tune-up. Oil-wetted, oil-bath, and dry-element air cleaners require different service procedures. Follow the recommended servicing procedures for the type used. *Caution*: If the air cleaner is held to the carburetor air horn by a clamp-and-screw arrangement, do not overtighten this clamp, or the air *horn may be distorted enough to cause the choke valve to stick.*

FUEL PUMPS

The fuel pump is used to move gasoline from the tank to the carburetor in sufficient quantity to supply the requirements of the engine under all operating conditions. These conditions vary over wide limits, from idle to full speed and during periods of sustained full acceleration.

The rocker arm of the fuel pump rides against an eccentric that is attached to the cam shaft or some other rotating engine part, as shown in Fig. 7. As the rocker arm is driven up and down, it actu-

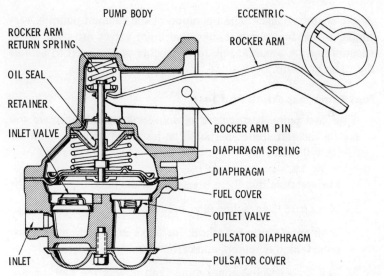

ROCKER ARM RETURN SPRING
PUMP BODY
OIL SEAL
RETAINER
INLET VALVE
INLET

ECCENTRIC
ROCKER ARM
ROCKER ARM PIN
DIAPHRAGM SPRING
DIAPHRAGM
FUEL COVER
OUTLET VALVE
PULSATOR DIAPHRAGM
PULSATOR COVER

Fig. 7. Illustrating a typical fuel pump.

ates a neoprene diaphragm. On the upward stroke a vacuum is created above the inlet and outlet valves, drawing gasoline through the inlet valves and closing the outlet valve. Fuel is stored in the chamber between the valves and the diaphragm.

On the downward stroke the inlet valve is forced against its seat and remains sealed. The outlet valve is forced open and fuel is forced through the valve, into the fuel lines, and to the carburetor.

Combination Pumps

A combination fuel pump and vacuum pump will be found on some automobiles. The vacuum portion has nothing to do with the fuel system, but has merely been added to the fuel pump because of convenience. Its purpose is to furnish a nearly constant vacuum to the windshield wipers so their speed will not vary as the load

153

on the engine changes. The operation of the vacuum pump is very similar to the fuel pump, except that more valves are used in the vacuum unit. A separate link to the rocker arm is used to actuate the vacuum pump.

Fuel Pump Inspection and Test

If the fuel pump is suspected of delivering an improper amount of fuel to the carburetor, it should be inspected and tested on the engine as follows:

1. Make certain that there is gasoline in the tank.

2. Make sure the gasoline filter is clean.

3. With engine running, check for leaks in the line at the gasoline tank, fuel pump, and carburetor.

4. Tighten any loose connections, and inspect the fuel line for flattening or kinks which would restrict the flow of fuel.

5. Inspect for leaks at the fuel pump diaphragm flange.

6. Disconnect the feed pipe at the carburetor. Ground the distributor terminal of the coil with a jumper wire so that the engine can be cranked without firing. Place a suitable container at the end of the pipe and crank the engine a few revolutions. If no gasoline (or only a few drops) flows from the pipe, the feed line is clogged or the fuel pump is inoperative. Before condemning the fuel pump, disconnect the feed line at the pump and blow through the line with an air hose to make sure that it is clear.

7. If gasoline flows in good condition from the fuel line at the carburetor, it may be assumed that the fuel pump and feed line are in good condition. It is advisable to make the fol-

lowing pressure test to make certain that the fuel pump is operating with sufficient pressure. *Caution: An air leak or restriction on the suction side of the fuel pump will seriously affect the pump output.*

Fuel Pump Pressure Test

The following procedure should be used when making a pressure test:

1. Disconnect the gasoline line at the carburetor and connect a suitable pressure gauge in series between the hose and the carburetor.

2. Start the engine and check the pressure with the engine running at slow idle speed. The fuel pump pressure should be approximately 3 to 5 pounds per square inch.

3. To test for leakdown of the fuel pump check valves or diaphragm, shut off the engine and observe the gauge. The pressure should not leakdown more than 1/2 lb. in 20 seconds. If excessive leakdown is detected, shut off the tester valve to determine whether the leakage is in the carburetor or fuel pump.

4. If the fuel pump pressure is below minimum, the pump must be replaced.

MAIN LINE FILTER

The fuel filter removes dirt and other particles that might otherwise get into the carburetor. Such particles could clog passages in the carburetor and prevent normal fuel system operation.

FUEL TANK AND LINES

The fuel lines carry the gasoline in liquid form from the fuel tank to the fuel pump, and from the pump to the carburetor, as illustrated in Fig. 8. The fuel line hose should be inspected oc-

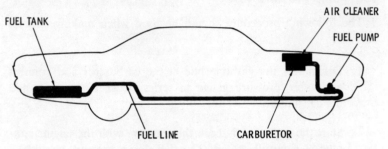

Fig. 8. Illustrating the fuel line and components.

casionally for chafing, cracks, brittleness, rotting, and kinks or collapse. The line can be tested for air leaks and restriction by using a vacuum pump.

The fuel tank stores gasoline in liquid form, and contains the fuel-gauge sending unit and an outlet to the fuel line. It usually has a drain to allow for cleaning if required.

FACTORS AFFECTING THE FUEL SYSTEM

Three items are essential to effective carburetor service—proper tools and gauges, correct specifications, and assurance that a carburetor problem is not in reality a problem caused by some other car component. The information which follows is aimed at checking out other areas of the car which might contribute to faulty carburetion or carry symptoms that could mislead one to believe that the carburetor is at fault.

Road test the car and check for dragging brakes. Unbalanced wheels, low tire pressure, any abnormal friction, etc., should be remedied. Check underneath the car for a damaged or defective exhaust system. Check inside the engine compartment—replace damaged wiring, check terminal connections, and check the fan belt for proper tension. Check the distributor points, spark plugs, ignition timing, and valve clearance. Make adjustments or replacements, as required. Check the cooling system for leaks. Tighten connections and replace defective hoses. Inspect fuel lines for damage and loose connections. Clean the fuel-pump sediment chamber and filter if one is used. If fuel-pump pressure is suspected of being low, check it with a pressure gauge tapped into the fuel line with a T connection.

Check the fuel tank for a clogged vent which will cause high-speed failure. Clean it, as required. Check engine heat control— the internal combustion engine derives its power from the expansion of a combustible gas mixture inside the combustion chamber. It is extremely important that combustion chamber temperatures be accurately controlled if the engine is to develop full power and not consume an excessive amount of fuel in its operation. The engine cooling system should be regulated to a controlled temperature. This is accomplished through the use of a thermostatic control valve. When a predetermined temperature is reached by the engine coolant that circulates around the engine heat-producing areas, the thermostatic valve will open and allow just enough coolant to circulate through the cooling system. This regulates engine temperatures to the manufacturer's specification. Engine temperature control is equally important in either hot or cold weather, since the engine is designed to operate efficiently at a given engine temperature.

Many engines use intake manifolds which are heated by water. The water temperature is directly controlled by the cooling system thermostat. The function of an intake manifold is to provide a passageway for distributing the carburetor fuel-air mixture to the engine cylinders. A carburetor mixes the air with fuel and puts both together into a vapor. The fuel and air are thoroughly mixed together and will support a good, even combustion. Intake manifold heat helps to further vaporize and mix the mixture together, keep it in a state of suspension, and evenly distribute it to all of the engine cylinders. A water-heated manifold spacer is used between the carburetor and the intake manifold on some engine applications. On these applications it is good practice to inspect the water passages in the spacer for any obstructions or blocked channels. Without proper heat to the carburetor, poor performance will result.

By recirculating engine exhaust gases through an area of the intake manifold, exhaust heat can also be transferred to the intake manifold. This is usually done by means of an exhaust control valve using a thermostatic coil spring that will change the valve position as the engine heat affects the thermostatic spring. When the temperature is low during the engine warmup, the valve will be closed and deflect a considerable portion of the exhaust gases to the heat passage around the carburetor intake manifold. As the engine warms up, it will supply a substantial amount of its own heat and the valve will open to bypass just the necessary amount of hot exhaust gas to the intake manifold to keep it at a predetermined temperature.

Not enough can be said about the need for carburetor heat and its accurate control. It is essential for good carburetion and engine performance. Exhaust control valves and engine thermostats should always receive attention on an engine tune-up. Check the engine compression pressure—when the compression stroke is performed in the internal combustion engine, the fuel-air mixture from the carburetor is sealed inside the cylinder and then compressed by the piston on the upward stroke. If the piston rings, which form the seal between the piston and cylinder wall, are worn, a loss of engine efficiency will result. This is due to the expanding gas being able to bypass around the piston and not exert its full pressure on the piston. A compression loss can also exist when the engine intake or exhaust valves fail to seal correctly and allow a portion of the expanding gas to escape. The condition of the cylinder seal can be determined by making a simple compression check with a pressure gauge. When performing this test, primary consideration should be given to any variation in pressure readings between cylinders. If a variation of more than the amount allowed by the engine manufacturer is recorded between cylinders, additional checks should be performed to determine the cause of the trouble. In a high-compression engine, carbon build-up within the combustion chamber can raise compression pressures. An abnormally high reading may indicate a source of trouble which may affect engine performance.

SUMMARY

The fuel system stores the fuel and supplies the combustible air-fuel mixture to the cylinders. The system includes the fuel tank, fuel lines, fuel gauge, fuel pump, carburetor, air cleaner, and intake manifold.

The components most often requiring service are the fuel and air cleaner, fuel pump, and carburetor. The fuel filter may be located in the fuel tank or lines, the fuel pump, or on the carburetor. The filter removes rust and other foreign particles that may accumulate in the fuel tank or lines and which would clog or affect the operation of the carburetor jets or the float needle and seat. Fuel filters may include sediment bowl and/or a ceramic, metallic, or treated paper filtering element.

The fuel pump moves fuel from the gasoline tank to the carburetor. It must supply adequate fuel for engine requirements ranging from idle to full speed during periods of sustained full acceleration.

The carburetor checks and adjustments required for engine tuneup are not difficult to perform. Often it is more of a problem to locate the correct rod or adjusting screw than it is to make the adjustment. Carburetors may be single, dual, or four-barrel. Dual, four-barrel, and triple, two-barrel carburetors will also be encountered, as well as separate single-barrel caburetors such as used on the small compact automobiles.

REVIEW QUESTIONS

1. What is the purpose of the power circuit in the carburetor?

2. What maintains an exact level of gasoline in the carburetor fuel bowl?

3. What are the advantages of an automatic choke?

4. What is the purpose of the fuel pump?

5. What is the purpose of the fuel filter?

CHAPTER 9

Ignition Systems

The internal combustion engine operates by forces created in expanding gases in the combustion chambers. These gases are the product of the burning air-fuel mixture which is ignited by a high-voltage spark. The function of the ignition system is to produce a high voltage and deliver it to the proper spark plug at the proper time to ignite the air-fuel mixture compressed in the cylinder.

The ignition system consists of the following components:

1. Battery.

2. Ignition switch.

3. Ballast resistor or ballast wire.

4. Ignition coil.

5. Distributor assembly.

   a. Body.

   b. Breaker Points.

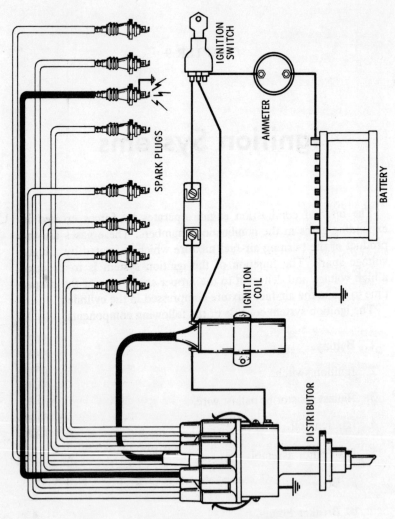

Fig. 1. Pictorial diagram of a typical ignition circuit.

     c. Cap.

     d. Condenser.

     e. Rotor.

     f. Advance Mechanisms.

6. High-tension leads.

7. Spark plugs.

The battery and generator (or alternator) are the source of power supplying low voltage to produce a current flow in the ignition primary circuit. The ignition switch is an On-Off switch that closes the ignition circuit between the battery and coil. When the ignition switch is closed, current will flow through the coil-distributor (primary) circuit and return by way of the car frame or engine block to the battery. The ignition switch may also serve as a bypass switch during engine starting. A pictorial diagram of an ignition system is shown in Fig. 1.

The ballast resistor in the ignition primary circuit is designed to permit the proper amount of current flow under all driving conditions. During cranking, it is frequently bypassed to permit maximum current flow through the coil for quick starting. The ignition coil transforms or "steps up" the low battery voltage to a voltage high enough to jump a spark gap at the spark plug. The distributor interrupts the flow of current in the primary winding by means of the breaker points. It also distributes the high voltage developed by the coil through the rotor and the distributor cap to the proper spark plug at the correct instant.

The high-tension or secondary leads conduct the high voltage produced by the ignition coil to the distributor, and from the distributor to the spark plugs. The spark plugs provide a spark gap in the combustion chamber. When high voltage jumps across this gap, the air-fuel mixture is ignited. The previous ignition system discussion is confined to the conventional systems found in most vehicles. Transistorized ignition systems will be discussed later in the chapter.

COILS

Perhaps one of the greatest reasons for using a 12-volt coil in the automotive ignition system was because of the limited output

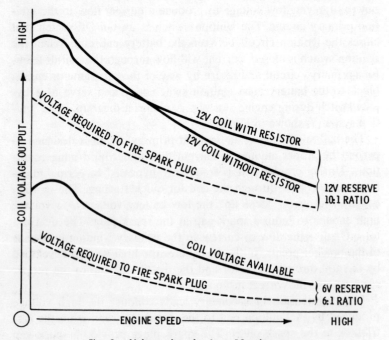

Fig. 2. Voltage chart for 6- or 12-volt system.

of the 6-volt system. As the compression ratio increased, so did the voltage or energy required to fire the spark plugs. The voltages required are shown in Fig. 2. It can be seen from the chart that the voltage required to fire a plug on a 6:1 compression ratio engine is much lower than the voltage required to fire a spark plug in a 10:1 compression ratio engine. The 6-volt ignition coil had plenty of voltage and energy reserve at starting or low engine speeds; however, at high engine speed the difference between what was available from the coil and what was required to fire the plug was very small. This difference is spoken of as the voltage reserve. As the engine wears, the spark plug gap becomes larger and the voltage requirement rises. As the ignition points wear, the energy input to the coil is reduced and, consequently, the coil voltage available is reduced. When these two curves meet, the spark plug will not fire and engine missing occurs. It is desirable in any ignition system to obtain as much voltage reserve as possible, and to follow the voltage requirement curve as closely as possible.

Among the first 12-volt ignition coils to appear was a "straight" 12-volt coil that used no resistor. This coil had plenty of voltage reserve for starting requirements, and although it had substantially more reserve at high speed than the 6-volt coil, the shape of the curve was such that the voltage reserve fell off rapidly at very high engine speeds. For this reason the resistor is used with the coil. With the resistor type system, lower starting reserve is obtained, but the secondary output very closely follows the voltage requirement curve and provides more voltage reserve at high engine speeds.

Principles of Coil Operation

The primary purpose of the automotive ignition coil is to provide an electric spark at the spark plugs of an engine sufficient to ignite, without failure, the gas mixture in the cylinder. The ignition coil accomplishes this task by supplying a high-voltage surge to the secondary system of an automobile. The amount of voltage produced by an ignition coil is dependent upon several important factors.

The spark-plug gap is preset, and a given amount of voltage is needed to "spark" the gap. Before an electric spark or flow of current can appear between two disconnected parts, such as the firing and ground electrodes of the spark plug, a potential difference (voltage) must be present across the gap. The ground electrode of a spark plug is electrically attached to the ground of the vehicle, and the firing electrode of a spark plug is electrically connected to the high-voltage terminal of the ignition coil, as shown in Fig. 3.

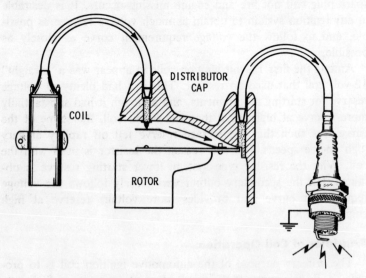

Fig. 3. Pictorial view of an automotive secondary circuit.

The voltage produced by the coil rises very fast to a point where the potential difference, or the electrical pressure, is great enough to force current to flow across the spark-plug gap. The potential, or electrical difference, necessary to fire a spark-plug gap is known as the firing voltage of the plug. The firing voltage of a plug depends on the width of the gap, the heat, and the pressure of the fuel mixture around the gap. There are other gaps in the secondary of an automotive system whose firing voltages must be added to the firing voltage of the spark plug in order to obtain the total amount of voltage necessary from the ignition coil. There is a gap between the distributor rotor and the distributor-cap terminal, and there may be a gap between the center terminal of the distributor cap and the rotor spring.

All of these gaps add up to a given amount of voltage necessary to push current through the system. It is this amount of voltage that the coil must produce before a spark can be established at the spark-plug gap. There are many coils in the automotive field that are capable of producing approximately 25,000 volts at idle speed; however, the firing voltage of the secondary system may only be 8,000 volts, and this is the level to which the coil will build. That is, the coil will build up to 8,000 volts, fire the circuit, and no more voltage is produced. The output of the coil depends not only on the voltage requirements of the secondary circuit, but also on the speed of the engine. At high engine speeds, the points do not remain closed for a long period of time, and sufficient energy is difficult to store in the ignition coil so that it will build over 8,000 volts under extremely high engine speeds. This is the reason why most racing cars, whose engines must turn at very high speeds, use magnetos or transistor ignition instead of the normal automotive system.

In Chapter 2 a discussion of how an ignition coil develops voltage is presented. It was pointed out that magnetic lines of force

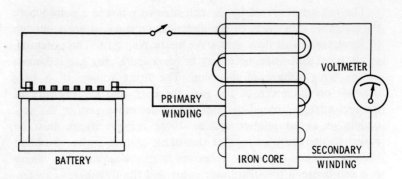

Fig. 4. Schematic diagram illustrating the ignition coil.

must cut conductors to generate electrical energy. Fig. 4 shows an electromagnet consisting of an iron core around which is wound a few turns of heavy wire. These few turns of heavy wire are referred to as the primary winding, and are connected to a battery by means of a switch. Between the primary winding, and directly on the iron core, is a secondary winding which consists of many thousand turns of fine wire. This secondary winding is connected to a voltmeter in Fig. 4.

When the switch is closed in the primary circuit, magnetic lines of force emerge from the steel core and completely surround the primary and the secondary windings of the coil. The magnetic field produced builds up in intensity. When the switch is first closed, only a few lines of force appear, but in a very short time the maximum amount of magnetic field is produced. The time it takes to build up this field to its maximum is very short, only the smallest fraction of a second. The circuit shown in Fig. 4 is electrically the same as an ignition coil and point-set installation in an automotive system. The switch in the circuit is replaced by a point set, and as the engine speed increases, the point set opens and closes at a faster rate than it would at slow speed. Because of the increased rate of operation of the point set, and the fact that it takes time to build the magnetic field of a coil to its maximum, it can be seen that at some point in engine speed, not enough time is available to build sufficient amounts of magnetic energy in the coil.

When the switch (ignition points) in the primary circuit is opened, the magnetic field collapses. The collapse of the magnetic field is very much faster than its build-up. The rapid collapse of the magnetic field is aided by the condenser. As the magnetic field collapses, each magnetic line of force cuts every turn of the secondary winding. Because of the speed of the collapse and the great number of secondary turns being cut by the magnetic lines of force, a very high voltage surge is produced that can be read on the voltmeter. It is this high-voltage surge that fires the spark plug.

Perhaps the best way to look at and understand the operation of an ignition coil is from the energy standpoint. When electromagnet or transformer windings are made, they are capable of storing energy. The primary winding is the energy input side, and the secondary winding is the energy output side. Energy can be neither created nor destroyed; however, the form of energy can be changed. The amount of energy that is stored in an ignition coil is directly proportional to the amount of current allowed to flow through the primary winding and, within limits, the time during which this current flow occurs. Some of the input energy is used in the coil and dissipated as heat. The remaining energy is transferred to the secondary winding of the coil and available for spark-producing purposes. In the automotive ignition coil, there is an energy input limitation and hence an energy output limitation. The energy input limitation is the amount of current that can be interrupted by the points. If too much current is interrupted, short point life will be encountered.

Because of the energy input limitation, there is no method known to obtain more output voltage than can be presently obtained from conventional 12-volt ignition coils without increasing the primary current flow. Winding more secondary turns does not accomplish an increase in output voltage, because the input energy cannot be increased, a problem partially solved by transistor ignition. Because of the energy input limitation and the fact that increasing secondary turns will not raise the output voltage of a coil, a true heavy-duty 12-volt ignition coil hasn't been produced to date.

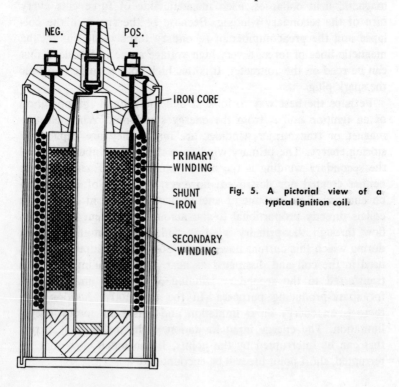

Fig. 5. A pictorial view of a typical ignition coil.

Construction

Many refinements are made on the elementary winding shown in Fig. 4 in order to construct a high-quality ignition coil. Pictured in Fig. 5 is a cross section of a conventional automotive coil. The core iron used in most coils consists of many laminations of high-quality magnetic steel. Also, around the outside of the coil are sheets of high-quality magnetic steel. This type of steel allows more magnetic energy to be stored in the coil and a faster collapse of the magnetic field than would be allowed in low-quality magnetic or ordinary steel.

The primary winding generally consists of about 250 turns of 18-22 gauge copper wire. The secondary winding consists of 36-42 gauge copper wire, and the amount of turns run from 18,000 to 30,000. The first turns on the inside or outside of the secondary winding are wound with considerable space between them. These turns are usually referred to as the spiral turns of the secondary winding. These few turns take the shocks of the voltage surge and are subjected to severe electrical stresses. If a coil fails, it is most likely that the spiral turns will be broken due to high electrical or physical stresses. Although all quality coil manufacturers take every known precaution to protect against this type of failure, it still occasionally happens.

In quality coil construction, all the insulation is checked so that it contains no acidic or basic material. If an acidic or basic material is present in the coil and moisture enters, they will intermix chemically and destroy the coil. Secondary windings are thoroughly coated with an impregnating wax or varnish. Impregnating the secondary removes all the moisture content and provides a coating through which moisture cannot enter. The entire coil is then hermetically sealed (after evacuation of all moisture), and filled with either a potting compound or oil.

171

Coil Resistor

Perhaps the easiest way to understand the function of the coil resistor is from the energy standpoint. In order to obtain sufficient reserve energy at high engine speed, a very high input energy will be obtained at low engine speeds. The input energy of a coil is directly proportional to the amount of current that flows through the primary winding. If an electrical device could be found that would use up more energy at low engine speeds than at high engine speeds, this device could be used with an ignition coil to control the amount of energy input to the coil. The device used is the coil resistor, as shown in Fig. 6. At low engine speeds the

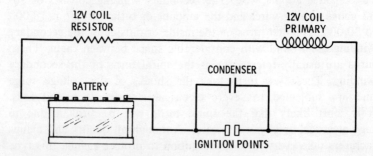

Fig. 6. A schematic wiring diagram of a coil resistor.

contact points remain closed a relatively long period of time, and an increased amount of current flows through the coil resistor and the coil primary winding. The energy dissipated by the resistor is measured by its *IR* drop (the current that flows through the resistor times the resistance of the resistor).

At high engine speeds the points do not remain closed for a long period of time, and the length of time that current can flow through the coil resistor and the coil primary is substantially reduced. Therefore, because of the variation in the amount of current flow, more energy is taken by the resistor at low engine speeds, than at high engine speeds. An increased amount of energy from low to high engine speed is presented to the primary of the ignition coil. The figures shown in Table 1 were taken from a 12-volt system of a modern vehicle. Notice the decrease in voltage drop (IR drop or energy lost) in the resistor, while the coil voltage (a measure of the energy available) rises as engine rpm increases.

Table 1. Coil Voltage in Relation to Engine RPM

RPM	Coil Voltage	Resistor Voltage Drop	System Current
600	8.9V	3.6V	2.60A
1000	11.2V	3.2V	2.30A
2000	12.5V	2.0V	1.80A
3000	13.0V	1.6V	1.55A

Factors Affecting the Coil

Coil caps are quickly covered with oil and dirt that may trap moisture on the surface of the cap. The moisture presents a low resistance path to current flow and may provide a path for current flow from the coil tower to a primary stud. Once the coil has "flashed-over," the cap material has been permanently damaged, leaving a thin, ragged, carbonized path that is referred to as "carbon-tracking." At first glance, carbon-tracking may appear as a thin crack in the cap.

Clean the top of the coil (Fig. 7) with a clean cloth and solvent before checking for carbon tracks or cracks. Loose high-tension wires and poorly seated rubber boots may permit a coil to flashover even in the absence of moisture.

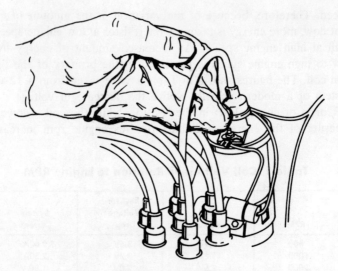

Fig. 7. Illustrating the cleaning of the ignition coil.

Always make sure that the high-tension wire and rubber boot are firmly seated, as illustrated in Fig. 8. Rotten or cracked rubber boots can cause a low-resistance path to ground due to dirt and grease collection. This can cause a spark jump to ground.

Coil Polarity

To keep the required firing voltage of the ignition system as low as possible, the ignition coil must be connected for the correct polarity. The primary terminals of the coil should be connected so that the polarity markings correspond to the polarity of the battery, with the distributor connection considered as ground. This will cause current flow through the spark plug from the center electrode to the ground electrode. This spark-plug polarity requires a lower voltage to fire the spark plug since the electrons

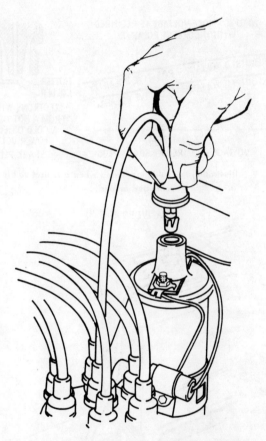

Fig. 8. Illustrating the importance of ignition wire boots.

will be emitted from the hotter center electrode easier than from the cooler ground electrode.

If secondary polarity is reversed, 20% to 40% more voltage is required to jump the spark-plug gap, as shown in Fig. 9. The

175

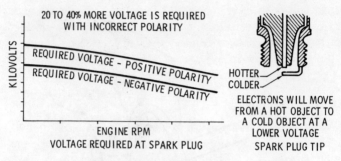

20 TO 40% MORE VOLTAGE IS REQUIRED
WITH INCORRECT POLARITY

KILOVOLTS

REQUIRED VOLTAGE - POSITIVE POLARITY
REQUIRED VOLTAGE - NEGATIVE POLARITY

ENGINE RPM
VOLTAGE REQUIRED AT SPARK PLUG

HOTTER
COLDER

ELECTRONS WILL MOVE
FROM A HOT OBJECT TO
A COLD OBJECT AT A
LOWER VOLTAGE
SPARK PLUG TIP

Fig. 9.   Illustrating the voltage required when a typical coil is not
connected properly.

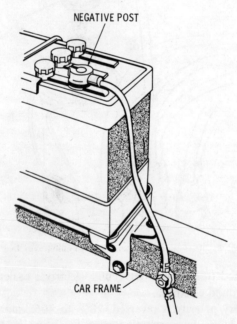

NEGATIVE POST

CAR FRAME

Fig. 10.   Illustrating battery polarity.

176

correct coil polarity is important to engine performance and plug life. To determine vehicle polarity, observe the battery connections. The battery post that is connected to the frame or engine block of the vehicle determines if it is a positive or negative ground. In Fig. 10 a negative ground is shown.

Coil Overheating

When a coil ballast resistor is shorted or incorrectly wired into the circuit (or the ignition is left *on* with the engine stopped), excessive current will flow through the coil. Under these conditions the coil may be overheated to such a degree that it literally "blows up."

DISTRIBUTOR

The distributor has three functions to perform. First, due to the action of the contact points, it opens and closes the primary circuit, allowing energy to be stored in the ignition coil and causes the collapse of the magnetic field, resulting in a high-voltage impulse. The second function is to time these impulses with regard to the engine requirement by means of a centrifugal advance and a vacuum advance system. The third function is to distribute the high-voltage surge to the spark plugs in the correct order.

There are two separate circuits through the ignition distributor. One is the primary or low-voltage circuit, which includes the contact points, condenser, coil primary and battery. The other is the high-voltage circuit, which includes the coil secondary, rotor, distributor cap, high-voltage wires, and spark plugs. In Fig. 11 a cross-sectional view of a typical distributor is shown. The primary circuit is opened and closed by means of the contact points and breaker cam. The cam is rotated by the distributor shaft through the centrifugal advance mechanism. The distributor shaft

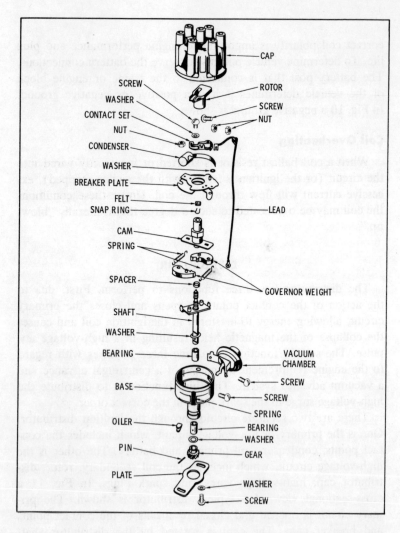

CAP

SCREW
WASHER
CONTACT SET
NUT
CONDENSER
WASHER
BREAKER PLATE
FELT
SNAP RING

CAM
SPRING

SPACER

SHAFT
WASHER
BEARING

BASE

OILER

PIN
PLATE

ROTOR
SCREW
NUT

LEAD

GOVERNOR WEIGHT

VACUUM
CHAMBER
SCREW
SCREW
SPRING
BEARING
WASHER
GEAR

WASHER
SCREW

Courtesy Dodge Div., Chrysler Motors Corp.

Fig. 11. Illustrating component parts of a distributor assembly.

and breaker cam are operated at one-half the engine speed. The breaker cam has the same number of lobes as the engine has cylinders. As each breaker cam lobe passes under the rubbing block of the contact points, the points are opened, collapsing the magnetic field in the coil and resulting in a high-voltage surge to the spark plugs.

The condenser is connected across the contact points, aiding the rapid collapse of the magnetic field in the coil and helping to retard the arcing that would otherwise occur across the contact points. After the high-voltage surge is produced in the ignition coil secondary, it is conducted through the high-voltage lead to the center terminal of the distributor cap. From there, it travels through the rotor to the outer cap elecrode at which the rotor is pointed at the time the high-voltage surge occurs. This outer terminal is connected, by means of a high-tension wire, to the spark plug.

SPARK ADVANCE

In order for an engine to develop maximum efficiency, it is necessary that peak pressures be developed in the cylinders near the start of the power stroke. It takes time for the fuel mixture in the cylinder to burn once ignition has been started by the spark plugs. Therefore, it is necessary for the spark to start the mixture burning before the piston reaches TDC at the end of the compression stroke and at the start of the power stroke. This is called *spark advance* and the advance which gives maximum engine power is called *optimum spark advance*.

The time it takes for a specific amount of mixture to burn does not vary greatly. The faster the piston moves, the earlier in the compression stroke the spark must occur in order to develop the maximum pressures at the top of the stroke. This results in a spark

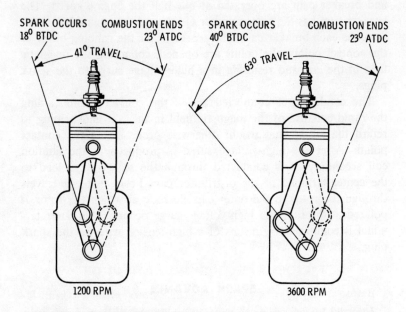

SPARK OCCURS 18⁰ BTDC COMBUSTION ENDS 23⁰ ATDC 41⁰ TRAVEL 1200 RPM

SPARK OCCURS 40⁰ BTDC COMBUSTION ENDS 23⁰ ATDC 63⁰ TRAVEL 3600 RPM

Fig. 12. Illustrating the spark advance which will vary due to engine RPM.

advance that varies directly with engine speed (Fig. 12), and is usually accomplished by a centrifugal advance mechanism, shown in Fig. 13. There is another action going on at the same time that must also be considered. As the throttle of an engine is opened, more fuel mixture is drawn into the cylinders. It takes a longer time to burn a larger charge of fuel, so another advance must be introduced which depends on how much fuel is going into the engine to ensure that maximum pressures are developed at the end of the compression stroke. This advance that must be added to the centrifugal advance is commonly called *vacuum advance.*

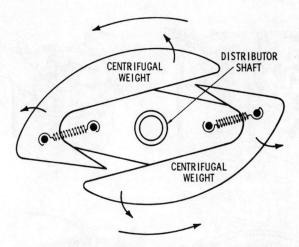

Fig. 13. Centrifugal weights which govern the spark advance.

FACTORS AFFECTING THE DISTRIBUTOR

Before installing new parts on the distributor plate it should be cleaned and checked for freedom of movement (Fig. 14). With the vacuum chamber removed, the plate should rotate easily, and downward pressure should not cause undue plate travel or wob-

Fig. 14. Checking the distributor breaker points for freedom of movement.

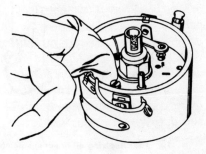

181

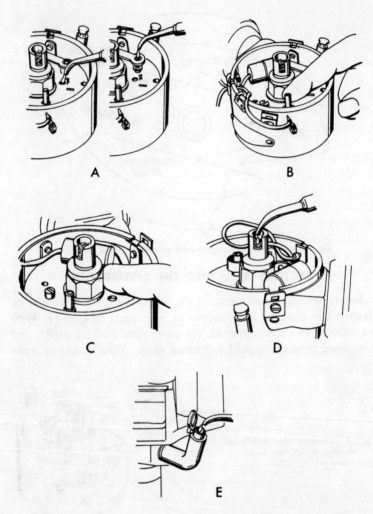

Fig. 15. Applying oil to various points on the distributor breaker plate.

ble. Experience will soon indicate the normal amount of movement in both directions. Breaker plates that require lubrication should have a drop or two of light engine oil applied at the proper location. This is illustrated in Fig. 15A.

Vacuum pivot arms and the point-set arms should have a drop or two of light engine oil applied. Apply oil to the point-set pivot shaft, using the "finger-method," as shown in Fig. 15B. The breaker cam (Fig. 15C) should have a light coating of *high-temperature grease* applied before the point set is installed. The minimum amount of grease should be used to prevent it from being thrown off during high-speed operation.

Place a few drops of light engine oil on the wick (Fig. 15D) in the center of the shaft under the rotor, if a wick is present. *Do not over-oil.*

Most distributors should be oiled at each vehicle lubrication period. When an oil reservoir tube is present (Fig. 15E), it should be filled with a light-weight engine oil. On distributors which have a grease cup, the cup should be removed and checked to make sure it is packed with grease. After replacing it, the screw cup should be tightened one or two turns, as shown in Fig. 16. Dis-

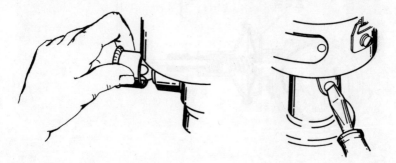

Fig. 16. Checking the distributor drive shaft for grease.

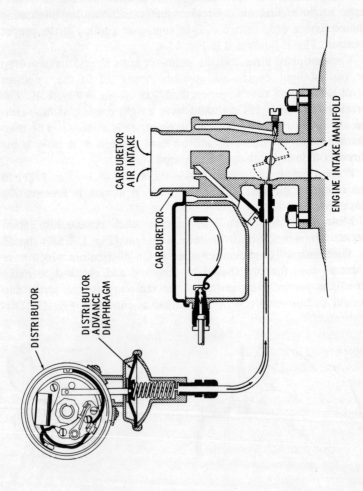

Fig. 17. Illustrating the vacuum advance mechanism.

tributors with oil plugs should have their reservoirs filled with light-weight engine oil until the oil level reaches the bottom of the plug hole.

VACUUM ADVANCE MECHANISM

As mentioned earlier, as the mixture flowing into the cylinder is increased, the spark advance must also increase. A simple way of measuring the amount of fuel flowing to the engine is through the use of an auxiliary venturi in the carburetor. This venturi will develop a vacuum that depends upon how much fuel is flowing into the cylinder. As can be seen in the diagram (Fig. 17), this vacuum is applied to one side of the diaphragm in the vacuum chamber. Atmospheric pressure acting on the other side of this diaphragm is opposed by the spring and, as a result, causes movement of the operating rod to the left.

With increasing vacuum, the rod will move in proportion to the amount of vacuum applied to the chamber. This rod is usually connected to the distributor plate so that, as vacuum is introduced into the chamber, the plate is rotated opposite to the distributor shaft rotation, causing an ignition advance which depends upon the amount of charge being drawn into the cylinders. Under very high engine loading (that is, when the throttle is floored), the spark must be retarded somewhat to prevent detonation or "ping." By connecting this diaphragm vacuum line through properly designed passages to the engine intake manifold, this effect is accomplished. When a wide-open throttle is approached, the engine manifold loses its vacuum and over-rides the normal effect, resulting in a loss of vacuum advance under high engine loading. The centrifugal advance and vacuum advance work together in an automotive engine to produce the total advance necessary for the maximum efficiency of the engine.

DWELL ANGLE

The total cam rotation of any automotive cam is 360 degrees. With any 6-cylinder cam, each face or lobe of the cam accounts for 60 degrees of the total cam rotation (360 ÷ 6 lobes). In an 8-cylinder engine, each lobe accounts for 45 degrees of cam rotation, and in a 4-cylinder engine each lobe accounts for 90 degrees of cam rotation.

As can be seen in Fig. 18, when a high point of the cam approaches the rubbing block of the lever arm, it exerts an upward

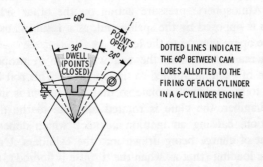

DOTTED LINES INDICATE THE 60° BETWEEN CAM LOBES ALLOTTED TO THE FIRING OF EACH CYLINDER IN A 6-CYLINDER ENGINE

Fig. 18.   Illustrating the dwell angle in a six cylinder engine.

pressure on the rubbing block, forcing the points to open. When the high point of the cam is directly under the rubbing block, the points are in their extreme open position, and as the cam continues to rotate, the points are again closed and remain closed until this cycle begins to repeat. The time that the points remain closed is called the *dwell angle*, and is the angle measured with a dwell meter.

During the time the breaker points are closed (or during the dwell angle), energy is stored in the ignition coil. Sufficient energy must be stored in the coil so there is enough energy to operate the engine through the entire speed range. If too much energy is stored in the coil, the engine will run well at high speeds but there is danger of point burning during low-speed operation. Obviously, an optimum setting must be reached, and this is determined by the car manufacturer. Too low a dwell reading will mean poor high-speed operation, as sufficient energy is not being stored in the ignition system. Too high a dwell reading will store too much energy in the system and lead to poor ignition-point life.

From the above discussion, it should be obvious the correct setting of the dwell is very important and that there is a definite relationship between the dwell angle and the maximum point opening. As an alternate, a feeler gauge can be used to set ignition points, and it is used when the points are in their maximum open position. However, due to the difficulty of obtaining two parallel surfaces on the ignition points, and holding a feeler gauge absolutely parallel to these surfaces, this method can never be as accurate as a dwell meter. Of course, the setting of used points is impossible with a feeler gauge.

IGNITION POINTS

Ignition points are a switch inserted into the primary circuit. The function of the points is to break the primary circuit to stop current flowing at the proper time. When current ceases to flow in the primary circuit the magnetic field in the ignition coil collapses, producing a high-voltage surge that fires the spark plugs.

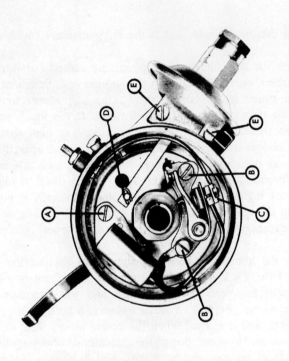

1. REMOVE CONDENSER
   HOLD DOWN SCREW "A"

2. REMOVE TWO POINT SET
   HOLD DOWN SCREWS "B"

3. LIFT POINT SET AND REMOVE
   PRIMARY TERMINAL NUT "C"
   REMOVE POINT SET AND
   CONDENSER

4. REMOVE SPRING CLIP "D"

5. REMOVE TWO SCREWS "E"
   LIFT VACUUM CHAMBER
   ARM OFF PLATE STUD
   AND REMOVE CHAMBER

Fig. 19. Illustrating a *Ford* distributor assembly with centrifugal weights.

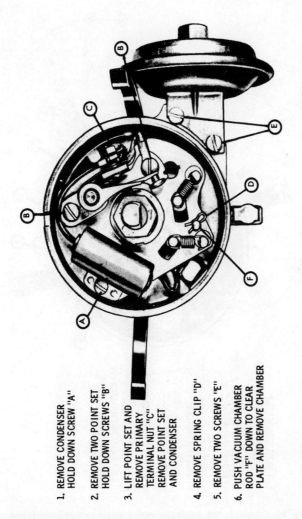

1. REMOVE CONDENSER HOLD DOWN SCREW "A"

2. REMOVE TWO POINT SET HOLD DOWN SCREWS "B"

3. LIFT POINT SET AND REMOVE PRIMARY TERMINAL NUT "C" REMOVE POINT SET AND CONDENSER

4. REMOVE SPRING CLIP "D"

5. REMOVE TWO SCREWS "E"

6. PUSH VACUUM CHAMBER ROD "F" DOWN TO CLEAR PLATE AND REMOVE CHAMBER

Fig. 20. A *Ford* distributor assembly which is vacuum operated.

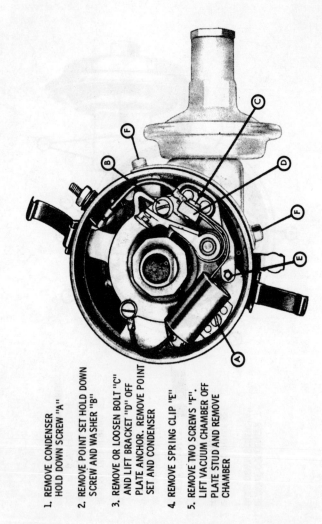

1. REMOVE CONDENSER HOLD DOWN SCREW "A"

2. REMOVE POINT SET HOLD DOWN SCREW AND WASHER "B"

3. REMOVE OR LOOSEN BOLT "C" AND LIFT BRACKET "D" OFF PLATE ANCHOR. REMOVE POINT SET AND CONDENSER

4. REMOVE SPRING CLIP "E"

5. REMOVE TWO SCREWS "F". LIFT VACUUM CHAMBER OFF PLATE STUD AND REMOVE CHAMBER

Fig. 21. An *Auto-Lite* distributor with a single-contact point system.

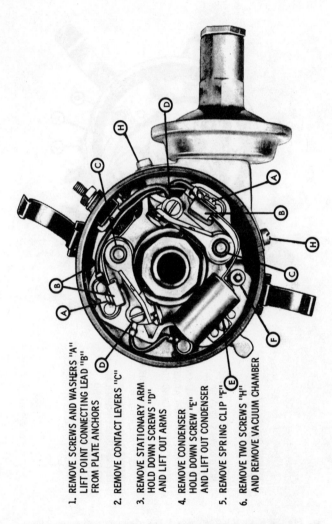

1. REMOVE SCREWS AND WASHERS "A"
   LIFT POINT CONNECTING LEAD "B"
   FROM PLATE ANCHORS

2. REMOVE CONTACT LEVERS "C"

3. REMOVE STATIONARY ARM
   HOLD DOWN SCREWS "D"
   AND LIFT OUT ARMS

4. REMOVE CONDENSER
   HOLD DOWN SCREW "E"
   AND LIFT OUT CONDENSER

5. REMOVE SPRING CLIP "F"

6. REMOVE TWO SCREWS "H"
   AND REMOVE VACUUM CHAMBER

Fig. 22. An *Auto-Lite* distributor with dual contacts.

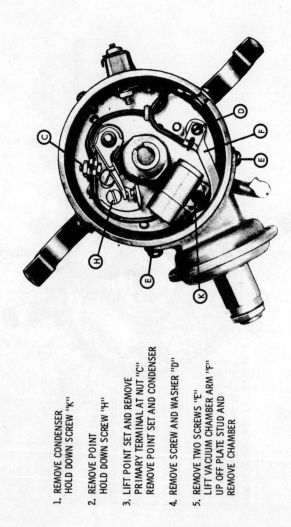

1. REMOVE CONDENSER
   HOLD DOWN SCREW "K"

2. REMOVE POINT
   HOLD DOWN SCREW "H"

3. LIFT POINT SET AND REMOVE
   PRIMARY TERMINAL AT NUT "C"
   REMOVE POINT SET AND CONDENSER

4. REMOVE SCREW AND WASHER "D"

5. REMOVE TWO SCREWS "E"
   LIFT VACUUM CHAMBER ARM "F"
   UP OFF PLATE STUD AND
   REMOVE CHAMBER

Fig. 23. A *Delco-Remy* distributor with internal contact adjustment.

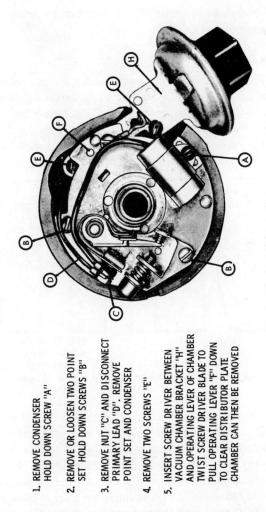

1. REMOVE CONDENSER HOLD DOWN SCREW "A"

2. REMOVE OR LOOSEN TWO POINT SET HOLD DOWN SCREWS "B"

3. REMOVE NUT "C" AND DISCONNECT PRIMARY LEAD "D". REMOVE POINT SET AND CONDENSER

4. REMOVE TWO SCREWS "E"

5. INSERT SCREW DRIVER BETWEEN VACUUM CHAMBER BRACKET "H" AND OPERATING LEVER OF CHAMBER TWIST SCREW DRIVER BLADE TO PULL OPERATING LEVER "F" DOWN TO CLEAR DISTRIBUTOR PLATE CHAMBER CAN THEN BE REMOVED

Fig. 24. A *Delco-Remy* distributor with external contact adjustment.

Figs. 19 through 24 illustrate typical distributor assemblies used in modern automotive engines.

Tungsten Contacts

Much has been said in the past about various contact shapes, finish, and alignment. Usually, one very important fact is overlooked. This fact is that under normal operating conditions, regardless of the contact shape or finish, the point faces will wear into two flat surfaces. The contacts will appear rough and grey in color, as shown in Fig. 25. The face of any contact can be polished

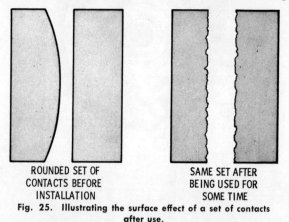

ROUNDED SET OF
CONTACTS BEFORE
INSTALLATION

SAME SET AFTER
BEING USED FOR
SOME TIME

Fig. 25. Illustrating the surface effect of a set of contacts after use.

so that, to the naked eye, it is very smooth and may even resemble a mirror. If a highly polished contact is examined under a microscope, however, it will be found that the face of the contact actually contains many hills and valleys, as illustrated in Fig. 26. Any two contact surfaces therefore must meet on the raised portion of the contacts. The little hills or valleys found on a set of contacts would actually make contact with the metal tips of the mating point.

194

Fig. 26. The contact surface as viewed through a magnifying glass.

It is impossible for all metal tips to be of the same height, therefore, only a few of the tips will make contact each time a pair of contacts closes. This action is very similar to that of a three-legged stool, as shown in Fig. 27. When three high points on a

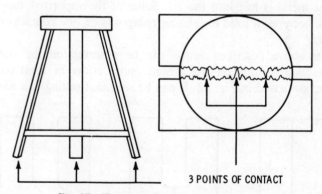

3 POINTS OF CONTACT

Fig. 27.   Illustrating the three points of contact.

pair of contacts come together, it is impossible to further close the contacts without condensing the contact material. Therefore, it is unlikely that in any set of contacts more than three areas would actually pass any amount of current when the contact points are closed.

In automotive operation, the primary current must pass through several small areas on the surface of the tungsten contact. As the contacts begin to open, all current-passing contact surfaces will open but one. Now, all the primary current passes through one very small contact area, and because of the high current that flows through such a small area, the temperature of the area can actually reach the melting point of tungsten—6100°F. As the contacts continue to open, the molten metal is stretched much like a rubber band and the cross-sectional area becomes smaller and smaller. This increases the temperature, which can reach a point where the tungsten explodes or vaporizes.

When the tungsten explodes, an arc appears. The heat of an electrical arc is extremely high, and more tungsten will be vaporized. Each time a minute amount of tungsten is vaporized, some of the metal is lost into the air. Some of the vaporized tungsten cools, becomes a solid metal, and redeposits on one contact or the other.

The above described action can be observed on the contact points as a buildup on one contact and a crater or a pit on the other, as viewed in Fig. 28. It can be seen that pitting is a normal

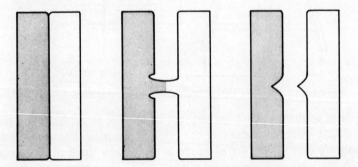

Fig. 28. Illustrating the deposits made on contact surface.

condition and will occur in all automotive vehicles. Some attempts have been made to help dissipate the heat developed and decrease the amount of transfer in a point set. One of these attempts is the ventilated point.

Rubbing Block Construction

The rubbing block in common use today is made of laminated phenolic. The laminations are made from cotton cloth, and are passed through baths of liquid phenolic or resin, resulting in sheets of impregnated cotton cloth. The sheets are stacked and placed in a heated press which forms the sheets to shape. The press is closed under great pressure, causing the phenolic in the cotton cloth to cure. The finished part is then removed from the press, cut, and ground to its finished shape, as shown in Fig. 29. Manufacturing

Fig. 29. Illustrating a typical contact rubbing block.

the rubbing block in this manner allows close dimensional tolerances.

The black line or black lamination frequently found in the laminated type rubbing block has no lubrication qualities. The black liner is used merely as a means of identification. Another type of rubbing block is made from nylon or a similar material. This type of rubbing block is molded and usually requires no grinding or other operations in the preparation of the material.

Lubrication

One of the most important and yet frequently forgotten procedures when ignition points are installed, is the lubrication of the rubbing block and cam. A good high-temperature grease is required, which will usually last the life of the point set. However, good lubrication is so vital that it is recommended that the cam and rubbing block be checked for adequate lubrication every 5000 miles. This is true regardless of the type of rubbing block used on the point set installed. In an emergency, any grease will do (even vaseline), but it should be removed as soon as possible and a good lubricant applied.

Two types of cam rotation are used. These are illustrated in Fig. 30. In one method, the cam rotates from the lever-arm

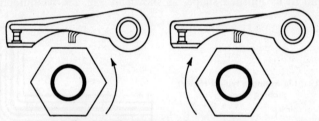

Fig. 30.   The two types of cam rotation.

bushing to the rubbing block to the contact. This is illustrated in Fig. 30A. In Fig. 30B, the opposite rotation is shown, where the cam rotates from the contact to the rubbing block to the lever-arm post. The stresses imposed upon the point set when the cam rotates as in Fig. 30B are considerably higher than those produced in Fig. 30A. The point set installed as shown in Fig. 30A may last slightly longer without lubrication than if installed like in Fig. 30B under the same conditions. Without lubrication, the lever-arm spring (or a copper strap, if used) may be broken in a few thousand miles. If no breakage occurs, the laminated rubbing block under a no-lubrication condition has a decided advantage over all other types. The laminations may "peel" or laminate, but the engine will not fail completely. The cam angle will be changed rapidly, resulting in poor engine operation, but the car may run long enough to reach a service station.

Timing

After new points have been installed, the timing should be checked and reset if necessary. An example of a timing light and a timing mark is shown in Fig. 31. See Chapter 13 on the use of the timing light.

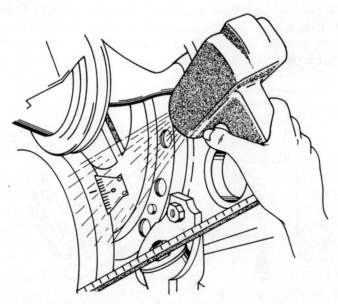

Fig. 31. Illustrating the timing mark and the use of a timing light.

FACTORS AFFECTING POINT SETS

Blue Points

Blue tungsten oxide will form on a tungsten contact whenever the surface of the contact is heated to more than 600°F. in the presence of oxygen. Blue tungsten oxide is an insulator, and when the working area of the contact is covered with oxide, primary current will not flow. During slow-speed driving or idling, the contacts remain closed a longer period of time than when the engine is at medium or high speed. Under these low-speed conditions, higher current will flow through the primary circuit.

Blue points can be a normal point condition over a long period of time. However, there are some conditions that lead to rapid blue pointing, and these conditions should be avoided if possible. It is peculiar but the blue tungsten oxide will usually form on the positive contact only. If a considerable amount of blue tungsten oxide is present, and the point set has not been in serv-

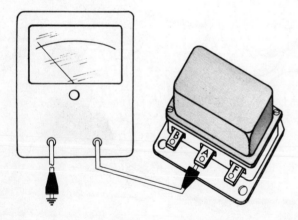

Fig. 32. Checking the voltage setting.

ice for a long period of time, several items should be checked to see if they are aiding the rapid formation of this oxide.

Perhaps the first thing that should be checked is the voltage regulator setting. If the generated voltage is above specifications, higher than normal currents will be forced through the primary circuit and the formation of blue tungsten oxide will be very rapid. The current (measured with an ammeter) that flows at idle is not the current that the contacts actually break. The actual break current is about twice the average current read at idle speeds.

As shown in Fig. 32, a voltmeter connected from the armature terminal of the regulator to ground, with the engine running at approximately 1500 rpm, will show the voltage regulator setting. The voltage read should be approximately:

6-volt systems	7.0- 7.5 volts
12-volt systems	14.0-15.0 volts

The blue point condition is especially common during cold weather. With a normal voltage setting, higher than normal currents can flow if the resistance of the primary circuit is low. On a cold morning, the resistance of the primary circuit is low; consequently, high primary currents will flow when the automobile is started. As the current flows, the coil and associated parts of the primary will warm up. This causes the resistance to rise so that normal current will flow shortly after the car is started. However, each time the engine is started on a cold morning, a small amount of blue tungsten oxide is formed, and over a period of repeated starts, the points will eventually be covered with blue tungsten oxide and made inoperative.

It might be well to keep in mind that excessive slow-speed driving or idling should be avoided during cold weather. Another cold-weather problem that can cause *blue points* in a hurry is when hard starting exists. If, for instance, a flooded carburetor is encountered, the engine is cranked over very slowly. On most 12-volt automobiles, the coil resistor is shorted out during this cranking period, and very high primary current flows. Under this condition, point sets can become blue and inoperative in a very few minutes.

During cold weather, it is wise to have, if possible, a good starting automobile and to avoid idling and slow-speed driving. Several devices have been used by various manufacturers to raise the primary resistance of an automotive system on a cold morning. On 6-volt, slow-moving vehicles, such as delivery trucks, taxi cabs, etc., a "slow-speed" coil can be used to help eliminate the blue-point problem. The slow-speed coil is essentially a 12-volt coil that contains a higher primary resistance than the normal 6-volt coil.

Discolored Movable Lever Arm

On 12-volt vehicles, if the point set is removed and, along with a heavy blue-point condition a discolored movable lever arm is noted (Fig. 33), the coil resistor should be checked. If the coil

Fig. 33.   Illustrating the discolored area on contact points.

resistor is shorted out in the primary circuit, either because of component failure or because it has been incorrectly wired, very high current will flow, and the point set will only last for a short period of time. Whether or not the coil resistor is wired properly in the circuit can be determined by using a voltmeter.

Black Points

Black deposits on the contacts indicate excessive oil vapors in the distributor, or indicate that oil or grease was on the face of the contacts when they were installed. Oil vapors can be present in a distributor because of poor crankcase ventilation, worn distributor bushings, or the use of an inferior cam lube.

Cam Lubrication

The rubbing block riding on the cam is essentially a bearing and must be lubricated regardless of the type of rubbing block material used. If the block and cam are not adequately lubricated with a high-temperature grease, the block may suffer from rapid wear, or the steel stamping may break.

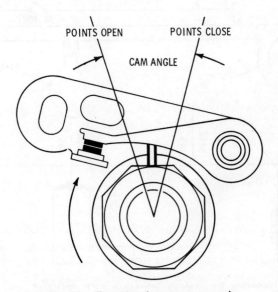

Fig. 34. Illustrating the proper cam angle.

Cam Angle

An excessively large cam angle prevents the points from opening enough to completely stop the arcing, causing rapid errosion of the point set. Cam angle or dwell is the time the points are closed, measured in degrees of cam rotation. Point opening, therefore, has a definite bearing on the cam angle, as shown in Fig. 34.

CONDENSERS

The function of the automotive condenser is something very difficult to understand. As an aid in understanding condenser

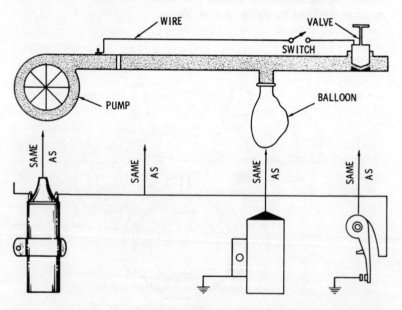

Fig. 35. Illustrating the similarity between a water system and the automobile electrical system.

action, a water analogy will be used. Shown in Fig. 35 is a water pipe containing a centrifugal pump, an outlet to a rubber balloon, and a valve. In our water system, we have to make several assumptions. One is, when the valve is nearly closed, the water pressure must not become excessively high or the valve will be damaged. The second assumption is the centrifugal pump has a large flywheel attached to the shaft. When a flywheel is set in motion, it is difficult to stop the rotation.

With the pump in operation and the valve open, water flows continuously through the pipe. Attached to the valve is an electrical switch which is used to remove the power from the pump when the valve is closed. If the valve is closed and the power is removed from the pump, water pressure will remain since the pump continues to operate due to its heavy flywheel. Excessive pressure against the valve, as previously stated, will result in damage to the valve.

A balloon is inserted in the circuit to help reduce this pressure. At the instant the valve is closed, water rushes into the balloon, filling it, and actually blowing up the balloon with water. The balloon full of water exerts a back pressure on the pump, or attempts to make water flow in a reverse direction. The back pressure produced by the balloon stops the flow of water much faster than the flow would normally stop. This action helps prevent system leakage and damage to the valve. When the pump finally stops rotating, the line pressure is reduced to zero, at which time the balloon will empty back into the line. This action is similar to the action that takes place in the primary circuit of any automobile electrical system.

In the automotive ignition system, the coil acts similar to the water pump, the point set action is similar to the action of the valve, and the condenser acts similar to the balloon. This is illustrated in Fig. 35.

Water Pump = Coil

Valve   = Point Set

Balloon   = Condenser

In Chapter 2, the electromagnetic action of a coil was discussed. It was mentioned in that chapter that when the magnetic lines of force collapse, each line of force cuts each turn of the secondary winding, producing a high-voltage output. These same lines of force also cut every turn in the primary winding and, in doing so, generate a voltage that tries to keep the current flowing in the primary circuit. This is why the coil acts similarly to the water pump shown in Fig. 35.

The peak voltage produced by the coil primary winding can be as much as 300 volts, and will help maintain an arc across the ignition points when they open. This would correspond to a bursting of the valve in the water system. The electrical pressure or voltage presented to the contact points is relieved by the condenser. The condenser absorbs the electrical pressure much like the balloon did in the water system. The absorption of the electrical energy by the condenser not only reduces the spark at the contact points, but also stops current flowing quicker than can be done without the condenser. Of course, the more rapid the current flow stops, the faster the collapse of the magnetic circuit in the ignition coil, and the higher the output voltage obtained from the coil.

Condenser Construction

A condenser is made from a series of aluminum sheets. The aluminum sheets have layers of insulation between each layer of conductive material, as illustrated in Fig. 36. The alternating layer of conductive material protrudes at either end of the wound con-

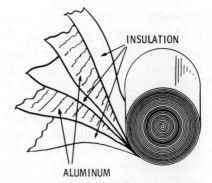

INSULATION

Fig. 36. The material used in
constructing a condenser.

ALUMINUM

denser. The condenser is wound from two continuous sheets of
conductive material, with the necessary insulation between sheets.
When the winding is completed, one conductive sheet appears at
each end of the winding in a spiral form. The over-lapped aluminum sheet is pressed together so that an electrical connection can
be made to an entire sheet from each end of the condenser. One
end of the winding is connected to ground, while the other end
of the winding is insulated from ground and connected to the
terminal of the condenser. A cross-sectional view of a condenser
is shown in Fig. 37.

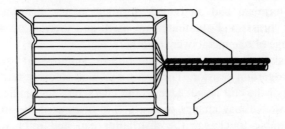

Fig. 37. A cross-sectional view of a condenser.

Capacity

The capacity of a condenser is a measure of its electrical storage ability. The capacity of a condenser has nothing to do with the physical size of the unit. The unit of capacity is called a *farad*. The *farad* means the same thing in an electrical system as a gallon means in a liquid system. Obviously there can be no "heavy-duty" type of condenser. The capacity of a condenser is determined by the car manufacturer and should be adhered to closely. If a condenser is low in capacity, the car will run well at higher speeds; however, excessive arcing will take place at slow engine speeds, resulting in rapid point failure. If a condenser is too high in capacity, poor high-speed performance may be expected from the automobile.

DISTRIBUTOR CAP AND ROTOR

Caps

A distributor cap is constructed of a high insulating material. Metal inserts are molded into the distributor cap to receive the secondary wire from the coil, and also to receive the spark-plug wires. The metal inserts extend downward inside the distributor cap so that the distributor rotor can provide a path between the center terminal and an outside terminal of the distributor cap. Copper, brass, and aluminum are used, and there is no apparent advantage of one metal over the others.

A resistor-type cap containing built-in suppression usually includes a carbon resistor. The resistor is built into the terminal on the cap of the coil tower. Due to the characteristics of the carbon, the resistance may change over a period of time; it therefore may be advisable to change the distributor cap and rotor when replacing the breaker points.

Distributor caps are keyed to the housing and the cap must be properly located before applying the hold-down clamps, as shown in Fig. 38. To replace a defective cap, place the old and new caps side by side in the same relative position, noting the locating lugs or slots. Remove one lead at a time from the old cap and place it in the same relative tower on the new cap. The lead must first be pushed to the bottom of the tower and then the rubber boot replaced securely.

Rotors

Distributor rotors are usually constructed of materials similar to those used in distributor caps. A metal strip on the rotor is

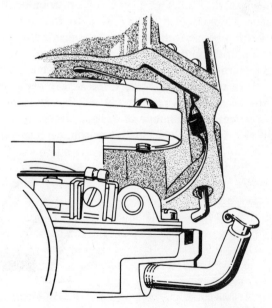

Fig. 38. Showing the distributor cap locating lug.

used to form a conductor which contacts the center button of the distributor cap. This metal strip provides a path for the high-tension current to the proximity of one of the secondary wire terminal posts inside the cap. The metal strip does not actually close the circuit between the center button and the outer terminal. There is always an air gap between the end of the rotor tip and the distributor cap terminals. This gap is very small so that not more than 2000 to 3000 volts are required to carry secondary ignition current across it.

Some rotors incorporate a carbon resistor in their construction to provide ignition suppression. Be sure to replace resistor-type rotors and caps with similar type units to retain the balance of the ignition system. Rotors are keyed to the distributor shaft, which places them correctly with relationship to the distributor cam. The relationship between the rotor and the distributor cam is critical, in that the rotor tip must be passing one of the secondary ignition wire terminals inside the cap at the time the ignition points open. If this relationship is incorrect, the air gap between the rotor tip and the secondary wire terminal will be excessive. This, in turn, will increase the amount of voltage necessary to complete the circuit to the spark plug. For this reason, care should be taken

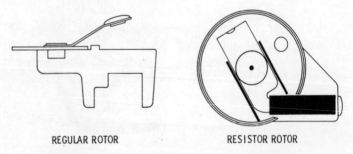

REGULAR ROTOR   RESISTOR ROTOR

Fig. 39. Showing the regular and resistor type distributor rotor.

to select the proper replacement rotor. Fig. 39 illustrates two types of distributor rotors.

To clean the rotor, wipe off any dirt, using a clean rag dampened in solvent, as shown in Fig. 40. Then examine the rotor for

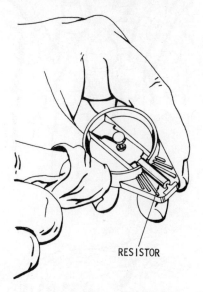

Fig. 40. Illustrating a method of cleaning a rotor.

RESISTOR

cracks or chips and inspect the rotor tip for excessive burning. If the rotor tip is badly corroded, scrape it clean and check the spring on the rotor for sufficient tension to ensure a good contact with the carbon button in the center of the distributor cap. The carbon resistor, if present, should be examined for cracks.

Many distributor caps are destroyed by loose high-tension leads. When the high-tension lead is not properly seated, an arc occurs each time the plug fires. The resulting heat carbonizes the phenolic material and eventually eats it away, as shown in Fig. 41.

211

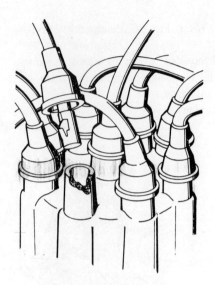

Fig. 41. Showing a portion of a distributor cap eaten away by high-voltage arc.

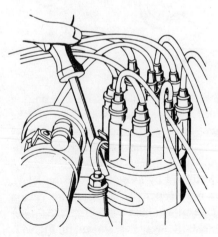

Fig. 42. The method used to remove the distributor cap when snap-on clips are used.

When using a screwdriver to remove the spring clips from a distributor cap, insert the screwdriver between the spring clip and distributor housing and pry outward, as shown in Fig. 42. Never apply pressure on the cap, as it may crack.

To remove a cap from a distributor containing spring-loaded screw clamps, press down on the screw and turn in either direction, as shown in Fig. 43. This action will release the clamps

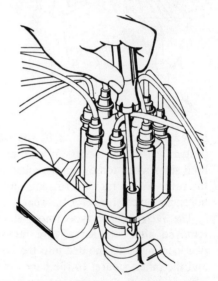

Fig. 43. The method used to remove the distributor cap when screw clamps are used.

from the housing, releasing the cap. Clean the cap with a rag and solvent on the outside as shown in Fig. 44, and with an air hose on the inside. Check the entire cap for carbon tracks, cracks, eroded terminals, and worn or lost carbon inserts.

Many older vehicles have a spring that fits between the rotor and the distributor shaft. If a push-on type rotor is loose on the shaft, check the spring for proper tension. If the rotor is allowed

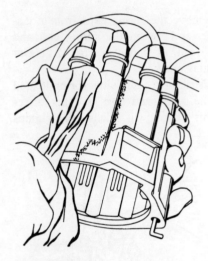

Fig. 44. Cleaning the distributor cap.

to remain loose on the shaft, the timing will be off and an improper spark will occur. Where possible, support the rotor on both sides when removing or replacing, as shown in Fig. 45. Clean the rotor with a rag and solvent, and check for carbon tracks, pin holes, and excessive rotor tip wear.

The *Delco-Remy* type rotor, shown in Fig. 46, can only be removed after two screws are removed. This type of rotor has two locating studs molded into the body. One of the studs is round and the other square. In the hands of a strong mechanic, it is possible to mount the rotor incorrectly. If enough screwdriver pressure is exerted, the round stud will be forced into the square hole and the square stud into the round hole.

SECONDARY CIRCUIT SUPPRESSION

In resistor spark-plug cable design, the copper wire formerly used is replaced with a carbon or carbon impregnated linen core.

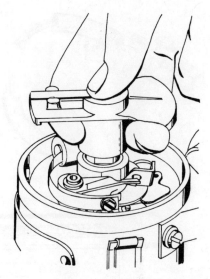

Fig. 45. Illustrating the push-on type rotor.

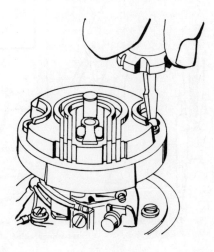

Fig. 46. Illustrating the *Delco-Remy* type rotor.

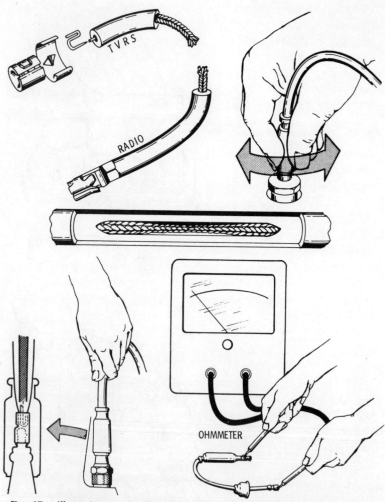

Fig. 47. Illustrating a resistance cable and the use of an ohmmeter to check the resistance value of cable.

These cables have a resistance value of approximately 4,000 ohms per foot. Because of their design, resistor cables are particularly susceptible to damage by rough handling. These cables should never be "yanked" from the spark plugs. Instead, the rubber spark-plug boot should be gently twisted to break the seal between the boot and the spark-plug insulator. The cable should then be gently lifted straight from the plug.

Rough handling can break the connection between the cable and the plug terminal, or it can stretch the cable sufficiently to change the resistance value. Any damage will be reflected in poor engine performance. Trouble of this nature may be difficult to locate since the symptoms are the same as spark-plug malfunction. An ohmmeter is an excellent instrument with which to check cable continuity and to measure the resistance value of resistor cables. Resistor cables are identified by the letters *TVRS* or the word *radio* printed on the cable insulation, as shown in Fig. 47.

To retain the balance engineered into the ignition system, always replace resistor cables with the same type when performing your tune-up. Resistor cables are *never* used with resistor plugs since the double resistance may cause ignition misfiring.

SPARK PLUGS

To provide proper engine performance, spark plugs must operate within a particular temperature range. If the spark-plug operating temperature is too cold (less than 700°F.), soot and carbon will deposit on the insulator tips which will cause fouling and misfiring. If the plugs run too hot (more than 1700°F.), the insulator will be damaged and the electrodes will burn away rapidly. In extreme conditions, hot plugs cause premature burning (preignition) of the air-fuel mixture. A spark-plug heat range chart is shown in Fig. 48.

	USUAL INSULATOR COLOR	AVERAGE GAP WEAR	RECOMMENDATIONS
	LIGHT TAN TO GRAYISH BROWN	.0005" TO .001" PER 1000 MILES	USE SAME HEAT RANGE AS REPLACEMENT
	WHITE OR DEAD GREY	MORE THAN .001" PER 1000 MILES	USE NEXT STEP COLDER PLUG
	BLACK	LESS THAN .005" PER 1000 MILES	USE NEXT STEP HOTTER PLUG

Fig. 48. A spark plug heat range chart.

The ability of a spark plug to transfer heat from the insulated center electrode tip is controlled by the design of the spark plug. The only escape path for heat is through the insulator tip, spark-plug shell and gasket, through the cylinder head, to the cooling liquid in the water jacket. By varying the length and shape of the insulator and shell, the manufacturer is able to produce spark plugs with different heat-range characteristics, and thereby control their operating temperatures.

A visual inspection of the spark plugs after they have been removed from the engine may reveal the existence of a variety of engine ailments. In addition, the spark plug will show with reasonable accuracy if the correct heat range plugs are being used.

The nature of the deposits collected on the plug insulator and the condition of the electrode gap also provide valuable clues. It is important, however, not to idle a cold engine for any length of time before removing the spark plugs for examination. The plugs taken from a cold engine that has been idling with partial choke will very likely be soot-fouled by the rich fuel mixture. This deposit will give a false impression of the true condition of the plug.

When replacing spark plugs during your tune-up, it is usually advisable to replace the plugs with those of the same heat range as used originally. If, however, the plugs in an engine constantly exhibit electrode wear and blistered insulators, a colder range of plugs should be used. If, because of constant low-speed city driving, the plugs are constantly fouled, a hotter range of plugs should be installed. When a change is made, change only one heat range number at a time. *Remember—a hotter spark plug can stand a higher temperature; it does not provide a hotter spark.*

Spark-plug reach is the length of the threaded portion of the plug, as illustrated in Fig. 49. If the reach is too short, the plug

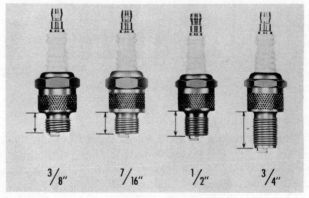

Fig. 49. Illustrating spark plug reach.

electrodes will be in a pocket and may misfire under certain conditions. The exposed threads in the cylinder head will "carbon up," making cleaning of the threads necessary before plugs of the proper reach can be correctly installed and torqued. If the reach is too long, the plug threads will be exposed and may overheat. The exposed threads will carbonize, making plug removal difficult. The danger of piston head damage also exists if the reach is too long.

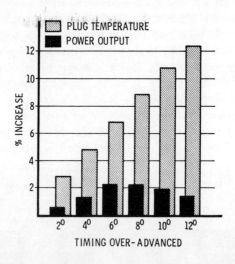

Fig. 50. Showing the effects of advance timing.

Fig. 50 shows how ignition timing advanced beyond the specified settings rapidly overheats the spark plugs, with little or no gain in power. Most manufacturers now warn against so-called "power timing," or timing on the basis of audible detonation. Distributor basic timing should be set in accordance with manufacturer's specifications, preferably with a timing light. This will greatly increase the life of spark plugs, valves, and other engine parts. Ignition timing should always be double-checked after new breaker points have been installed or after point spacing has been adjusted, since dwell angle affects timing.

Carbon Deposits

A rich mixture caused by improper carburetor jets or by choke action leaves excessive carbon deposits on the spark plug that will lead to plug shorting and erratic operation, as indicated in Fig. 52. The oil-fouled plug is usually wet due to oil leakage into the cylinder via the valves or past the piston rings. An oil-fouled plug is shown in Fig. 53.

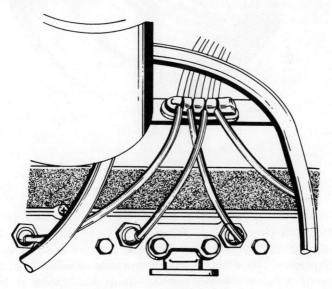

Fig. 51. Illustrating cross-fire in spark plug cables.

Fig. 52. Illustrating carbon deposits on a spark plug.

REVERSED COIL POLARITY

Polarity of the high-tension current should always be *negative* at the spark-plug terminal. When the polarity is reversed, the voltage required to fire a spark plug may increase as much as 20 to 40 percent. This occurs under all operating conditions and can encourage rough idling and misfiring during acceleration or high speeds. Polarity can be reversed by improperly installing the battery, but it is almost always traced to reversed primary leads at the coil, as shown in Fig. 54.

Fig. 53.   Illustrating an oil-fouled spark plug.

CROSS-FIRE

Induced leakage, or "cross-fire," has become an important factor in modern engines, since higher compression ratios have increased sparking voltages. Such leakage between ignition cables does not depend on insulation strength, but rather is caused by cables bunched closely together and running parallel, as shown in Fig. 51. For best ignition performance on all high-compression

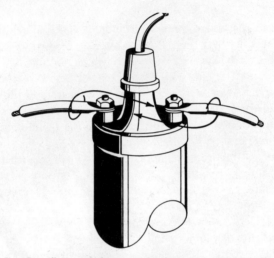

Fig. 54. Illustrating the reversed polarity of an ignition coil.

engines, make sure that the spark-plug cables are as widely separated as possible. Remember that cross-fire is most likely to occur between consecutively firing cylinders when these cylinders are located on the same engine bank.

IGNITION TIMING

Correct ignition timing is one of the most important factors relative to efficient and economical engine operation. If the initial timing setting is not correct, the entire range of the spark-advance curve will be out of limits. Ignition timing is checked and set with the aid of a power timing light. The light is energized by battery current and triggered by the voltage of the spark plug that it is connected to (usually the plug in cylinder No. 1). The procedure for ignition timing an engine is as follows:

1. Locate the timing marks on the crankshaft pulley, harmonic damper, or flywheel. If they are not readily visible, wipe with a cloth and mark them with chalk or paint.
2. Operate the engine until normal temperature is reached.
3. Stop the engine and connect the tachometer and timing light as instructed by the instrument manufacturer. Disconnect the distributor vacuum line and tape the manifold opening, if this operation is recommended.
4. Start and idle the engine. The light will flash each time the No. 1 spark plug fires.
5. Operate the engine at the specified speed and aim the timing light at the timing marks.
   CAUTION: Be very careful of the revolving fan blades.
6. Reset the ignition timing if the timing mark appears on either side of the reference pointer. Reconnect the distributor vacuum line, if disconnected.
7. The ignition timing is adjusted by slightly loosening the distributor hold-down screw and slowly turning the distributor body opposite to the rotor rotation to *advance* the timing, or with the rotor rotation to *retard* the timing. When the specified mark is aligned with the pointer, securely tighten the distributor hold-down screw. Then recheck the alignment of the timing marks.

Fig. 55 illustrates a method of easily determining the direction of rotor rotation without removing the distributor cap or cranking the engine, by merely observing the position of the vacuum

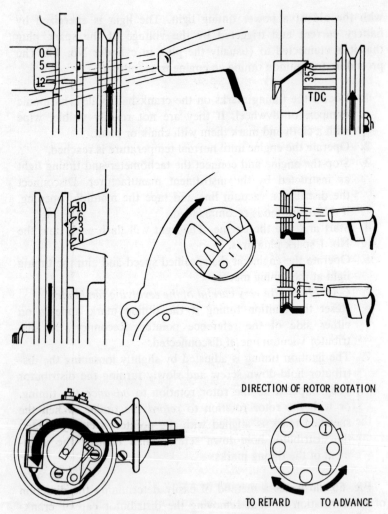

DIRECTION OF ROTOR ROTATION

TO RETARD   TO ADVANCE

Fig. 55. Illustrating the use of a timing light.

advance unit on the distributor body. Rotor rotation can be determined by visualizing an arrow passing through the vacuum line and around inside the distributor cap. As illustrated, the rotor turns counterclockwise. Had the vacuum advance unit been positioned below the centerline of the distributor, rotor rotation would have been clockwise.

The timing mark should appear steady as the light flashes. If the mark appears to "fan out" or "wander" as the light flashes, trouble is indicated. This condition can be caused by pitted breaker points, misaligned points, improper point spring tension, loose or worn breaker plate, worn distributor shaft, worn distributor-shaft bushings, or excessive lash anywhere in the distributor drive mechanism. These conditions must be corrected before an engine can be properly tuned.

After the initial timing is set, slowly accelerate the engine to approximately 1500 rpm while observing the timing mark with the light. The timing mark should move steadily away from the pointer. This is an indication that the spark advance mechanism is in operation. If there is little or no indication of spark advance, the distributor should be removed from the engine for a complete test.

TRANSISTOR SYSTEMS

The transistor, being able to pass relatively large currents from the battery to the coil, enables the coil to store more energy. Increasing the coil input increases the coil output at all engine speeds. The transistor used with a specially designed coil will produce much higher output voltages than the conventional ignition system. See graph shown in Fig. 56.

Increased coil output at all engine speeds may eliminate acceleration and/or high-speed engine missing. Fig. 57 illustrates

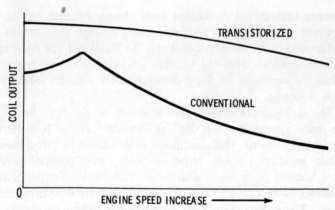

Fig. 56. Showing output voltage versus engine speed.

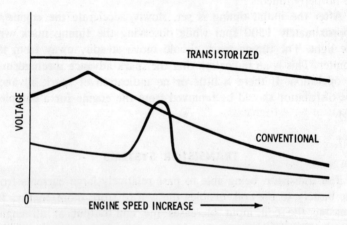

Fig. 57. Illustrating acceleration or high speed misfiring.

the voltage change that can occur in the secondary while accelerating if plugs misfire. When all cylinders are firing, maximum efficiency can be obtained, resulting in fuel savings.

Point Set Life

The transistor ignition system greatly increases point set life as the contacts carry relatively small amounts of current. In the conventional ignition system, the average current flowing through the primary wiring and the contacts is approximately 2 amperes. The peak current is approximately 5 amperes. The high current flow leads to blue pointing, excessive pitting, and short contact life. In the transistor system, the current flowing through the contacts is 1 ampere maximum. The decrease in current flow through the contacts greatly increases contact life. Reports of 40,000 to 60,000 miles is not uncommon with the same set of points.

Spark-Plug Life

When a spark-plug gap increases to .050 inch, the conventional ignition system may not be able to "fire" the plug consistently. The plugs must then be removed, cleaned, and regapped. The transistor system will continue to "fire" a .050-inch gap and increase the time between spark-plug maintenance intervals. This is the explanation of "longer spark-plug life" frequently found in transistor advertisements.

Coil

A specially designed high-ratio coil is used with all-transistor ignition systems. The coil used in the conventional ignition system has approximately 200 turns in the primary winding, and from 20-26,000 turns in the secondary winding. The turns ratio of a 20,000-turn secondary, 200-turn primary is 100:1. Coils used with transistorized ignition systems have a turns ratio of approximately 270:1 or 400:1. If a 26,000-turn secondary is being used on a 275:1 turns-ratio coil, the primary winding will contain approximately 95 turns.

Starting Circuit

In a conventional ignition system, the output voltage during cranking is greatly affected by the battery voltage of the vehicle. If the engine is hard to start due to cold weather, or other trouble, the battery voltage may be reduced from 12.6 volts to a lower value very rapidly. The lower battery voltage available greatly reduces the coil output and there may not be enough energy to "fire" the spark plug.

The coil output voltage of the transistor ignition system is also affected by battery voltage under starting conditions. Many transistor ignition systems contain a special starting circuit that will help maintain a high coil-output voltage under the severest starting conditions. The special starting circuit utilizes a second coil ballast resistor. During cranking, the two ballast resistors supplied with the kit are automatically paralleled, greatly increasing the coil input current, even though the battery voltage has been reduced.

The condenser used in the conventional system does not have to be removed when a transistor ignition system in installed, but it may be if desired. The rubbing block should always be lubricated with a good quality lubricant when new points are installed, and be properly aligned. Failure to follow these procedures may lead to rubbing block wear, a change in basic timing, and poor engine operation.

Do not remove a high-tension lead while the engine is running without first checking the installation instructions; many systems will be permanently damaged by the high voltage produced. When in doubt, remove one plug, re-attach the high-tension lead, and ground the side of the plug to the engine block. When the engine is turned over, a spark will jump the spark-plug gap if the system is operating.

The installation instructions should be checked before using a dwell meter, as its use on some systems will destroy the transistor. The dwell angle is not too critical on a transistorized system. A + or −3° from original specifications can be tolerated. Be sure to reset the timing according to the original specifications of the automobile manufacturer.

DWELL METERS

The word *dwell* refers to the number of degrees through which the distributor shaft rotates from the time the points open until they close again. The dwell meter may be used to check the dwell on the car with the engine operating at idle speed, or off the car in a distributor tester. Hook up the dwell meter according to the manufacturer's instructions, as shown in Fig. 58.

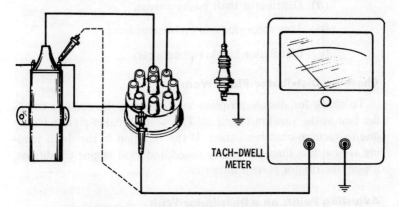

TACH-DWELL
METER

Fig. 58.   A method used to connect a dwell meter.

1. Start the engine with the meter connected; the meter will read degrees of point dwell.

2. On cars equipped with an external distributor point-adjustment feature, set the points according to the specifications. Normal setting tolerance is plus or minus 1°. In the absence of exact tune-up specifications:

    Eight-cylinder engines may be set at 30°.

    Six-cylinder engines may be set at 38°.

    Four-cylinder engines may be set at 45°.

3. Run the engine from idle to high speed. The dwell angle should not change more than 3°.

    NOTE: On some distributors, the distributor plate operates on an off-center pin. On distributors of this type, the dwell angle will change more than 3° as the engine speed is increased; a 4° to 6° change in dwell may be normal on this type of distributor.

    Loss of dwell angle can mean:

    (a) Distributor shaft bushing wear.

    (b) Low spring tension on breaker lever.

    (c) Distributor breaker-plate wear.

Checking Distributor-Plate Wear

To check for distributor-plate wear, remove the vacuum modifier line at the vacuum chamber. This stops breaker-plate advance due to vacuum-chamber action. If the variation in the dwell reading is now less than previously noted under all engine conditions, a worn distributor plate is indicated.

Adjusting Points on a Distributor With External Adjustment Feature

1. Hook up the instrument according to the manufacturer's instructions.

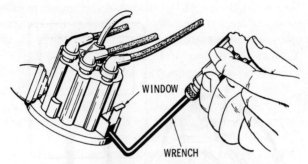

Fig. 59. Adjusting contact points on distributor with external adjustment.

2. Insert the adjusting tool through the distributor cap into the adjusting mechanism of the point set, as shown in Fig. 59.

3. Turn the ignition "On" and crank the engine over with the starter, or use a remote starter switch. Engine may be started if desired.

4. Observe the meter reading and adjust the point gap to the proper dwell angle, according to specifications.

5. Check the engine timing and reset if necessary.

Adjusting Points on a Distributor
Without an Internal Adjustment Feature

1. Hook up the instrument according to manufacturer's instructions.

2. Remove the high-tension lead from the coil at the distributor cap and ground it at the engine to prevent shock. Remove the distributor cap and rotor.

3. Turn the ignition "On" and crank the engine over with the starter, or use a remote starter switch, as illustrated in Fig. 60.

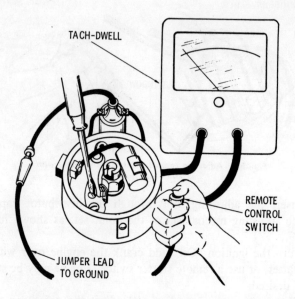

TACH-DWELL

REMOTE
CONTROL
SWITCH

JUMPER LEAD
TO GROUND

**Fig. 60. Cranking engine to set dwell angle on internal
point adjustment.**

4. Observe the meter reading and adjust the point gap to the
proper dwell angle, according to specifications. If the meter
reads too low, the point gap is too large. If the meter reads
too high, the point gap is too small. To facilitate this adjustment, loosen the hold-down screw and place a screwdriver on the adjusting slot, as shown in Fig. 61. Turn the
engine over and adjust the point set while watching the
dwell meter. When the proper dwell has been obtained,
stop the engine and tighten the hold-down screw. The dwell
should again be checked to make sure that it has not
changed from its original setting.

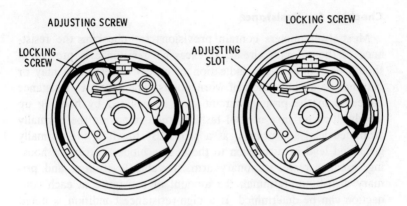

ADJUSTING SCREW   LOCKING SCREW

LOCKING
SCREW   ADJUSTING
SLOT

Fig. 61. Breaker point locking and adjusting method.

5. Replace the rotor, distributor cap, and high-tension lead in the distributor cap, and start the engine.

6. Check the engine timing and re-set if necessary.

   NOTE: Most meters load the ignition system. If hard starting is encountered, disconnect one lead, start the engine, and replace the lead.

Adjusting Dual Points

1. Dual points are adjusted in the same manner as previously described, except one set at a time is blocked open with an insulator, such as clean paper placed between the contact points. Adjust the other point set to the proper dwell angle.

2. Remove the block from the first set and block the second set. Adjust the first set to the proper angle.

3. Remove the block and check the total dwell.

4. As a rule of thumb, each individual point set can be set to 28° dwell. The resulting total dwell should be 32-36°.

Checking for Resistance

Most dwell meters contain provisions for checking the resistance of the primary circuit. If excessive resistance is present, it should be removed. An indication of excessive resistance may or may not be an indication of worn points. The excessive resistance indicated in the primary circuit may be isolated by hooking up the dwell meter in a normal fashion, then removing the normally grounded lead and using it as a probe. By touching the normally grounded lead in succession to the engine block, distributor housing, breaker plate, stationary arm, movable lever arm, and primary distributor terminal, the amount of resistance at each connection can be determined. If a high-resistance condition is noted in the primary circuit, it may be found that most of this resistance lies in the distributor lead-to-coil terminal connection. When checking the resistance drop of dual contact points, one point set at a time should be checked by blocking open the other point set with a piece of clean paper, or other type of insulation material.

SUMMARY

The function of the ignition system is to fire the spark plugs. The system provides a hot spark at each plug in the right sequence and at the correct time to ignite the air-fuel mixture in the cylinders to provide maximum usable power.

The essential components in the ignition system are:

1. Ignition switch.

2. Coil.

3. Primary wiring.

4. Ignition points and condenser.

5. Distributor cap and rotor.

6. High-tension cables.

7. Spark plugs.

The ignition switch simply closes the circuit to the battery which starts and operates the engine, and also opens the circuit to stop the engine.

The battery and generator voltage is increased by the coil which is a step-up transformer. The cables conduct high voltage current from the coil to the distributor cap center tower and from the spark-plug terminals in the cap to the spark plugs.

The ignition points, also called breaker points, serve as a switch to make and break the primary ignition circuit through the coil. The condenser absorbs voltage from the primary circuit, as the points open, to help prevent point arcing. The condenser also assists in quickly collapsing the magnetic field in the coil, resulting in a hotter spark.

REVIEW QUESTIONS

1. When the ignition switch is turned on what happens to the battery current?

2. What is the purpose of the ignition points?

3. What is the purpose of the condenser?

4. What happens if you have a cracked distributor cap?

5. Why should all electrical components be free of grease and dirt?

CHAPTER 10

Charging Systems

Water pressure concepts are usually easy to understand. Consequently, water systems are frequently used to explain electrical systems. Voltage, or electrical pressure, has the identical meaning in an electrical system as water pressure has in a water system. Without pressure, neither system will function.

An elevated water tank supplies water at a certain pressure due to the height of the water above the outlet level of the tank. As the level of the water in the tank is reduced, the pressure is reduced. An automotive battery can be thought of as a tank that stores electrical pressure or voltage for the automotive electrical system. As the electrical energy level of the battery is reduced, the electrical pressure or voltage is reduced. This is illustrated in Fig. 1.

Another water-pressure producing device is a pump. An automotive cooling system would not operate very efficiently if the water did not circulate through the motor block and radiator. The water pump supplies the pressure to force the water through the system. An automotive generator or alternator functions in the same manner as the water pump; however, the electrical pressure they produce is called *voltage*. It is this *electrical pressure or voltage* that forces current through the automotive electrical system.

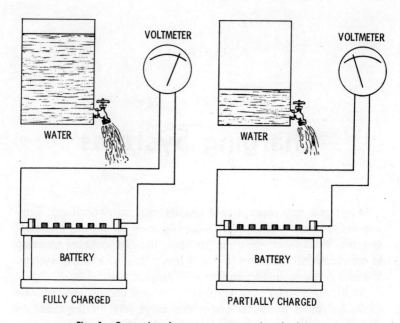

Fig. 1. Comparison between a water tank and a battery.

In an automatic lawn-sprinkling system, water flows through underground pipes to the sprinklers. The amount of water that flows depends upon the water pressure, the roughness of the pipe surface which tends to retard the water flow, and the energy lost in driving the sprinkler. Simply stated, the amount of water flow depends upon the water pressure which is supplied by the pump, and the resistance of the system, as shown in Fig. 2. Just as a water pump or a storage tank does not make water, a generator, alternator, or a battery does not make electricity. They do make or create an electrical pressure called voltage, which moves the electricity, and this movement we measure as *current.*

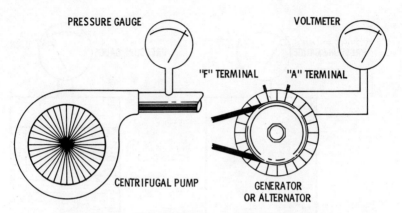

Fig. 2. Comparison between a water pump and generator.

In an automotive charging system there are two sources of electrical pressure—the generator and the battery. The generator (or alternator) acts similar to a water pump, and the battery similar to a water storage tank. If a water tank is practically empty, the flow of water into the tank will be greater than when the tank is practically full. As the tank fills up with water it exerts a back pressure upon the pump. This back pressure must be overcome by the pump and, therefore, less pump pressure is available to push the water into the tank.

Similarly, the battery pressure rises as an automotive battery is charged, just like the water illustrated in Fig. 3. When the battery, being the storage tank of the system, loses some of its energy, the energy loss is replaced by the generator, or alternator, as shown in Fig. 4. If the battery has lost considerable energy, the generator or alternator attempts to replace the lost energy as fast as possible with a high charging rate. The actual amount of current that flows from the generator to the battery depends upon the pressure differential; which is the difference between the voltages

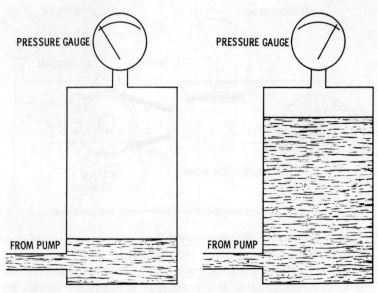

Fig. 3. Illustrating water back pressure.

of the two units. If the voltage of the generator or alternator is, for example, 14.5 volts, and the voltage of the battery is 12.6 volts, a certain current will flow due to the difference of electrical pressure. (See Fig. 5.) When the battery is charged to 13.1 volts less charging current will flow, and when the battery voltage has risen to 14.4 volts very little current will flow.

The battery is frequently referred to as *floating* on the line. Under normal driving conditions, the generated output falls to a value near or below the battery voltage at idle, and increases as the engine speed increases. During idle periods, it is possible that all the electrical energy used in the automobile is taken from the battery. As the engine speed increases, the electrical energy lost by the battery is replaced by the generator. The generated output

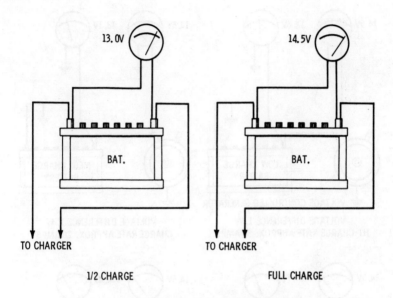

Fig. 4. **Illustrating electrical back pressure.**

above idle speeds is substantially a constant voltage; therefore, the battery takes what it needs to be recharged.

COMPLETE CHARGING SYSTEM

In the water system illustrated in Fig. 6, the pump feeds the tank through a pipe. When the tank is full, the pump must be shut off so that the pressure of the system does not build up and burst the walls of the tank. A pressure-operated switch can be used to remove the power from the pump when the pressure reaches a predetermined limit. With the pump off and the tank full, water will drain from the tank through the pump. To prevent this drain-

243

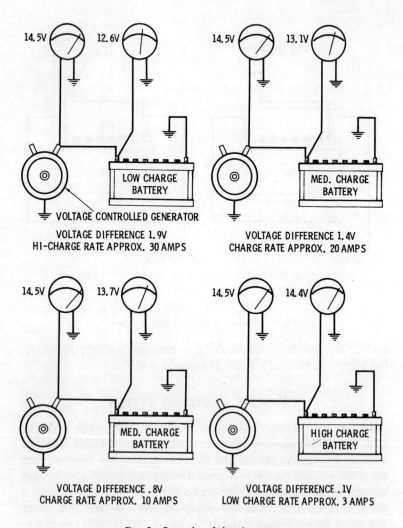

VOLTAGE CONTROLLED GENERATOR

VOLTAGE DIFFERENCE 1.9V
HI-CHARGE RATE APPROX. 30 AMPS

VOLTAGE DIFFERENCE 1.4V
CHARGE RATE APPROX. 20 AMPS

VOLTAGE DIFFERENCE .8V
CHARGE RATE APPROX. 10 AMPS

VOLTAGE DIFFERENCE .1V
LOW CHARGE RATE APPROX. 3 AMPS

Fig. 5. Examples of charging rates.

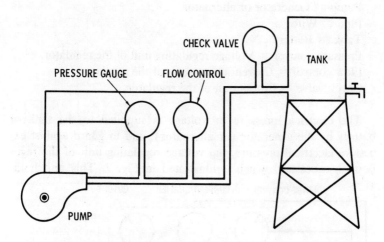

Fig. 6. Illustrating the similarity between a completely controlled water system and a voltage regulator.

age, a check valve can be inserted in the line. The check valve will operate any time the water tries to reverse its direction flow.

In addition to the above two controls, another control is needed to guard against excessive water flow. If a break occurred in the pipe or tank, a great deal of water would be pumped; however, the pressure probably would never be great enough for the pressure control to shut off the pump. Under this condition the pump would be overloaded, and in a short time it would break down or burn up. Another control that is sensitive to the amount of water flowing through the system must therefore be used. This control will shut the pump off whenever the amount of water flowing reaches the setting of the control.

An automotive charging system and the controls act in the same manner as the above water system:

Pump = Generator or alternator.
Pipe = Wire.
Tank = Battery.
Pressure control = Voltage regulating unit of the regulator.
Flow control = Current limiter unit of the regulator.
Check valve = Cutout unit of the regulator.

The electrical pressure or voltage is supplied to the tank or battery by the generator (or alternator), and to guard against excessive electrical pressure, the voltage regulating unit of the regulator is necessary, which is illustrated in Fig. 7. This unit holds

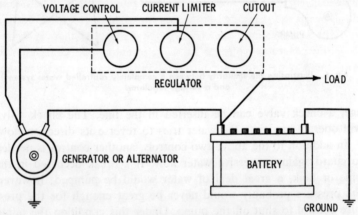

Fig. 7. The complete automobile charging system.

the generated voltage constant, and in doing this, the contacts of this unit are constantly vibrating. The current limiter of the regulator (found only in generator systems) serves the same purpose as the flow gauge of the water system. It is sensitive to the amount of current being forced from the generator to the battery. If the current flowing reaches the designed limit of the generator and regulator, the current limiter reduces the electrical pressure or voltage of the generator, thereby reducing the current flow.

The *check valve* of the charging system is the cutout unit of the regulator (the diodes in an alternator). This unit closes when the generator is capable of charging the battery, and opens when the generator is not capable of charging the battery. This action prevents the current from flowing from the battery to the generator. All of the above control units of the regulator are sensitive to the voltage produced by the generator. The voltage regulating unit is the prime control of the voltage produced by the generator. The current limiter is sensitive to load current, but it adjusts for high load currents by lowering the generated voltage. The cutout closes when the generated voltage is high enough to force current into the battery, and opens when the battery voltage is higher than the generator voltage. In the alternator-type charging system, there is no cutout or current limiting unit in the regulator. These two units have been replaced by diode rectifiers which regulates the current flow.

Summary

In reviewing both the water and the electrical systems, it is evident that the proper functioning of both systems depends on good pressure or voltage control. In the water system, if the pressure is low the storage tank will not be filled to the correct level, and when a large quantity of water is needed, it will not be available. In the electrical system, low generator voltage will result in the battery being only partially charged, and when a hard-starting condition is encountered, the battery will not be charged sufficiently to handle the job.

High water pressure can be dangerous in a water system—the storage tank may burst, or the pump, working against excessive pressure, may be damaged. In the electrical system, high voltage (pressure) will not only result in overcharging and damaging the battery or generator, but may also lead to ignition troubles, plus short headlight and accessory life. In both the water and electrical systems, the systems will function properly if the pressure is maintained at the correct value. In the water system, the pump can continue to run indefinitely as long as the pressure is maintained at the proper value. The storage tank will fill to the proper level and then cease taking in additional water because the tank pressure is equal to the pump pressure. In the electrical system, if the generator or alternator is in good working order and if the voltage regulator holds the generated voltage to the correct value, the battery will be charged.

This charging action will cease when the battery is fully charged, because the voltage of the battery will be equal to the generator voltage (pressure). All other components of the electrical system, such as lights, ignition, and accessories, will give their best life expectancy as they are being operated at the voltage for which they have been designed.

ALTERNATORS

The alternator possesses the ability to produce a current output at engine idle speed and at low car speed. This factor makes it a superior charging unit to the direct current generator which must be rotated at reasonable speed before a current output is developed. The basic alternator charging system components include the battery, the self-rectifying alternating voltage generator, a voltage limiting relay, and interconnecting wiring. The circuit may include either an ammeter or an indicator light. (See Fig. 8.)

Every *AC* charging system is controlled by a voltage regulator. The battery initially supplies the current for the alternator field coil. At this time, and during idle and low-speed operation, there

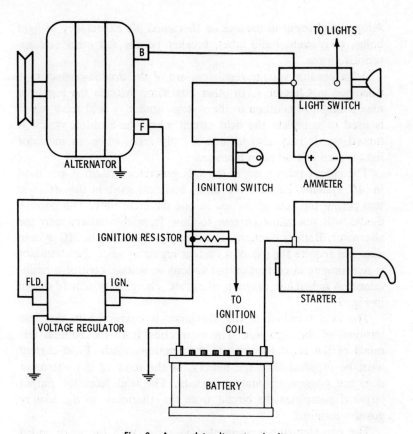

TO LIGHTS

B

LIGHT SWITCH

ALTERNATOR

F

IGNITION SWITCH

AMMETER

IGNITION RESISTOR

FLD.   IGN.

TO
IGNITION
COIL

STARTER

VOLTAGE REGULATOR

BATTERY

Fig. 8. A complete alternator circuit.

is no voltage control problem. However, as the alternator speed increases with engine speed, the voltage increase developed by the alternator would be imposed on the field coil. This increases the field strength and further raises the voltage output. Unless this voltage rise condition is kept under control, the high voltage de-

249

veloped will result in damage or shortened life expectancy of light bulbs, relay coils, radio tubes, breaker points, and other voltage-sensitive units.

All alternator voltage regulators are of the double-contact type discussed in Chapter 4. In other alternator systems the regulator may contain, in addition to the voltage limiter, a field relay which is used to complete the field circuit when the ignition switch is turned on. It may also include a lamp relay when an indicator light is used instead of an ammeter.

The cutout relay used in the *DC* generator system is not used in *AC* systems, because the diode rectifiers used in the *AC* system permit the flow of current in one direction only. The positive diodes will not allow current to flow from the battery into the alternator. Battery discharge is thereby prevented. The *AC* system does not require the use of a current regulator since the alternator is self-limiting in current output as long as voltage control is maintained. A schematic diagram of an *AC* charging system is shown in Fig. 9.

The field terminal of the alternator is connected to the field terminal of the regulator. The connection from the ignition terminal of the regulator goes to the ignition switch. Field current must be supplied from the battery, as the rotor of the alternator does not possess residual magnetism. The lead from the output terminal completes the circuit from the alternator to the battery positive terminal.

The car ammeter is connected in series with the ungrounded lead to the battery. In that location, it will register charge only when the alternator output is greater than the electrical load. The ammeter will register discharge only when the alternator output is less than the electrical load. The ammeter does not register the alternator output. It registers only the current flow into or out of the battery.

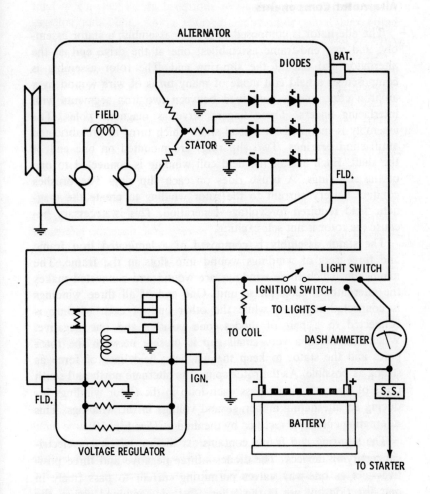

Fig. 9. A complete schematic diagram of an alternator circuit.

Alternator Components

The alternator is composed of a rotor assembly, a stator assembly, and two end-frame assemblies; one at the drive end of the alternator and one at the slip-ring end. The rotor assembly is composed of a field coil made of many turns of wire wound over an iron core, and is contained between two iron segments with interlacing fingers. These fingers serve as magnetic poles. The assembly is mounted on a steel shaft which turns in prelubricated antifriction bearings. Two slip rings are mounted on one end of the shaft. Each end of the field coil winding is connected to one of the slip rings. A brush rides on each slip ring. The brushes conduct battery current to the rotor winding to create the magnetic field required for voltage generation. This is necessary because the rotor is not self-exciting.

The stator assembly is composed of a laminated iron frame and three sets of windings wound into slots in the frame. The manner in which these windings are wound and connected makes the alternator a three-phase unit. One end of all three windings is connected together, while the other end of each winding is connected to a pair of diodes, one positive and one negative. When assembled a very small gap is present between the rotor poles and the stator to keep the magnetic field lines of force as strong as possible. As the rotor spins, the alternate north and south poles of the rotor finger pass each loop in the stator windings inducing an alternating amperage and voltage in the windings. This alternating current is rectified by the diodes. (See Fig. 10.)

The slip-ring end frame contains six diodes, which are electrical rectifying devices. The diodes—three negative and three positive—act as one-way valves permitting current to pass freely in one direction but not in the other. By their combined action, the alternating current generated is rectified to direct current.

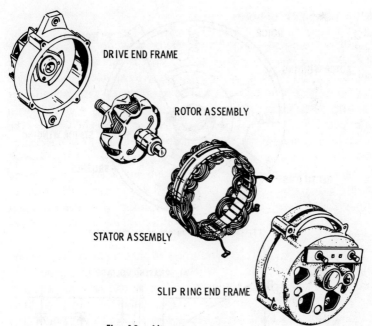

DRIVE END FRAME

ROTOR ASSEMBLY

STATOR ASSEMBLY

SLIP RING END FRAME

Fig. 10. Alternator component parts.

Alternator Action

A schematic end view of an alternator is shown in Fig. 11. The actual generation of electrical energy in the alternator uses exactly the same principle as the conventional *DC* generator. The strength of the magnetic field is controlled by allowing current to flow through the field windings, strengthening the magnetic field and stopping or limiting the field current flow to reduce the magnetic field.

Only one phase of the load-carrying winding and two rectifiers are shown. In the actual alternator, there are three phases and six rectifiers. An *AC* voltage is produced in the stator winding

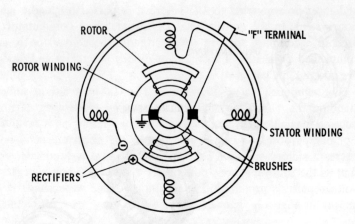

Fig. 11. Schematic diagram of an alternator.

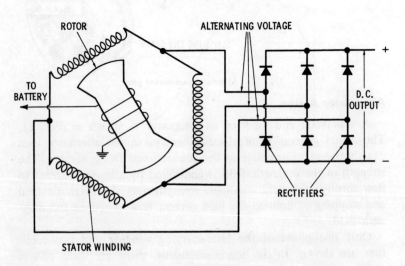

Fig. 12. Schematic diagram of the alternator and rectifiers

and must be converted to *DC* before it is passed on to the ignition system. In the conventional *DC* generator, a commutator is used to accomplish this. In the alternator, the conversion is accomplished by means of rectifiers or diodes. Rectifiers and diodes are covered in Chapter 4.

The simplified wiring diagram in Fig. 12 may aid in understanding the alternator action. The rotating electromagnet produces a magnetic field that *cuts* each stator winding as it revolves. For our purpose, we can assume that as the north magnetic pole passes a stator winding a positive voltage pulse is produced, and that as the south magnetic pole passes a stator winding a negative voltage pulse is produced. The resulting voltage wave shape is as shown in Fig. 13. The *AC* wave is fed to a pair of rectifiers

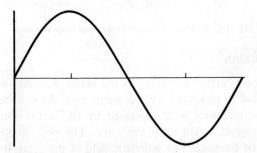

Fig. 13. The AC sine-wave that is fed to the rectifiers.

where the positive and negative voltage pulses are separated electrically and a *DC* voltage is obtained.

Because of the rectifier action, no cutout is needed on the alternator-type system (see Chapter 4). Another unit necessary for the control of the conventional *DC* generator, but not necessary with the alternator, is the current limiting relay. In Chapter 4, the action of an electromagnet was described. If the steel core of an electromagnet is removed, a magnetic field will still appear when current is passed through the wire coil. In the alternator, the rotating magnet (or rotor) rotates directly under the coils of the stator windings.

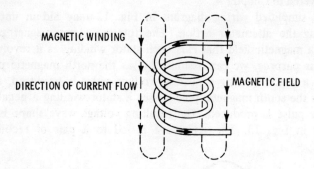

MAGNETIC WINDING

DIRECTION OF CURRENT FLOW

MAGNETIC FIELD

Fig. 14. Illustrating current flow versus magnetic field.

Stator Winding

As the load current increases in the stator winding, a stronger magnetic field is produced by the stator coil. As can be seen in Fig. 15, the magnetic field produced by the stator winding opposes the magnetic field from the rotor. The two magnetic fields are said to be *bucking*. The magnetic field of the rotor starts from some small residual value, and builds up in intensity until the field is strong enough to produce the rated current output of the alternator (approximately 30 amperes in standard units). At this point, any further build up of the rotor magnetic field is *bucked* or cancelled by the magnetic field produced in the stator winding. The magnetic field produced in the stator winding is due to the load current, which cancels out only enough of the rotor magnetic field to limit the current output of the alternator. This is how the alternator limits the amount of current that can flow and,

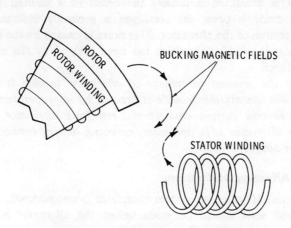

Fig. 15. Illustrating the opposed magnetic fields.

therefore, the need for an external current limiting control relay is eliminated. The above described action is frequently referred to as *armature reaction*.

Troubleshooting

Failure of the *AC* charging system to function normally is revealed either by an indicator lamp that does not light when the ignition switch is turned on or by a lamp that stays lit after the engine starts running. An alternator with a faulty diode can deliver enough current to supply the ignition system demands and yet be incapable of keeping the battery fully charged, especially when the lights and accessories are used.

When an alternator diode is defective, an obvious indication is a whine or hum with the engine idling or operating at low speed. Since the alternator is a 3-phase machine, when one diode is defective the machine is out-of-phase, sound wise, resulting in a whine. This condition is usually the result of a shorted diode. When a diode is open, the condition is generally indicated by noisy operation of the alternator. This noise is caused by the physical unbalance of the unit which has been created by the electrical unbalance.

By far the greatest percentage of alternator trouble is diode trouble. But usually this trouble is created by improper test procedures, reverse current connections, removing alternator leads while the alternator is in operation, reversing battery connections, and other abuses.

Factors Affecting AC Systems

When an *AC* charging system complaint is encountered, a few checks and tests should be made before the alternator is condemned or disassembled. Proceed as follows:

1. Check the tension of the drive belt, and inspect its condition. Stretched, frayed, or oil-wetted belts should be replaced. The smaller alternator drive pulley has less wraparound drive-belt action, making the belt tension particularly critical. Since the alternator has an output even at idle, it is possible for the belt to be slipping at idle speed. Care must be exercised when adjusting the belt tension so that the alternator housing is not broken.

2. Test the condition of the battery. A sulfated or internally defective battery will resist being charged even when the charging system is functioning normally.

3. Excessive resistance in the charging system can cause a lower-than-normal charge rate, and will result in a discharged battery. Conduct circuit tests using your test equipment.

4. Make an alternator field current draw test and an output test.

5. Test the regulator. A malfunctioning field relay may be restricting field current, thereby reducing alternator output. A low voltage regulator setting can also be responsible for an undercharged battery condition.

GENERATORS

In Chapter 4, a basic rule of generation is described—that is, electrical energy can be generated in any conductor when the conductor is moved through a magnetic field. The amount of electrical energy that is produced depends on:

1. The number of conductors.

2. The speed with which the magnetic lines of force *cut* the conductors.

3. The strength of the magnetic field.

In any generator the physical size of the unit is limited and, therefore, the number of conductors are limited. In the automotive generator, the speed with which the conductors *cut* the magnetic field (conventional *DC* generator), or the speed with which the magnetic field *cuts* the conductors (alternator) is controlled by the speed of the engine. The strength of the magnetic field is used to regulate or control the amount of energy developed by the generator.

The energy produced is measured by the amount of voltage produced by the generator. The automotive electrical load can be thought of as substantially constant and, therefore, at any given time the resistance remains constant. The current that flows will then be directly dependent upon the electrical pressure or voltage. If the generated voltage rises, the current rises. If the generated voltage falls, the current must fall. *To control the current output of a conventional DC generator, the voltage—and voltage only—must be varied.*

The automotive engineer has only two factors to use in designing the control circuit of a generator:

1. External controls must be sensitive to the generator output voltage.

2. The output voltage must be controlled by varying the strength of the magnetic DC generator field.

In the conventional *DC* generator, the controlling units are the voltage and current limiting relays of the regulator.

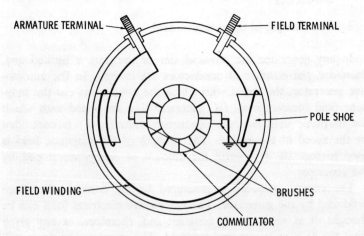

Fig. 16. End view of an externally grounded generator.

Commutating Type DC Generator

In Fig. 16, the standard *Delco* or *Auto-Lite* generator (end view) is shown. An initial magnetic field exists from one field shoe to the other, due to the slight magnetism of the field shoes. As the armature rotates in the weak magnetic field, electrical energy is produced in each conductor in the armature. The energy is collected by the brushes and a voltage can be read from the armature terminal to ground. The voltage produced by the residual magnetism is usually from 1 to 3 volts, depending upon engine speed and generator design.

The small amount of voltage due to the residual magnetism of the field shoes forces a small amount of current through the field coils. The small amount of current that flows in the field circuit enables the field shoes to become electromagnets and increases the magnetic field. The voltage that appears at the brush, due to the armature rotating in the residual magnetic field, forces a small amount of current through the field windings. The electromagnets now formed strengthen the magnetic field and higher voltage appears at the brushes. This cycle keeps repeating until very high and damaging voltages are produced or until *the field circuit is opened.* Opening the field circuit stops the field current flow and reduces the magnetic field in the generator. Opening the field circuit at the proper time is the function of the voltage regulator.

One other type of conventional *DC* generator is used by some automotive manufacturers, which is the *Delco heavy duty* or *Ford* type system. In this system (Fig. 17), the generator field is grounded inside the generator. For this reason, this type of system is usually referred to as an *internally grounded system.* To complete the field circuit, in order that field current may flow, an electrical connection must be made from the field terminal to the armature terminal. Both systems operate and produce electrical en-

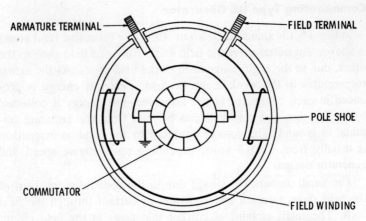

Fig. 17. End view of an internally grounded generator.

ergy in the same manner. The only difference in the two systems is the connections necessary to close the field circuit.

Generator Polarity

The generator will build up voltage that will cause current flow in either direction. It depends upon the polarity of the residual magnetism in the pole shoes, which in turn is determined by the direction of current flow in the field coils. The generator polarity must be in agreement with battery polarity in order for current to flow in the proper direction to charge the battery, and to prevent damage to the regulator relay points. Reverse polarity causes these points to flutter, arc, and burn, and can even cause burning of the generator armature and charging system wiring.

Whenever the leads have been disconnected from a generator, or after a generator has been repaired, it must be polarized. It is important that the generator be polarized *before* starting the engine. This will ensure correct polarity and cause current to flow

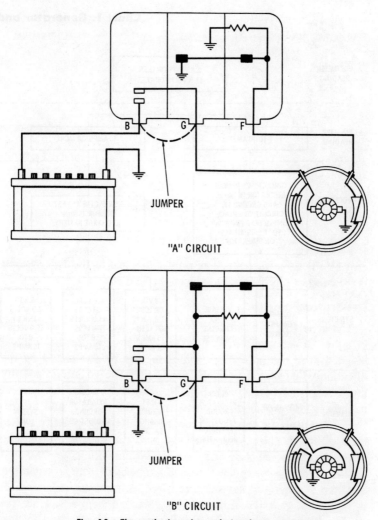

"A" CIRCUIT

"B" CIRCUIT

Fig. 18. The method used to polarize the generator.

Chart 1. Generator and

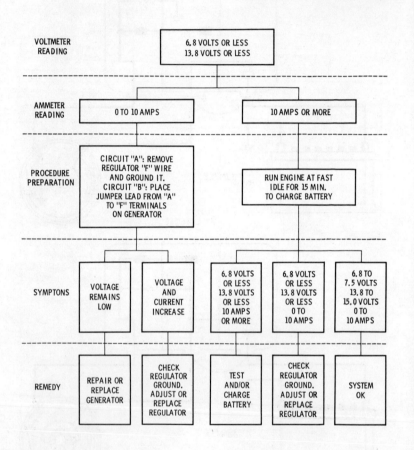

VOLTMETER READING	6.8 VOLTS OR LESS 13.8 VOLTS OR LESS				
AMMETER READING	0 TO 10 AMPS		10 AMPS OR MORE		
PROCEDURE PREPARATION	CIRCUIT "A": REMOVE REGULATOR "F" WIRE AND GROUND IT. CIRCUIT "B": PLACE JUMPER LEAD FROM "A" TO "F" TERMINALS ON GENERATOR		RUN ENGINE AT FAST IDLE FOR 15 MIN. TO CHARGE BATTERY		
SYMPTONS	VOLTAGE REMAINS LOW	VOLTAGE AND CURRENT INCREASE	6.8 VOLTS OR LESS 13.8 VOLTS OR LESS 10 AMPS OR MORE	6.8 VOLTS OR LESS 13.8 VOLTS OR LESS 0 TO 10 AMPS	6.8 TO 7.5 VOLTS 13.8 TO 15.0 VOLTS 0 TO 10 AMPS
REMEDY	REPAIR OR REPLACE GENERATOR	CHECK REGULATOR GROUND. ADJUST OR REPLACE REGULATOR	TEST AND/OR CHARGE BATTERY	CHECK REGULATOR GROUND. ADJUST OR REPLACE REGULATOR	SYSTEM OK

Regulator Service Chart

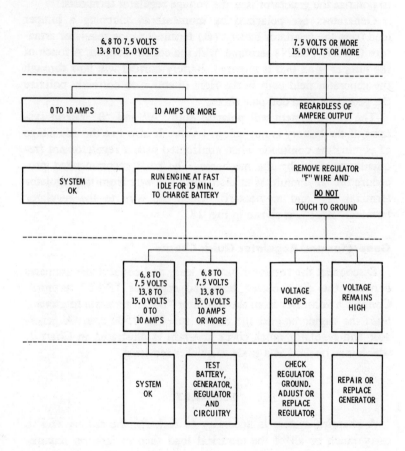

in the proper direction to the battery. An easily accessible place to polarize the generator is at the voltage regulator terminals.

Generators are polarized by momentarily touching a jumper lead from the regulator battery (B) terminal to the regulator armature (ARM) (GEN) terminal, with the engine stopped. A touch of the jumper is all that is required. Battery current will flow through the generator field coils in the right direction to correctly polarize the generator field coil pole shoes.

The above system will polarize both "A" and "B" circuit systems, if the battery is not below 4 volts. It also has the advantage of eliminating confusion when confronted with a regulator not frequently serviced by the mechanic. The most recommended procedure on "B" circuits is to disconnect the wire from the regulator terminal "F" and momentarily touch the wire to the regulator terminal "BAT", as shown in Fig. 18.

Generator and Regulator Quick Checks

Disconnect the regulator battery lead, and connect the ammeter between the disconnected lead and regulator "BAT" terminal. Connect a voltmeter from the regulator "BAT" terminal to ground. Start the engine and set the engine speed at 1500 rpm. A generator and regulator quick check diagram is illustrated in Chart 1, which may be used as a guide to quicker servicing.

SUMMARY

A charging system is necessary to recharge the battery and to carry much or all of the electrical load such as ignition requirements, lights and accessories whenever the engine is operating above idling speeds.

The essential components in the charging system are:

1. Battery.

2. Generator or alternator.

3. Voltage regulator.

4. Charging indicator.

The battery provides the stored power to operate the starter, the electrical accessories, and the ignition system. When the engine is started and reaches sufficient speed for the generator to produce voltage, the battery and generator work together to provide electricity according to the car's needs.

The voltage regulator protects the generator from excessive output which would burn up the generator, and protects the electrical circuits from damage by excessive voltage. The charging indicator may consist of an indicator light or an ammeter. It will show any change that takes place in the charging system such as an overcharge or discharge.

REVIEW QUESTIONS

1. What voltage output is produced by an alternator?

2. What are the functions of a voltage regulator?

3. What is the purpose of a charging indicator?

4. What is the purpose of the charging system?

5. What is the function of the stator windings?

CHAPTER 11

The Starting Circuit

The starter is a specially designed electric motor made for the specific purpose of cranking internal combustion engines. The starter works on the principle that like magnetic poles repel each other. Two magnets can easily demonstrate the principle that like poles repel and unlike poles attract. This is illustrated in Fig. 1.

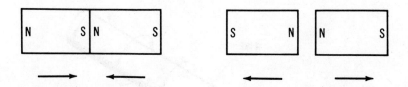

Fig. 1. Demonstrating that like poles repel and unlike poles attract.

A magnet attached to a shaft cannot back away from another magnet, but must rotate if a repelling force is present, as shown in Fig. 2.

In Fig. 2, let us assume the repelling force to be great enough to rotate the shaft magnet to point "A." At this point the magnet again would be repelled and rotate in the reverse direction. In

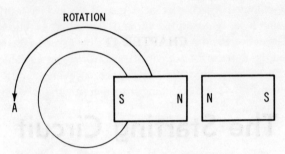

Fig. 2. Illustrating shaft rotation by magnetic force.

order to obtain a constant rotational direction, one or the other of the magnets must change polarity so that the unlike poles will attract each other. When the magnets are opposite each other, the polarity must change again so that like poles repel each other and the rotation is continued.

This is essentially how a starter motor operates. Electromagnets are used instead of permanent magnets, so that the polarity can

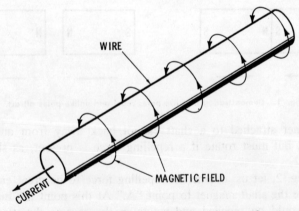

Fig. 3. Magnetic field generated around a conductor.

be easily changed. When current is passed through a copper wire, a magnetic field is generated around the wire, as illustrated in Fig. 3. Reversing the direction of current flow reverses the magnetic field, and in a sense, we have an electromagnet capable of reversing its polarity. Bending the copper wire into a "U" shape, as shown in Fig. 4, and attaching it to a commutator, will provide

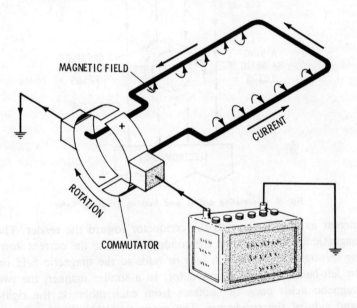

Fig. 4. Illustrating the basic movement of an armature.

the means for changing current direction. This is the same action that takes place in the generator, except in the generator we receive current *from* the armature, while in the starter we feed current *to* the armature.

As can be seen in Fig. 4, the current flow in the armature conductor changes direction each time the conductor contacts a different brush via a commutating segment. In Fig. 5, consider the

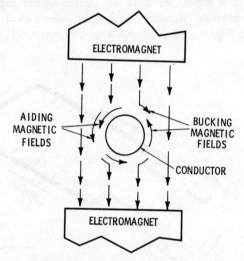

ELECTROMAGNET

AIDING
MAGNETIC
FIELDS

BUCKING
MAGNETIC
FIELDS

CONDUCTOR

ELECTROMAGNET

Fig. 5. Illustrating aiding and bucking magnetic fields.

current as flowing through the conductor toward the reader. The magnetic field surrounding the conductor, due to the current flowing through the conductor, *aids* or adds to the magnetic field on the left-hand side of the conductor. In a similar manner, the two magnetic fields *buck* or subtract from each other on the right-hand side of the conductor. The magnetic fields therefore repel on the left and attract on the right, pushing and pulling the conductor to the right.

Using this principle, and attaching a magnet to a shaft like the permanent magnet shown in Fig. 2, a rotating member is obtained. Varying the strength of the magnetic fields will vary the

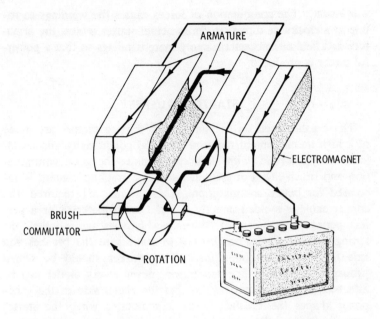

Fig. 6. Showing the direction of rotation of the armature.

strength of the motor. In the simple motor shown in Fig. 6, the armature would be forced in a clockwise direction, due to the action of the magnetic field surrounding the armature conductor. When the circuit between the battery and the motor is closed, current will flow from the battery, through the armature winding, through the field coils, and back to the battery.

The current flow through the armature winding generates circular magnetic fields. In the left-hand side of the winding, the current is flowing toward the reader. This causes an upward force on this half of the winding. Since the current is flowing in the opposite direction in the other half of the winding, the force is downward on it. The combination of forces causes the windings to rotate in a clockwise direction. In an actual starter motor, the armature and field circuit contain many more windings so that a powerful motor is produced.

STARTER BRUSHES

The brushes used on 6- and 12-volt starting motors are made of a high metal content material for good conductivity and excellent starting torque, with sufficient graphite for good commutation and brush life. For 24-volt units, the graphite content is increased for better commutation. Where shunts are required, the copper cable is molded directly into the brush material for a perfect permanent connection. When new brushes are installed, the spring tension should be checked to make sure the brushes will ride firmly on the commutator. The brushes should be *seated* properly. A piece of fine sandpaper (never emery cloth) can be attached to the commutator, so that the rough side of the sandpaper shapes the brushes to the commutator when the starter armature is manually rotated.

STARTER DRIVES

In order to develop sufficient torque to crank an engine, gear reduction must be used between the starting motor and the engine. This ratio is usually from 15:1 to 20:1. Therefore, it is necessary to have a drive mechanism which can engage the starter to the engine, crank it, and disengage once the engine starts. This need is evident from the fact that if disengagement did not occur and the engine accelerated to 4000 rpm, the starter would be driven to a possible 60,000 rpm which, of course, would destroy the armature.

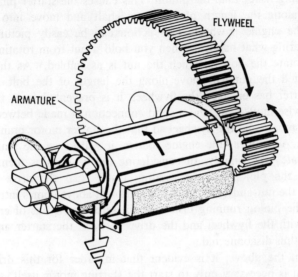

FLYWHEEL

ARMATURE

Fig. 7. A typical starter drive gear.

There are many types of drive mechanisms (Fig. 7), but all are based mainly upon two fundamental types—the *Bendix* and the *overrunning clutch*. The *Bendix* type of drive utilizes a lead screw on the motor shaft as a connection between the starter drive pinion and the starter drive shaft. Whenever there is relative motion between the pinion and the starter drive shaft, the starter pinion will move lengthwise back and forth on the starter drive shaft, due to this screw action. This will depend on whether the starter motor is running slower than, or faster than, the starter drive pinion.

In this type of drive, the starter motor starts to spin rapidly when it is energized. The inertia of the starter pinion holds it stationary for just a moment, and for this instant the starter motor

275

is running faster than the pinion. This causes the starter pinion to move along the length of the drive shaft and move into mesh with the engine flywheel. This action can be easily pictured by considering what happens when you hold a nut from rotating and then rotate the bolt to which the nut is assembled. As the bolt is rotated the nut will move along the length of the bolt. When the starter has engaged the flywheel, it is prevented from further lengthwise movement, and a solid connection is made between the starter motor and the flywheel so that the starter motor cranks the engine. As soon as the engine rotates, it will cause the pinion to accelerate very rapidly. In considering the gear ratios mentioned above, the pinion will be rotating faster than the drive shaft. Again, the nut-and-bolt principle mentioned above comes into play. With the pinion running faster, it will screw itself out of engagement with the flywheel and the drive between the starter and engine is thus disconnected.

From the above, it is evident that in order for this drive to work, it is necessary only to start the starting motor itself, and of course, to shut it off once the engine is started. This requires only a simple switch, and in all modern vehicles, this is accomplished by the magnetic starter switch which is described at the end of this chapter. The other type of drive makes use of what is called an *overrunning clutch,* but might better be described as a one-way drive mechanism. In this mechanism, spring-loaded balls or rollers are used as a driving mechanism between a shaft and a collar which rides on the shaft. The collar is so machined, and the rollers so placed, that when the shaft tries to turn faster than the collar, the shaft will drive the collar. Whenever the collar runs faster than the shaft, the rollers run out of engagement between the two and effectively there is no connection between the collar and the shaft. This makes it an ideal device for a starter arrangement.

In an *overrunning clutch* type drive, the starter drive pinion is attached to the collar and the entire arrangement is connected to the starter drive motor through the means of a splined drive shaft. In the use of this type drive, the first action that takes place is that of the *overrunning clutch* mechanism. The clutch mechanism slides along the drive shaft until the drive pinion engages the flywheel. When the pinion is fully engaged, electrical contact is made to the starter motor and it starts to spin, thereby cranking the engine. When the engine starts, and runs up in rpm, the starter pinion is driven to very high speeds. But due to the overrunning clutch arrangement, the starter armature cannot be driven to speeds higher than those due to electrical action. In this manner the armature is protected from the destructive speeds mentioned earlier. When the engine starts, the electrical connection is broken to the motor and the overrunning clutch assembly is allowed to slide out of engagement with the flywheel. This sliding action of the overrunning clutch assembly is accomplished through what we call a *shifter fork*.

Years ago, this action was accomplished by a long stroke, floor mounted, starter button. Most of the stroke was utilized to operate the shifter fork to engage the drive mechanism. The latter portion of the stroke operated a starter switch. On present day cars, the solenoid starter switch is used. These are very powerful solenoids, mounted directly on the starter, which contain contact assemblies within the solenoid switch. When the solenoid is energized, it causes movement of a solenoid plunger which is connected to the shifter fork. Just as the shifter fork fully engages the pinion, the solenoid plunger also closes contacts and causes the starter motor to be energized.

As is to be expected, there are many modifications of these basic drives in use, but they all operate on one of these two principles. As a general guide, *General Motors* utilizes the overrunning clutch type drive almost exclusively. *Chrysler Corporation* uses the overrunning clutch on their larger cars and *Bendix* drive on their smaller cars. *Ford Motor Company* utilizes the *Bendix* system, and *American Motors* the overrunning clutch.

REMOTE CONTROL STARTER SWITCHES

Two types of magnetically operated switches are in common use in present day starting systems. One of these is a magnetic starter switch, the function of which is to close heavy contacts that are capable of carrying large amounts of starter current. The other type is a solenoid starter switch which, in addition to performing the operation of the magnetic starter switch, magnetically operates the necessary linkage to engage the starter motor with the flywheel of the engine.

Magnetic Starter Switch

The magnetic starter switch consists mainly of two large copper contacts, a large copper contact washer, and an energizing winding. This type of starter switch may or may not contain the coil resistor shorting contact. All of these switches are basically the same; however, there are a variety of electrical connections used in conjunction with the magnetizing winding. Various types of winding connections are shown in Fig. 8.

When the starter button is closed on any of the circuits shown in Fig. 8, the battery voltage pushes current through the energizing winding. The magnetic field produced by the winding pulls the iron core down in the solenoid, closing the circuit between the heavy copper contacts by means of the copper contact washer. When these contacts are closed, the circuit is completed to the starter and the starter motor begins to rotate. When the starter button is released, current ceases to flow in the magnetizing wind-

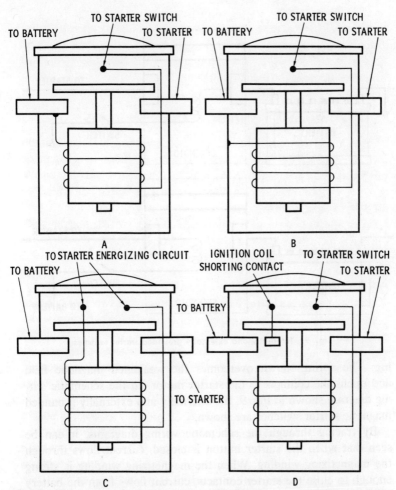

Fig. 8. Various types of magnetic starter switch diagrams; (A) Externally grounded magnetic; (B) Internally grounded magnetic; (C) Starter switch with independent energizing studs; (D) Internally grounded starter switch with coil resistor shorting contacts included.

279

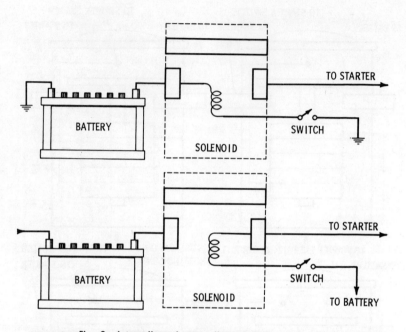

Fig. 9. Internally and externally grounded starter switches.

ing. The spring shown overcomes the weakened magnetic field and opens the contacts to the starter motor. In the schematic wiring diagram shown in Fig. 9, the internally and externally grounded magnetic starter switches are shown.

By tracing through the schematic wiring diagrams, it can be seen that when the starter button is closed, current flows through the magnetizing winding. When the magnetizing winding is strong enough to close the starter contacts, current flows from the battery to the starter motor. The starter switch may be located on the dashboard in the form of a push-button switch or in the ignition key lock assembly.

Solenoid Starter Switch

The solenoid starter switch (Fig. 10) functions electrically the same as the magnetic starter switch; however, in this type of

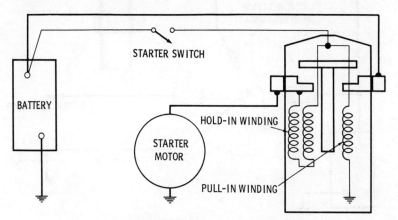

Fig. 10. A schematic diagram of a typical starter solenoid.

switch there are two magnetizing windings. When the starter switch is closed, current flows through the *pull-in* and the *hold-in* windings.

The magnetic pull of the two windings closes the large starter contacts, allowing starter current to flow. In addition, the closing of the solenoid contacts shorts out the pull-in winding and this winding loses its magnetic ability. The hold-in winding remains energized until the starter switch is released, at which time current ceases to flow in the winding and the return spring opens the solenoid contacts. The heavy steel core is attached to the appropriate linkage, so that when the core is drawn into the center of the solenoid the gear end of the starter motor is forced out to engage the gear with the flywheel of the engine. This type of solenoid frequently contains a coil resistor shorting contact.

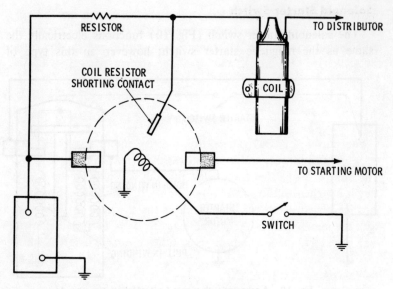

Fig. 11. Schematic diagram of the primary ignition circuit showing the coil resistor shorting contacts.

The coil resistor (Fig. 11) is a desirable element in the ignition primary system. However, when the coil resistor is used, the starting output of the ignition coil is substantially reduced. In an effort to raise the secondary ignition output under starting conditions, the coil resistor is shorted out or bypassed by the shorting contacts in the solenoid. This procedure allows maximum voltage to be impressed on the coil primary and the maximum secondary output can be obtained.

Remote Control Starter Switch

When using a solenoid starter switch (remote control switch), *follow the hook-up instructions* that came with the switch to avoid the possibility of damaging the starter control circuit on the vehicle. For example, if the remote control switch lead is clipped to the solenoid terminal of the transmission neutral switch, the neutral switch will be burned out when the remote control switch is actuated.

SUMMARY

The starter is a low-voltage direct-current motor capable of developing high torque, and is supplied with current from the battery. The starter may drive the engine through a pinion or by a dog clutch attached to the starter armature shaft. This drive is brought into mesh with teeth cut on the rim of the flywheel, or into mesh with the mating half of the dog clutch. The drive must be equipped with an overrunning clutch or some other means. The great speed reduction required is effected in the majority of cases utilizing the flywheel as a driven gear.

REVIEW QUESTIONS

1. What type of mechanical connection is made between the starter drive and the engine?

2. What is the purpose of the starter solenoid?

3. What gives the starter its high torque?

4. What two types of starter drives are used?

5. What indication will be given if the circuits between the battery and starter are not in good condition?

CHAPTER 12

Positive Crankcase Ventilation

When an automotive-type engine is in operation, a certain amount of the fuel and exhaust fumes pass by the piston rings and into the crankcase. These fumes, called *blow-by*, must be removed to prevent severe contamination of the engine oil. The traditional way to remove these fumes is through a road draft tube leading from the crankcase. Most cars also have a fresh-air inlet on the oil fill pipe (see Fig. 1). Movement of the vehicle creates a slight vacuum at the draft tube outlet under the car and a slight pressure of air under the hood around the oil fillpipe. These pressure differences draw in fresh air to ventilate the crankcase and exhaust the contaminated air.

To ensure that no contaminated air will be exhausted into the atmosphere, *Positive Crankcase Ventilation* (*PCV*) systems have been developed which recycle the engine blow-by fumes back into the engine's combustion chambers where these hydrocarbons can be burned (see Fig. 2). In the state of California, where the problem of air pollution has reached national prominence, all new cars sold since 1961 have had to be equipped with a *PCV* system. Further evidence of the effectivensss of *PCV* is the fact that

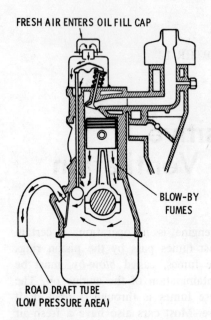

FRESH AIR ENTERS OIL FILL CAP

BLOW-BY
FUMES

ROAD DRAFT TUBE
(LOW PRESSURE AREA)

Fig. 1. Illustrating air vent pipe
on the crankcase.

most cars built in this country since the introduction of 1963 models have been so equipped.

While the road draft tube does a good job of removing blow-by fumes, the system has three disadvantages:

1. At low speeds (including idling), air does not move through the system fast enough to properly ventilate the crankcase.

2. The unburned gases vented into the atmosphere at higher speeds contribute to air pollution.

3. The unburned portion of the blow-by fumes are wasted in the atmosphere, reducing the vehicle's potential miles per gallon.

286

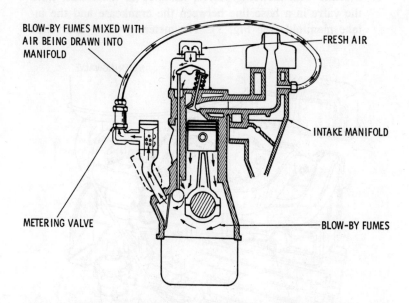

BLOW-BY FUMES MIXED WITH
AIR BEING DRAWN INTO
MANIFOLD

FRESH AIR

INTAKE MANIFOLD

METERING VALVE

BLOW-BY FUMES

Fig. 2. Illustrating one type of positive crankcase ventilation.

The disadvantages of the road draft tube system are eliminated by the *PCV* system. Unlike the road draft tube system, *PCV* does not rely on vehicle movement, but maintains a positive movement of air through the crankcase at idle and at all engine speeds. This greatly reduces the accumulation of harmful deposits when driving in heavy stop-and-go traffic. An unexpected advantage of the *PCV* system is increased fuel mileage. Unburned fuel fumes from the crankcase are drawn into the engine and burned, rather than being lost to the atmosphere.

At the present time, the various types of *PCV* systems installed as original equipment can be classified as follows:

1. Systems with metering valves, installed in most cars, have the valve in a hose line between the crankcase and the intake manifold (see Fig. 3). The metering valve, controlled

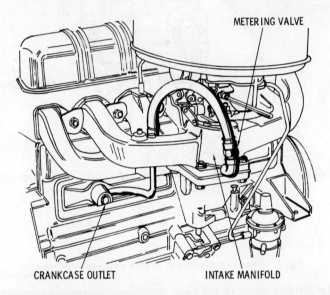

Fig. 3.   A typical *PCV* valve installed in the return hose.

by the engine vacuum, regulates the flow of air through the line (see Fig. 2). Fresh air is introduced through the oil fill cap.

2. Systems without valves utilize a large diameter hose which connects the crankcase outlet to the carburetor air cleaner (see Fig. 4). This system does not incorporate a valve, and therefore the service required is reduced. This system is used on many imported cars and several domestic cars.

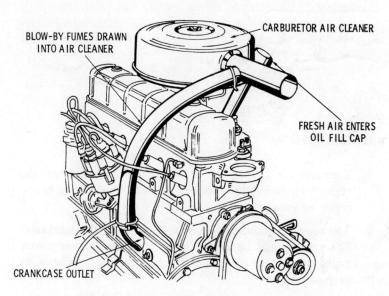

BLOW-BY FUMES DRAWN
INTO AIR CLEANER

CARBURETOR AIR CLEANER

FRESH AIR ENTERS
OIL FILL CAP

CRANKCASE OUTLET

Fig. 4. A PCV system without the use of a valve.

3. Closed systems which may or may not have a metering valve will all have a sealed-type oil fill cap in place of the usual ventilated type. Air enters the crankcase through a hose connected to the carburetor air cleaner.

In all open systems, the oil fill cap (see Fig. 5), serves as a fresh air breather, which is a basic function of the *PCV* system. For closed systems, either the carburetor air-cleaner element or a separate element is used to filter the crankcase ventilating air.

PCV systems require regular service. If the breather opening becomes obstructed, or the valve becomes clogged with varnish-like deposits and fails to operate, many things can happen:

289

Fig. 5.   A ventilator type oil
filler cap.

WIRE GAUZE FILTER ELEMENT

1. Excessive air flow in the *PCV* system can unbalance the engine's air-fuel ratio. This will result in rough idling of the engine or even prevent it from idling.

2. Too rapid air movement may pull oil out of the crankcase. The result could be engine failure because the car owner might not expect the engine oil level in the crankcase to drop so rapidly.

3. Too little air flow will not carry off the blow-by fumes and the crankcase oil will quickly become contaminated, resulting in rusting and corrosion of engine parts. Such a condition definitely shortens engine life due to the wear of moving parts.

4. Should the vent valve and breather filter become completely plugged, the build-up of blow-by fumes will create a pressure in the crankcase. This pressure can force oil out of the dipstick hole and the crankshaft seals, perhaps causing expensive damage.

PCV service is comparatively simple. The important point is to be sure that service is not neglected.

EXHAUST SYSTEM CONTROLS

For several years, the state of Calfifornia has been passing legislation regarding the control of automotive hydrocarbon emission. The emissions from automobile engine crankcase and exhaust systems have acted as air pollutants and smog producing agents. In addition to the smog producing emissions vented from the crankcase, it has been decided that unburned hydrocarbons from the exhaust system tail pipe were also offending agents. California now has laws limiting the amount of smog producing hydrocarbons that may be emitted from the tail pipe of motor vehicles sold in California in the year 1966.

Since other states are expressing an interest in air pollution control, it is probably just a matter of time until all cars sold in the United States will be equipped with a built-in exhaust emission control device in addition to the *PCV* system. An interesting explanation of the nature of air pollution and smog has been offered by the *Chrysler Corporation*. In general, it states that when we talk about smog, we are not talking about smoke. Smoke is an air pollutant of another type. Smog results from the action of sunlight on two invisible gases, partially burned hydrocarbons and nitrogen oxides. Both of these invisible gases are present in relatively small amounts in the normal automobile engine exhaust. In the atmosphere, in the presence of sunlight, they react to form an eye irritating haze referred to as smog. These are the elements that the new exhaust emission control systems have been designed to reduce to acceptable proportions.

To conform to California's requirements on pollution control, the car manufacturers have been submitting various exhaust emission control devices to California for approval. In 1965, California's Motor Vehicle Pollution Control Board officially certified *General Motors Corporation's* smog control system to be installed on 1966 model cars built for sale in California. At the same time, the MVPCB also certified the exhaust fume control systems for the 1966 car models of the *Ford Motor Company* and *American Motors Corporation.* The Board had previously approved the *Cleaner Air Package* designed by *Chrysler Corporation* for all 1966 Chrysler-built cars for sale in California.

General Motors calls their exhaust emission control device the *Air Injector Reactor* system. *Ford Motor Company* calls their device the *Thermactor* system and the *American Motors* unit is called the *Air-Guard.* All of these systems have much in common. The heart of each of these systems is a high-speed, high-volume, low-pressure air pump. The pump is much the same in size and shape as an alternator. The pump is front mounted on the engine and is driven by a belt the same as other accessories.

Air to the pump is filtered through the carburetor air cleaner or through a separate small air filter. Air from the pump enters an air manifold and piping that permits the injection of the air into jets mounted in the exhaust manifold. The position of the jets is directed toward each exhaust valve. The air supply into the exhaust manifold is continuous regardless of the piston stroke in the cycle. The object of the air pump is to inject air into the combustion chamber as soon as the exhaust valve opens. This air contains the oxygen necessary to support and complete the combustion of the unburned hydrocarbons and monoxide gases as they leave the combustion chamber. In this manner, the smog producing elements are consumed in the engine instead of being liberated into the atmosphere.

The air pump is equipped with a relief valve that by-passes air from the pump into the engine compartment when a predetermined pressure is reached. This limits the pump's output at sustained high-speed operation when large quantities of additional air are not desired. A check valve is placed in the pump's output line to prevent exhaust gases from entering the pump should pump pressure fall below exhaust manifold pressure at any time. An anti-backfire valve is also employed. *Chrysler Corporation's Cleaner Air Package,* called *CAP,* employs slight modifications to existing engine components as a means of controlling smog. *CAP* components are a modified carburetor, a slightly altered distributor and a sense valve to control spark advance during periods of deceleration. The function of the *CAP* is to burn the air/fuel mixture more completely in the engine's combustion chambers, thereby reducing the unburned hydrocarbons in the exhaust.

The carburetor modifications include a choke that opens more quickly during the warm-up cycle to lean the air/fuel mixture sooner; an idle adjustment that is set to a leaner mixture combined with a slightly increased throttle opening at idle; and main jets are set to operate close to the lean setting to provide a lean mixture that burns more efficiently at cruising speeds. The only alteration to the distributor is a greater range of breaker plate travel to acquire a substantial spark retard at idle while retaining the same maximum spark advance for cruising as is designed into the conventional distributor. The sensing valve, the only new unit in the system, is a vacuum sensitive device that is located in the vacuum circuit between the distributor and the carburetor. It functions only during closed throttle deceleration when it advances the spark timing to improve combustion during this period.

Regardless of the type of emission control system employed on an engine, it is imperative that the engine be expertly tuned at least once a year. Included in the tune-up should be the proper inspection and servicing of the *PCV* and exhaust emission control devices. The following are *PCV* and emission control system maintenance requirements that have been approved by California's motor vehicle pollution control board.

General Motors Corporation Air Injection Reactor System—As an annual service:

1. Replace the crankcase ventilation valve in the *PCV* system.
2. Check the condition of the air pump belt and adjust the belt tension as required.
3. Service the air pump air filter on those vehicles employing a separate air cleaner unit.

Ford Motor Company Thermactor System—As an annual service:

1. Replace crankcase ventilation valve.
2. Service the air pump air filter element.
3. Inspect the condition of the air pump drive belt and adjust tension as required.

American Motors Corporation Air-Guard System—As a 12,000 mile interval service:

1. Replace the crankcase ventilation valve.
2. Service the *Air-Guard* air filter.
3. Inspect the condition of the air pump drive belt and adjust tension as required.

Chrysler Corporation states that the tune-up requirements of California engines equipped with *CAP* require only the same adjustments recommended for all *Chrysler Corporation* cars. The only additional operation required during tune-up for a *CAP* equipped car is the checking of the sensing valve located between the distributor and carburetor.

A *CAP* equipped engine has its initial spark timing set at 5 degrees *after* TDC, at 600 rpm idle speed. This is contrary to the popular before TDC setting. The retarded ignition timing at idle speed is an aid to more complete combustion of the air/fuel mixture in the cylinders. In addition to improved combustion at idle, the new distributor design also provides optimum timing for all driving ranges above idle.

The vacuum sensing valve used in the *CAP* system functions in the following manner. With the engine idling, the vacuum in the manifold port is not strong enough to overcome the spring pressure of the sensing valve. This makes the valve inactive and the vacuum advance unit on the distributor functions as it does on a conventional engine. When the car is decelerating with the throttle closed, the high manifold vacuum created by the engine overcomes the spring in the sensing valve and opens the alternate vacuum line to the distributor vacuum advance unit. The spark timing is thereby advanced during deceleration to permit maximum burning efficiency of the air/fuel mixture in the engine's combustion chambers.

At all other periods of engine operation, the sensing valve does not function, and the standard vacuum control unit on the distributor operates in the usual manner. The changes in the *CAP* carburetor permit the use of a specific amount of air over and above the normal air intake. Basically stated, *Chrysler's CAP* emission control system functions through the precise control of ignition timing and carburetion. If you operate your shop in California it is imperative that you understand the state's requirements relative to crankcase and exhaust emission control testing and servicing. Or, it may be that the only California cars that you will be tuning are those that are driven into your area by tourists. In either event, it pays to be informed since some form of exhaust emission control device may be built into every engine before long.

SUMMARY

All automobile engines use a crankcase ventilation system of some kind to remove corrosive fumes and vapors from the engine and to reduce the formation of sludge. On early engines, a ventilator outlet tube extends below the engine. As the car is driven, the air flow past the lower opening of the tube creates a vacuum at the outlet end. This pressure difference causes fumes and vapors to flow out of the tube.

Fresh air also enters the oil filler cap to replace the air, fumes, and vapors that pass out the vent tube from road draft. The air which enters the crankcase must be filtered to remove airborne abrasives which could cause permature engine wear. Therefore, an air filter of some type is placed in the oil filler cap.

Late-model engines use a positive crankcase ventilation system (PCV) that routes crankcase fumes and vapors to the intake manifold so that they can be consumed during fuel combustion. A mechanical crankcase ventilation valve, controlled by engine manifold vacuum, meters the amount of crankcase ventilation according to the engine operating conditions.

The fumes and vapors carried by this system promote the formation of sludge, gum, and carbon. Consequently, the mechanical crankcase ventilation valve and tubing should be removed from the engine and thoroughly cleaned as part of a major tune-up. This system requires cleaning at about 5,000 mile intervals and more frequently in cold weather or with stop-and-go operation.

REVIEW QUESTIONS

1. What is the purpose of the crankcase ventilator?
2. How many types of crankcase ventilation are in use?

3. How often should the PCV valve be replaced?

4. Why must fumes be removed from the crankcase?

5. What are the disadvantages of the road draft tube to remove fumes from the engine?

CHAPTER 13

Engine Tune-Up
Equipment and Procedures

Heat, wear, and vibration gradually change the clearances between the engine parts and the adjustment within the electrical, fuel, and other systems. These changes cause a gradual falling off of engine performance which may not be noticeable at any given moment because the deterioration has been slow.

Car servicing should include engine tune-ups, preferably every spring and fall, and oftener if necessary or justified by the car mileage. A good tune-up follows a definite sequence of tests and adjustments that will restore the original performance, power, and economy of the car as completely as possible. In addition to improved performance, a good tune-up reduces major repair bills, since minor parts failure or defective adjustments are often caught before major engine trouble can result.

Tuning the modern automotive engine requires a knowledge of how to do the job. It also requires dependable test instruments and equipment, such as a voltmeter, ammeter, compression tester, timing light, tachometer, dwell meter, and the necessary hand tools. Accurate test specifications, which are generally supplied by the manufacturer, plus quality replacement parts, are the secret to successful engine tune-ups.

FUEL PUMP AND COMBUSTION EFFICIENCY TESTER

In order to assure an adequate quantity of fuel and a constant fuel level for all driving conditions, it is necessary that both fuel-pump pressure and volume be within specifications. A test of the fuel-pump should be made with the pump on the engine, and using the following procedure:

1. Remove the vehicle's air cleaner and disconnect the main fuel line at the carburetor, or at the "T" or junction (Fig. 1) if the vehicle is equipped with more than one carburetor.

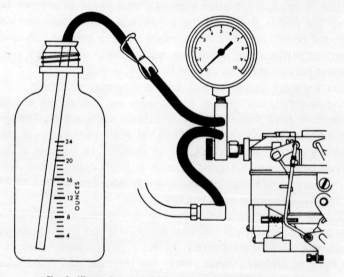

Fig. 1. Illustrating a method of connecting fuel pump tester.

2. Mount the tester to the carburetor inlet. Use adapters if necessary; the fittings need only be "finger tight."

3. Connect the vehicle's fuel line to the fitting on the fuel pump tester hose. Use adapters if necessary; the fittings need only be "finger tight."

4. Close the shut-off valve on the fuel discharge hose of the tester.

Pump Pressure and Volume Tester

Start the engine and adjust its speed to approximately 500 rpm, unless otherwise specified. Use the following procedure:

1. Insert the volume test hose into the graduated container and open the shut-off clamp. When the fuel reaches the 4-oz. level in the container, submerge the end of the hose in the fuel and observe for bubbles.

2. Note the time required to pump one pint of fuel, then close the shut-off clamp securely. (*Be sure to dispose of the fuel in the graduated container to avoid a fire hazard.*)

3. With the engine still running at the test speed, note the gauge reading on the fuel pump tester.

4. Compare the volume and pressure test readings with the vehicle's specifications.

Results and Indications

(a) *Pressure and volume within specifications.*
Pump and fuel lines in satisfactory condition.

(b) *Pressure and volume low.*
Defective pump, restricted or leaky line.

(c) *Pressure low with correct volume.*
Defective pump (pressure spring too weak).

(d) *Insufficient volume with normal pressure.*
Restricted or leaky fuel line, defective pump (stroke too short).

(e) *Air bubbles on volume test.*
Leaky fuel line, leaky pump.

CARBURETOR TESTING

Combustion efficiency is a very reliable indication of the carburetion system operation, if the engine is mechanically sound and properly tuned, and if its ignition system is in proper operating condition. Combustion efficiency is tested by utilizing exhaust gas samples picked up at the tail pipe to determine the fuel-to-air ratio. To obtain accurate test results, the engine must be at operating temperature.

Before testing, determine if both the compression and ignition of the engine to be tested are in good condition, and that the exhaust system doesn't leak. While oil smoke from a car does not materially affect the accuracy of a tester during the test, repeated use under such conditions is not recommended.

Preparation for Tests

1. Connect a tachometer to the engine.

2. Connect a vacuum gauge to the intake manifold.

3. Connect the battery leads of the combustion tester to either a 6-volt or 12-volt battery, as shown in Fig. 2. (Red lead to positive battery post, and black lead to negative battery

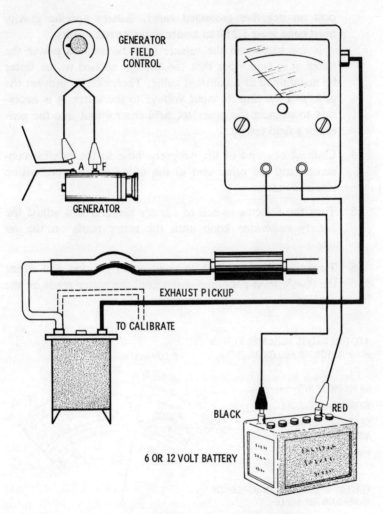

Fig. 2. Hooking up the combustion efficiency tester.

GENERATOR
FIELD
CONTROL

A   F

GENERATOR

EXHAUST PICKUP

TO CALIBRATE

BLACK

RED

6 OR 12 VOLT BATTERY

post on negative grounded cars). Battery specific gravity must be at least 1.250 to assure accurate test results.

If the battery in the vehicle is to be used to power the tester, it is important that the voltage applied to the tester be maintained at a constant value. Therefore, to prevent the generator varying its input voltage to the tester, it is necessary to connect the generator field control unit into the generator's field circuit.

4. Connect one end of the neoprene hose to the exhaust condenser and the other end to the fitting on the combustion efficiency tester.

5. Turn the selector switch to *battery* position and adjust the *battery calibrator* knob until the meter reads on the *set line*.

6. Turn the selector switch to *combustion* position and adjust the *combustion calibrator* knob until the meter reads on the *set line*.

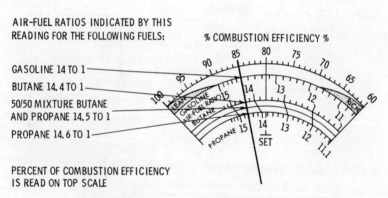

AIR-FUEL RATIOS INDICATED BY THIS
READING FOR THE FOLLOWING FUELS:

% COMBUSTION EFFICIENCY %

GASOLINE 14 TO 1
BUTANE 14. 4 TO 1
50/50 MIXTURE BUTANE
AND PROPANE 14.5 TO 1
PROPANE 14.6 TO 1

PERCENT OF COMBUSTION EFFICIENCY
IS READ ON TOP SCALE

Fig. 3. A pictorial view of the combustion efficiency dial.

7. Start the engine and insert the metal pick-up hose in the tail pipe of the vehicle. (*With dual exhaust, use the side opposite the manifold heat control valve.*) A pictorial view of the combustion efficiency dial is shown in Fig. 3.

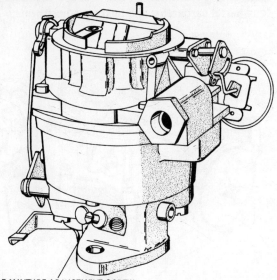

IDLE MIXTURE ADJUSTMENT SCREW

Fig. 4. A single-barrel carburetor showing one idle mixture adjusting screw.

Idle Mixture

To adjust the idle mixture screw, proceed as follows:

1. Adjust the engine speed to the specified idle rpm.

2. Note the reading on the combustion efficiency meter. The most desirable idle mixture on most passenger vehicles is 72% to 76%.

3. Make fine adjustments, moving each carburetor idle mixture screw to obtain the desired setting.

4. Note the idle speed and reset, as necessary, to the manufacturer's specifications. Figs. 4 and 5 illustrate single- and four-barrel carburetor idle mixture adjustments.

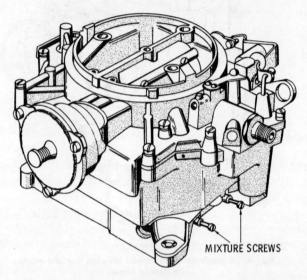

MIXTURE SCREWS

Fig. 5. A four-barrel carburetor which has two idle mixture adjusting screws.

Results and Indications

(a) *Idle mixture reading ranges from 72% to 76%.*
Idle speed and idle mixture screw settings satisfactory.

(b) *Too lean.*
Incorrect idle mixture adjustments, low float level, plugged idle jets, or air leaks.

(c) *Too rich.*

Incorrect idle mixture adjustment, high float level, or plugged air vents.

(d) *Little or no change in meter reading when idle mixture is changed.*

Plugged idle passages or carbon over idle ports.

(e) *Meter reading drifts.*

1. Worn needle and seat.

2. Fuel pull-over from: high-speed nozzle, accelerator pump jet, improper float level, leaky power valve, or plugged air vents.

Intake Manifold Leak

Using a squirt can, apply a mixture of engine oil and kerosene to the carburetor flange gasket and intake manifold gaskets. (*Do not apply this mixture near the choke heat riser tube as it will cause a false meter indication.*) Observe the combustion tester meter for any unusual deflections towards the rich side. *Caution should be exercised because this mixture is combustible. Keep a fire extinguisher handy.*

Results and Indications

(a) *No meter deflection observed.*
Manifold and gaskets airtight.

(b) *Meter pointer deflects more than 3% to the right (rich).*
Leaky intake manifold gaskets, cracked or warped intake manifold, loose carburetor, or loose manifold mounting bolts.

Carburetor Mixture Curve

Accelerate the engine very slowly, pausing at each designated speed long enough to permit the combustion efficiency meter to stabilize. Observe for readings recommended by the manufacturer.

NOTE: The following readings have been found to be the most desirable for economy during no-load carburetor testing. The readings pertain to most passenger cars and light trucks.

RPM	COMP. EFF.	RPM	COMP. EFF.
800		1500	
1000	78% to 82%	1800	84% to 88%
1200		2000	
		2200	

Results and Indications

(a) *Meter reading is within the specification for the listed engine speeds.*
Carburetor action satisfactory.

(b) *Too lean.*
Low float level, incorrect metering rod adjustment, or plugged metering jets, high-speed passages or jets, or air leaks in the manifold or carburetor.

(c) *Too rich.*
High float level, leaky power valve, leaky accelerator pump check valve, incorrect metering jets, plugged air vents, or restricted air cleaner.

(d) *Meter reading drifts.*

1. Worn needle valve and seat.

2. Fuel pull-over from: high-speed nozzle, accelerator pump jet, improper float level, leaky power valve, or plugged air vents.

Accelerator Pump

To check the accelerator pump, proceed as follows:

1. Set the engine speed to 1000 rpm and allow the combustion reading to stabilize.

2. Accelerate quickly to approximately half throttle, and immediately drop the speed back to 1000 rpm.

3. Observe the combustion meter for the amount of temporary

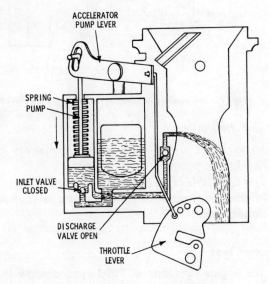

Fig. 6. The accelerator pump system during acceleration.

enrichment. Deflection to the right should be a minimum of 8%. The accelerator pump system during acceleration is illustrated in Fig. 6, with deceleration shown in Fig. 7.

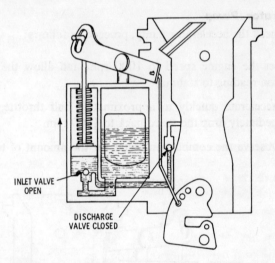

INLET VALVE
OPEN

DISCHARGE
VALVE CLOSED

Fig. 7. The accelerator pump system during deceleration.

Results and Indications

(a) *Meter shows a minimum of 8% temporary enrichment.*
Accelerator pump action satisfactory.

(b) *Too lean, little or no change in meter reading.*
Insufficient pump stroke, leaky check valve, worn linkage, worn plunger.

Air Cleaner Test

With the engine operating at 2000 rpm, observe the combustion meter reading with the air cleaner in place on the carburetor.

Observe the combustion meter reading with the air cleaner removed from the carburetor and compare with the meter readings observed in the previous step.

Results and Indications

(a) *Little or no difference indicated in the two meter readings just observed.*
Air cleaner not restricting flow of air.

(b) *Greater than 5% difference noted in the two meter readings just observed.*
Air cleaner restriction is indicated.

NOTE: *Some air cleaners have a built-in restriction which will cause considerable leanness of the air-fuel ratio when the air cleaner is removed. Consult the manufacturer's data.*

Final Idle and Adjustment

Reduce the engine speed to idle and observe the idle rpm, combustion efficiency reading, and vacuum readings. Adjust the carburetor idle mixture for the highest and smoothest vacuum. The idle should be smooth, with the mixture and speed within specifications. The vacuum reading should also be steady.

NOTE: *Experience is the best guide in determining the normal vacuum for any given engine. Normal manifold vacuum will range from 15 inches to 22 inches on various engines. On late-model engines, lower and less steady vacuum is becoming increasingly common because of the greater use of high-lift cams and more valve overlap.*

311

Results and Indications

(a) *High, steady vacuum. Mixture and speed within specification.*
Proper carburetor adjustment, correct timing.

(b) *Vacuum reading lower than normal but steady.*
Late ignition timing, late valve timing, low compression, and excessive mechanical drag in engine.

(c) *Vacuum reading abnormally unsteady.*
Improper carburetor idle mixture, distributor points faulty, spark plugs improperly gapped, faulty valve adjustment, fouled or dirty spark plugs, manifold air leaks, uneven compression, and improper carburetor action.

After completing the test series, stop the engine before disconnecting the test equipment. Be sure all vehicle electric, fuel, and vacuum connections are secure before restarting the engine for final adjustments.

NOTE: Allow the combustion tester to operate approximately five minutes after removing the hose to expel any moisture that has accumulated in the unit.

Load Testing

The combustion efficiency tester will make accurate tests and diagnose troubles in an engine operating under load (either on the road or on a dynamometer), up to an air-fuel ratio of 15:1. The proper air-fuel ratio for load tests on passenger cars is best determined by comparison tests and experience with several engines of the same make and model. Consideration must be given to engine conditions, temperatures, grades of fuel, etc.

Dynamometer and Road Testing

If the combustion efficiency tester is used for road testing, or in conjunction with the dynamometer to determine combustion efficiency of the engine at various loads, an auxiliary condenser must be used to prevent moisture from entering the tester element. The tester should be placed at a level considerably above the tail pipe to further guard against water being forced into the tester. When making road or dynamometer tests, it is a good practice to remove the pick-up hose from the tester panel except for periods when actual test data is being recorded. This is a very effective means of keeping moisture out of the tester element.

Use and Care of the Combustion Tester

The combustion tester is a precision instrument and, like any precision instrument, must receive proper care and usage if long life and accuracy are to be obtained. Never use the combustion tester on an engine while gum solvents or oils are being introduced into the combustion chamber through the carburetor or by any other means. Do not use the combustion tester on an engine that is burning oil badly. The oil leakage must be stopped before efficient combustion can be obtained. The oil smoke will eventually decrease the sensitivity of the combustion tester.

Check the vehicle for exhaust leaks at the manifold, exhaust gasket, exhaust pipe, muffler, and tail pipe. Leaks will allow the exhaust gases to be diluted with outside air, causing the meter test readings to be inaccurate. Always insert the pick-up tube as far as possible into the tail pipe of the vehicle. After completing the combustion tests, pull the exhaust hose off the meter panel and allow the booster to continue running for about ten minutes to evaporate any trace of moisture in the instrument.

Drain all water from the pick-up hose, and remove the water from the auxiliary condenser, and then store hose in a dry place.

Meter Indications

If the meter will not calibrate to the *set line* with the selector switch in the battery position, check for a low battery or for a poor connection. The meter calibration with the selector switch in the combustion position is very critical and touchy. Rotate the combustion calibrator knob several times, then re-adjust to the *set line*. When the meter is constantly floating in the combustion position, or showing a fixed reading, it indicates moisture in the tester. Dry out the tester by leaving it in operation with the combustion hose disconnected at the tester for ten minutes or more, if necessary.

CAUTION: Under no condition should compressed air be used in an attempt to remove moisture from the tester.

VOLTMETER-AMMETER

The physical condition of a battery can be determined by performing a light load test. This test is conducted by measuring and comparing individual cell voltages while the battery is supplying a comparatively light current flow of approximately 10 amperes. A low-reading voltmeter equipped with a scale graduated in 1/100 volt increments is required for this test. The procedure for performing the light load test (shown in Fig. 8) is as follows:

1. Place an electrical load on the battery by cranking the engine for 3 seconds. If it starts, turn the ignition off immediately. When testing a battery *out of the vehicle*, place a 150-ampere load on the battery for 3 seconds, using a battery/starter tester. Turn the headlights on *low* beam. The cranking load and headlight load conditions the battery so an accurate voltage comparison test can be made between

OPERATE STARTER - 3 SECONDS HEADLIGHTS ON - 1 MINUTE AND DURING TEST

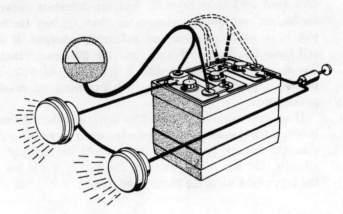

CELL VOLTAGES	CELL VOLTAGE VARIATIONS	BATTERY CONDITION
1. 95 VOLTS OR MORE ON ALL CELLS	LESS THAN . 05 VOLT DIFFERENCE	IN GOOD CONDITION, FULLY CHARGED, READY FOR SERVICE
LESS THAN 1. 95 VOLTS ON ANY CELL	LESS THAN . 05 VOLT DIFFERENCE	IN GOOD CONDITION BUT NEEDS CHARGING
1. 95 VOLTS OR MORE ON ANY CELL	MORE THAN . 05 VOLT DIFFERENCE	DEFECTIVE BATTERY, SHOULD BE REPLACED
LESS THAN 1. 95 VOLTS ON ALL CELLS		TOO DISCHARGED TO TEST CHARGE AND RETEST.

Fig. 8. **Illustrating the light load test.**

cells. For *out of the vehicle* tests, a battery/starter tester can be used to maintain a 10-ampere load.

2. After one minute, and with the lights still *on*, measure the individual cell voltages. Observe the proper polarity when

315

connecting the voltmeter across each individual cell. If all cells read 1.95 volts or more, and the difference between the highest and lowest reading is less than .05 volt, the battery is in good condition and sufficiently charged. If any cell reads less than 1.95 volts, and the difference between the highest and lowest reading is less than .05 volt, the battery is good but should be fully recharged for reliable performance.

If any cell reads more than 1.95 volts, and the difference between the highest and lowest reading is more than .05 volt, the battery is defective and should be replaced. If all cells read less than 1.95 volts, the battery is too low to test properly. Charge the battery and retest.

CAPACITY TEST

Most engine starting failures are caused by the inability of a battery to maintain a voltage high enough to provide effective ignition while cranking a cold engine. The function of the battery capacity test is to duplicate the battery drain of a cold engine start, while observing the battery's ability to maintain voltage. A battery that passes the capacity test will provide dependable service.

The battery/starter tester has an ammeter, a voltmeter, and a carbon pile (which is a battery loading device), as shown in Fig. 9. The charged battery is discharged for 15 seconds at a rate of three times its ampere-hour rating while its voltage is observed. The voltage of a 12-volt battery should not drop below 9.0 volts, or that of a 6-volt battery below 4.5 volts. A reading below this specification indicates a defective battery that should be replaced. A battery that is not fully charged may be tested with a fast battery charger and a *three-minute charge test*. A fast battery charger

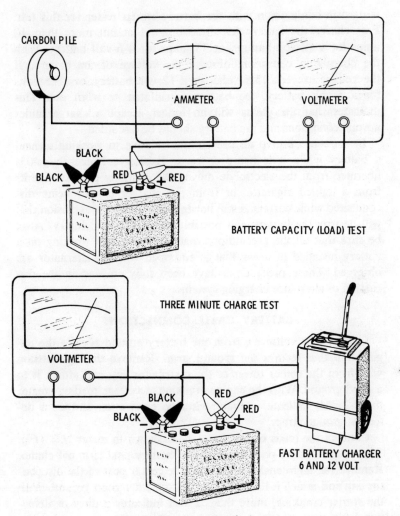

CARBON PILE

AMMETER

VOLTMETER

BLACK

BLACK

RED

RED

BATTERY CAPACITY (LOAD) TEST

THREE MINUTE CHARGE TEST

VOLTMETER

BLACK

BLACK

RED

RED

FAST BATTERY CHARGER
6 AND 12 VOLT

Fig. 9. Capacity testing the battery.

317

is used in conjunction with the battery/starter tester for this test. Fast charge the battery for three minutes at not more than 40 amps for a 12-volt battery, or 75 amps for a 6-volt battery. With the charger in operation, observe the voltage of the battery. If the voltage exceeds 15.5 volts for a 12-volt battery, or 7.75 volts for a 6-volt battery, the battery is sulfated or worn out. This indicates that the plates will no longer accept a charge under normal conditions and the battery should be discarded.

Be sure to observe all precautions relative to working around a battery while it is being charged. Explosive hydrogen gas is liberated from the electrolyte during the charging process. Sparks from a lighted cigarette, or from the charger clamps being disconnected while current is still flowing, may cause an explosion that will destroy the battery and possibly inflict personal injury. Also, be sure that all the precautions that are relative to working on a battery installed in a car that is equipped with an alternator are observed. These precautions have been fully covered in the discussion of alternator charging systems.

BATTERY CABLE CONNECTIONS

Connect the voltmeter from the battery ground post to the engine bolt that secures the ground strap. Remove the high-tension wire from the center tower of the distributor cap and attach it to a good ground. With the engine cranking, a voltage reading greater than .2 volt indicates a high-resistance connection and/or a defective ground strap.

Connect the leads of a voltmeter, as shown in meter "C" (Fig. 10), to the battery post terminal and battery post terminal clamp. Remove the high-tension wire from the center post of the distributor cap and attach it to the engine bolt or other good ground. With the starter cranking, more than .2 volt indicates a dirty or defective cable connection.

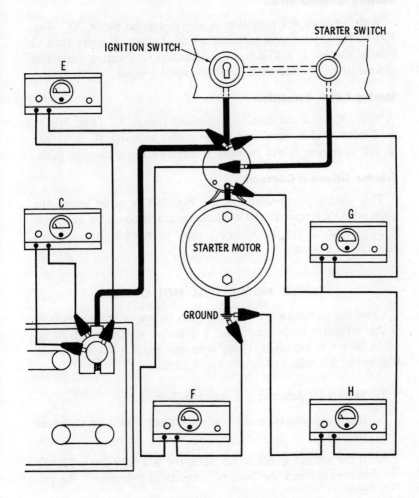

IGNITION SWITCH

STARTER SWITCH

E

C

STARTER MOTOR

G

GROUND

F

H

Fig. 10. Connecting meters for various voltage readings.

Battery Ground Strap

With the same test condition as above, connect meter "D" (Fig. 10) to the ground post terminal on the battery. If more than .2 volt is shown, it will indicate a defective connection, defective ground strap, or a defective frame-to-engine ground.

Starter Cable Condition

With the same test condition, connect meter "E" (Fig. 10) to the battery post terminal and to the starter solenoid. If more than .2 volt is shown, it will indicate a defective connection or cable.

Starter Solenoid Contacts

This voltmeter connection ("G" Fig. 10) is made across the large solenoid terminals and with the same test condition as above. If more than .2 volt is indicated, dirty or worn starter solenoid contacts are evident.

STARTER MOTOR WILL NOT OPERATE

Close the starter switch with the push button or ignition switch. If the voltmeter reads zero volts, a defective starter switch or ignition switch is indicated. If the voltmeter reads 4.5 volts (6-volt battery) or 9.0 volts (12-volt battery), or more:

1. Solenoid is defective if it does not click.

2. If solenoid clicks, make test with meter ("H") as shown in Fig. 10.

3. If the voltage is below 4.5 volts (or 9.0 volts for a 12-volt battery), check the battery connections throughout the circuits.

Starter Motor

If a voltage of at least 4.5 volts (or 9.0 volts) is read on the voltmeter, a defective starter motor is indicated. To check the starter motor, connect meter ("H") as shown in Fig. 10 using the same procedure as before.

Fig. 11. A starter current tester.

Starter Current Indicators

This instrument (Fig. 11) is an inductive ammeter, influenced by the magnetic field surrounding the cable on which it is placed. Select any portion of the starter cable, running between the starter and battery, which is straight for approximately 6 inches and away from the car body. Hold the indicator over the middle of this section so that the cable lies in the slot in the back of the meter, and touching both sides of the slot throughout its length. Press the starter switch; the meter will immediately indicate the approximate current drawn by the starting motor.

Engine temperature and the type of oil used are important factors in determining the amount of current the starting motor will draw. Readings obtained with a cold engine may be higher than those obtained when the engine is at operating temperature. For best results, have the engine at operating temperature before using the instrument. High readings indicate worn bushings, or grounded fields or armature coils. Low readings with a sluggish starting motor operation indicate high resistance in the starter circuit.

6-volt automobiles and trucks—100 to 300 amps.
12-volt autos   — 75 to 150 amps.
12-volt trucks   —100 to 350 amps.

PRIMARY IGNITION CIRCUIT
(12-volt resistor system only)

Turn the ignition on and crank the engine until the distributor points are closed. Connect voltmeter "A" as shown in Fig. 12. If the voltage shown on the voltmeter is less than the battery voltage, a defective ignition switch or connections are indicated. (To determine the battery voltage, connect the voltmeter leads directly

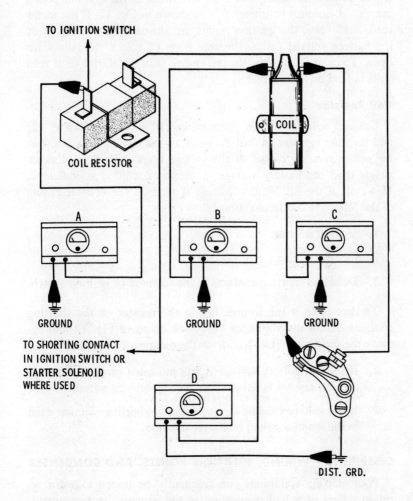

TO IGNITION SWITCH

COIL

COIL RESISTOR

A

B

C

GROUND

GROUND

GROUND

TO SHORTING CONTACT
IN IGNITION SWITCH OR
STARTER SOLENOID
WHERE USED

D

DIST. GRD.

Fig. 12. Checking the ignition circuit.

to the battery terminal posts). To determine if the ignition points are closed, connect voltmeter "C" as shown in Fig. 12. If the meter reads zero volts, the ignition points are closed. If the meter reads the battery voltage (approximately 6 or 12 volts) the points are open. To close the points, jog the engine with the starter until zero volts is read on the voltmeter.

Coil Resistor

Connect voltmeter leads from meter "B" as shown in Fig. 12, and turn the ignition on, but do not start the engine. *The distributor points must be closed.* If the voltage reading on the voltmeter is less than the battery voltage, a normal condition is indicated. However, if the full battery voltage is read on the voltmeter, one of the following conditions most likely exists:

1. Shorted resistor.

2. Incorrectly connected resistor.

3. Defective shorting contacts in the solenoid or ignition switch.

To determine if the trouble lies in the resistor or the shorting contacts, retain the voltmeter "B" hook-up as in Fig. 12 and remove the shorting contact lead from the coil resistor terminal:

1. If the full battery voltage is still indicated on the voltmeter, the coil resistor is either shorted or incorrectly wired.

2. If the voltage reading drops, defective shorting contacts exist in the ignition switch or starter solenoid.

DISTRIBUTOR WIRING, IGNITION POINTS, AND CONDENSER

Poor starting conditions can frequently be traced to worn ignition points or a bad connection in the primary ignition circuit.

If a typical ignition circuit is traced from the coil primary terminal (distributor side) to ground, the following locations are possible high-resistance areas:

1. The connection at the coil terminal.

2. The connection at the distributor housing.

3. The connection at the primary stud of the point set.

4. Contact condition.

5. The connection of the stationary ignition point contact to the breaker plate.

6. The breaker plate to the distributor housing.

The connection shown with meter "C" (Fig. 12) tests the entire primary circuit, and the connection of meter "D" tests the contact points alone. If an abnormal condition is noted with the connection of meter "C", yet the mechanic finds the ignition points to be in good condition with the connection of meter "D", then all wiring connections should be thoroughly cleaned and reconnected.

Distributor Wiring

Connect the meter leads on meter "C" as shown in Fig. 12 and turn the ignition on, but do not start engine. *The distributor points must be closed.* A reading of 0 to .2 volt indicates a normal distributor electrical condition. More than .2 volt indicates worn ignition points or defective connections.

Ignition Points

Connect the leads from meter "D" as shown in Fig. 12 to determine if the ignition points are excessively worn. Remove the distributor cap and rotor and turn the ignition on, but do not start engine. *The distributor points must be closed.* Touch one of the meter leads to the movable lever arm and ground the other lead. More than .2 volt with this connection indicates excessive contact resistance. Replace the points.

Condensers

Connect the meter leads from meter "D" as shown in Fig. 12. Insert a clean piece of paper between the contact points. *The distributor points must be open.* Touch one of the meter leads to the movable lever arm and ground the other lead. If the voltmeter now reads zero, a shorted condenser exists in the circuit.

Ignition Point Burning

Connect the meter leads from meter "B" as shown in Fig. 12. When a set of ignition points are removed and the movable lever arm is discolored due to overheating, it is an indication the coil resistor is not functioning properly in the primary circuit. A normal operating resistor will produce a voltmeter reading of 8 to 10 volts at idle speed, and 11 to 12.5 volts at high engine speed. Higher readings indicate a shorted resistor or defective shorting contacts in the solenoid or ignition switch. To determine the exact location of the trouble, refer to test with meter "B" above. On 6-volt and 12-volt systems, where no resistor is used, test meter "B" does not apply. Test meter "A" can be performed by connecting the voltmeter from the coil terminal (hot side) to a good ground.

LIGHTING CIRCUIT

Connect the meter leads from "A" as shown by the solid black line in Fig. 13. With this connection, the battery voltage should

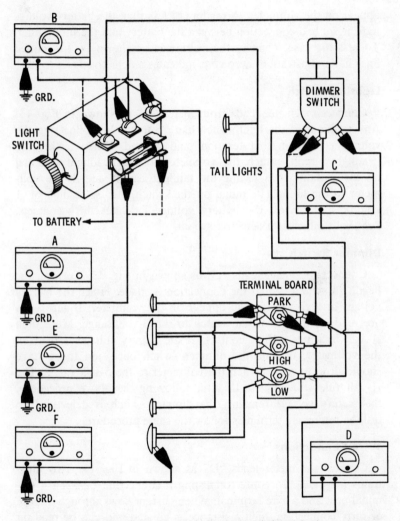

Fig. 13. Meter connections for checking lighting circuit.

appear on the voltmeter. A reading of less than the battery voltage indicates a bad connection between the battery and the fuse holder. To test the fuse, connect the voltmeter as shown by the dotted lines in the illustration. Zero volts indicates a defective fuse.

Lighting Switch

Connect the meter leads from meter "B" as shown in Fig. 13. Any terminal of the light switch can be tested by connecting the voltmeter between that terminal and ground. When testing the headlight circuit, attach the voltmeter to the headlight terminal on the switch; when testing the taillight circuit, attach the voltmeter to the taillight terminal on the switch, etc. A reading of .1 volt or more below the battery voltage indicates dirty contacts. Zero volts indicates a defective switch.

Dimmer Switch

Connect the meter leads "C" as shown in Fig. 13. Turn on the headlight switch. When the connection is made, either the battery voltage or zero voltage will appear on the voltmeter. If zero volts are read on the voltmeter, switch to the 5-volt range. More than .1 volt indicates a dirty contact. If the battery voltage is read on the voltmeter, operate the dimmer switch once and the voltage should drop to zero. Switch the voltmeter to the 5-volt range. The .1-volt rule still applies. If, after following the above procedure, the battery voltage remains, the dimmer switch is defective. To test the remaining terminals follow the same procedure.

Wire Connections

Connect the meter leads "D" as shown in Fig. 13. This illustrates a typical procedure for testing a connection between a terminal post and a wire terminal. When current flows through a loose or dirty connection, high resistance is created and can be read on the voltmeter in the form of a voltage drop. As a rule, more than .1 volt in light, accessory, horn, and regulator control circuits indicates a dirty or defective connection.

Lamp Condition

Connect the meter leads from "E" as shown in Fig. 13. This connection should be made at the terminal connector that attaches to the light, or at the terminal block. The connection will vary with each automobile and must be determined by the mechanic. If the voltage read on the voltmeter is more than .1 volt below the battery voltage, perform tests with meters "B" through "D" (Fig. 13) to locate the poor connection. If the battery voltage appears in this test and the lamp does not light, either a poor ground exists or the lamp is defective.

Lamp Ground Condition

Connect meter "F" as shown in Fig. 13. The ground connection of the lamp will vary depending upon the type of automobile being tested. The voltmeter should be connected from the ground frame of the lamp or the ground terminal of the lamp to battery ground. Any needle movement with the lamp *on* indicates a poor ground.

Checking Coil Polarity

By connecting a voltmeter as shown in Fig. 14, the coil polarity can be easily checked. The positive lead of the voltmeter should be attached to a good ground, such as an engine bolt. The negative lead of the voltmeter is momentarily attached to the end of a spark-plug wire. The engine should be started, and if an upscale reading is noted, then the coil polarity is correct. If the voltmeter needle attempts to read less than zero volts, the coil secondary polarity is reversed and the connections to the primary

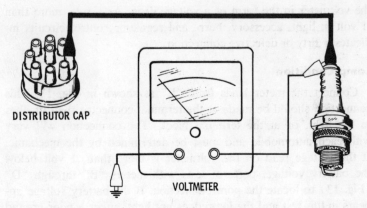

DISTRIBUTOR CAP

VOLTMETER

Fig. 14. Checking the coil polarity.

terminals of the coil should be interchanged. Keep in mind that the connection to the high-voltage lead should be made only long enough to read the meter.

VOLTAGE REGULATOR CHECK (GENERATOR SYSTEMS)

After installing a new regulator, or during a tune-up, the unit should be checked to ensure proper operation. The regulator must be heated to normal operating temperature before taking any readings. To test the voltage, current limiter, or cutout settings, connect the voltmeter and ammeter as shown in Fig. 15. If either meter reads backwards, reverse the leads to that meter.

Voltage Regulator

Connect the voltmeter leads as shown in Fig. 15, and insert a 1/4-ohm resistor in series with the battery lead. Run the engine at approximately 1500 rpm. The voltmeter will read the regulator

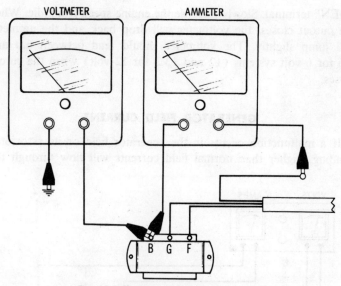

Fig. 15. **Checking voltage regulator output.**

setting. A setting between 7.0 and 7.5 for 6-volt systems (14 and 15 for 12-volt) is satisfactory.

Current Limiter

Discharge the battery slightly by turning on all lights and accessories for 3 to 5 minutes with the engine off. With the ammeter connected as shown in Fig. 15, accelerate the engine to medium speed and read the maximum current output on the ammeter. This is the current limiter setting and should be the rating of the regulator.

Cutout

Change the voltmeter connections for this test. Move the voltmeter clip connected to the "B" terminal over to the "G" or

"GEN" terminal. Slowly increase the engine speed from idle. When the cutout closes, the voltmeter will drop back and the ammeter will jump slightly. The voltmeter should read between 6.0 and 6.6 for 6-volt systems (12 and 13.2 for 12-volt) when the cutout closes.

GENERATOR FIELD CURRENT

If a malfunction occurs in the generator field or its associated winding, higher than normal field currents will flow through the

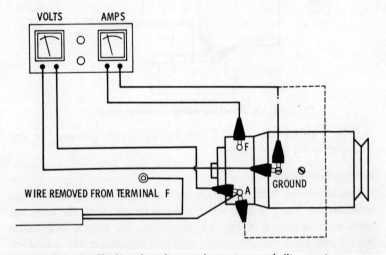

Fig. 16. Checking the voltage and current on a rebuilt generator.

regulator contacts. This will usually show up as short regulator life. Two of the most common causes for high generator field current are (1) a grounded generator field, or (2) a 6-volt field coil inadvertently placed in a 12-volt generator. The following test should be used each time a rebuilt generator is placed in an automobile.

1. Hook up the voltmeter as shown in Fig. 16.
2. Slowly increase the engine speed from idle until the voltmeter reads 7.5 volts on a 6-volt system or 15 volts on a 12-volt system. When the proper voltage has been obtained, read the current on the ammeter.
3. On a 12-volt system, if the current reading in *Step 2* is 4.0 to 5.0 amperes, the generator probably contains a 6-volt field winding. In either a 6- or 12-volt system, if the current in *Step 2* is 3.0 to 4.0 amperes or higher, a defective generator field winding is indicated. The field winding should be repaired, replaced, or the entire generator replaced.
4. In either 6- or 12-volt systems, the normal maximum field current should not exceed 2.5 amperes.

REGULATOR FUSES

Since 1958, some automobiles have been equipped with regulator fuses. This fuse is attached to the regulator battery terminal In some *General Motors* repair manuals, it is stated that the intent of this fuse is to prevent a discharged battery in the event the regulator cutout remains closed when the engine is shut off. It is also possible that the fuse will furnish protection against generator burn out and battery overcharging in the event that the generator field becomes grounded or because the regulator is misadjusted or malfunctions.

A quick test can be made with a voltmeter to determine if the fuse is OK. This test is performed with the engine shut off. Set the selector knob on the voltmeter to 20-volt scale and ground the negative lead of the voltmeter by attaching it to an engine head bolt. Touch the positive lead of the voltmeter to the "BAT"

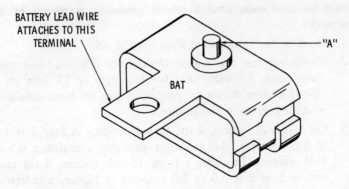

BATTERY LEAD WIRE
ATTACHES TO THIS
TERMINAL

"A"

BAT

Fig. 17. Illustrating a regulator fuse.

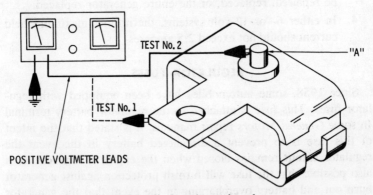

TEST No. 2

"A"

TEST No. 1

POSITIVE VOLTMETER LEADS

Fig. 18. Checking the regulator fuse.

terminal of the fuse; a battery voltage of approximately 12.6 volts should be noted (see Test 1, Fig. 18). Then, move the positive lead of the voltmeter from the battery terminal of the fuse to the screw marked "A" (see Test 2, Fig. 18). If the battery voltage is read with this connection, the fuse is OK. If zero (0) volts is read, the fuse is blown and must be replaced.

Generator regulator testing can be conducted by removing the fuse from the circuit. To remove the fuse, unscrew the screw marked "A" and remove the battery wire connected to the "BAT" terminal of the fuse. Reconnect the battery wire to the "BAT" terminal of the regulator and follow the regulator testing procedures. The fuse should be replaced after the testing has been completed. Keep in mind that a fuse of this type can be inserted any place in the wire that attaches to the "BAT" terminal of the regulator. Wherever the fuse is found, the above procedures can be used to determine if the fuse is in good working order. A troubleshooting chart is shown in Table 1, which includes continuous high-charge and low- or no-charge symptoms.

ALTERNATOR SYSTEMS

Current control is essential in the alternator, eliminating the need for the current limiting relay used in the conventional charging system. The diodes used in an alternator convert AC power to DC power, and prevent reverse current flow through the alternator, eliminating the need for the cutout used in the conventional charging system.

Because of the two factors listed above, quick and complete checking of the alternator charging system can be accomplished by checking voltage output. Two precautions must be observed when testing alternator systems:

1. Never allow the output voltage to exceed 16 volts.

2. Never operate the alternator with the battery disconnected.

Hook up the tester on all systems as shown in Fig. 19, start the engine, and increase the speed. As the engine speed is increased, the output voltage will increase until the operating voltage is obtained. Do not continue to increase the engine speed if the volt-

Table 1. Regulator and Generator Troubleshooting Chart

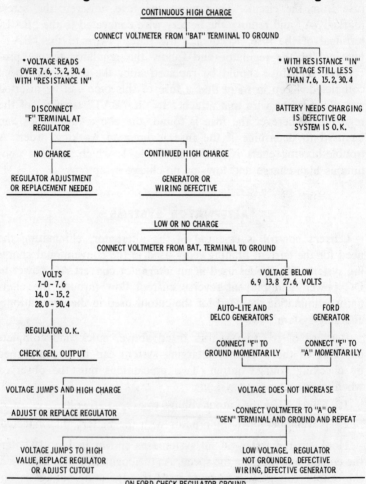

CONTINUOUS HIGH CHARGE

CONNECT VOLTMETER FROM "BAT" TERMINAL TO GROUND

• VOLTAGE READS
OVER 7.6, 15.2, 30.4
WITH "RESISTANCE IN"

• WITH RESISTANCE "IN"
VOLTAGE STILL LESS
THAN 7.6, 15.2, 30.4

DISCONNECT
"F" TERMINAL AT
REGULATOR

BATTERY NEEDS CHARGING
IS DEFECTIVE OR
SYSTEM IS O.K.

NO CHARGE

CONTINUED HIGH CHARGE

REGULATOR ADJUSTMENT
OR REPLACEMENT NEEDED

GENERATOR OR
WIRING DEFECTIVE

LOW OR NO CHARGE

CONNECT VOLTMETER FROM BAT. TERMINAL TO GROUND

VOLTS
7-0 - 7.6
14.0 - 15.2
28.0 - 30.4

VOLTAGE BELOW
6.9 13.8 27.6, VOLTS

AUTO-LITE AND
DELCO GENERATORS

FORD
GENERATOR

REGULATOR O.K.

CHECK GEN. OUTPUT

CONNECT "F" TO
GROUND MOMENTARILY

CONNECT "F" TO
"A" MOMENTARILY

VOLTAGE JUMPS AND HIGH CHARGE

VOLTAGE DOES NOT INCREASE

ADJUST OR REPLACE REGULATOR

• CONNECT VOLTMETER TO "A" OR
"GEN" TERMINAL AND GROUND AND REPEAT

VOLTAGE JUMPS TO HIGH
VALUE, REPLACE REGULATOR
OR ADJUST CUTOUT

LOW VOLTAGE. REGULATOR
NOT GROUNDED, DEFECTIVE
WIRING, DEFECTIVE GENERATOR

ON FORD CHECK REGULATOR GROUND

• INSERT 1/4 OHM, 100 WATT RESISTOR IN SERIES WITH BATTERY TERMINAL AND AMMETER LEAD

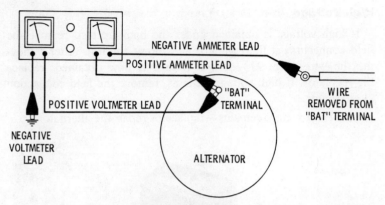

Fig. 19. Checking output voltage on alternator.

meter reaches 16 volts. One of three conditions will exist under this test:

1. Low voltage (13.5 volts or less).
2. Normal voltage (13.5 to 15.0 volts).
3. High voltage (15 volts or more).

A typical voltmeter dial is shown in Fig. 20.

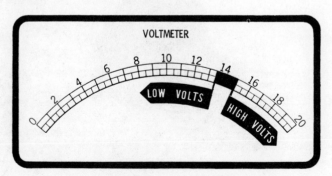

Fig. 20. Illustrating a typical voltmeter dial.

High Voltage

If high voltage is obtained under the hook-up test, remove the field connection at the regulator and repeat the test. After removing the wire (Fig. 21), if low voltage is now obtained, replace the regulator. If high voltage remains, remove the field connection at alternator.

(a) High voltage remains—replace or repair the alternator.

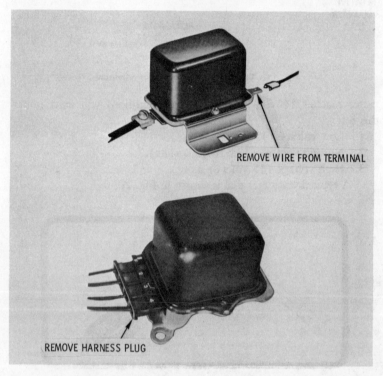

Fig. 21. Two typical voltage regulators used in an alternator system.

(b) Low voltage is now obtained—replace the field wire from the alternator to the regulator.

Low Voltage

If low voltage is obtained under the hook-up test, the alternator field must be directly connected to the battery and the test repeated. *CAUTION: Do not allow the voltage to exceed 16 volts.* Remove the field wire from the "FLD" terminal and attach it to the "IGN" terminal of the regulator, using a jumper wire as shown in Fig. 22.

Fig. 22. Testing for low voltage.

Insert an adaptor into the "F" and "3" slots of the harness plug shown in Fig. 23, and connect a jumper wire between the adaptors. Insert an adaptor into the "A" and "F" slots of the harness plug shown in Fig. 24, and connect a jumper wire between the adaptors. If low voltage remains, check the alternator brushes for good contact—repair or replace the alternator. If high voltage is now obtained—replace the regulator.

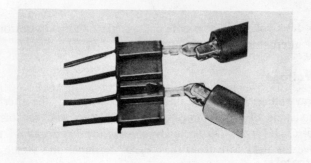

Fig. 23. Illustrating the test lead connection used on some Delco-Remy regulators.

Fig. 24. Illustrating the test lead connection used on some Ford regulators.

TRANSISTOR IGNITION SYSTEMS

Some transistor ignition systems use one transistor while others use two, thus the amount of voltage drop across each system will be different. The ballast resistors may vary between .3 ohm and 1.2 ohm, and the voltage drop across the resistor cannot be predicted with any degree of accuracy. Because of the above factors, actual voltmeter readings not shown in the test procedures are listed in Figs. 25 and 26. The voltmeter reading will usually be compared to the first test—the battery voltage on a preceding test.

Two general types of transistor systems can be identified by tracing the wiring of the system through the first two components. Complete both *points-open* and *points-closed* tests before making a decision.

Before making any tests, remove a spark plug. Attach the spark-plug wire and ground the plug to the engine block—*use insulated pliers*. Crank the engine observing the spark between the electrodes. If no spark is observed, the coil may be at fault. Replace the coil if all other components test OK. If the voltmeter reads backwards, reverse the leads.

COMPRESSION GAUGE

Before making any tests, *warm the engine thoroughly,* and make all tests with the throttle *open*. Remove all of the spark plugs from the motor. On cars equipped with automatic starters, ground the high-tension wire from the coil, as shown in Fig. 27. Use extreme care in removing spark plugs by first removing all dirt or foreign substance which may have collected on the cylinder head around the base of the plugs. On occasion, when removing a spark plug, particles of heavy carbon will become loosened and lodge under a valve when making the test. When this condition exists, run the motor for several minutes, which should dislodge the carbon from the valve seat.

With the ignition switch off (and the compression gauge inserted in the plug hole), spin the engine with the starter until the piston has pumped five times. Be sure and have the throttle wide open in making all compression tests. Make a note of this reading and open the valve on the gauge to release pressure. Repeat this procedure for all cylinders. Test all of the cylinders and note all

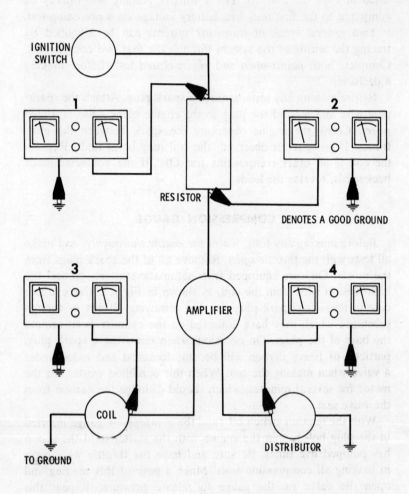

Fig. 25. **Transistor ignition**

"POINTS CLOSED - IGNITION ON"		
READ AND RECORD BATTERY VOLTAGE		
VOLTMETER POSITION	VOLTAGE READING	TEST RESULTS
1	BATTERY VOLTAGE	O. K.
	LESS THAN BATTERY VOLTAGE (MORE THAN 1/2 VOLT DROP)	CHECK WIRING—SWITCH TO BATTERY IGNITION SWITCH, ALL CONNECTIONS
2	LESS THAN BATTERY VOLTAGE	O. K.
	NO VOLTS	DEFECTIVE RESISTOR
3	.5 TO 2 VOLTS LESS THAN VOLTAGE IN #2	O. K.
	NO VOLTS OR SAME VOLTS AS IN #2	CHECK ALL CONNECTIONS IF O. K. AMPLIFIER IS DEFECTIVE
4	0 TO .2 VOLTS	O. K.
	.2 VOLTS OR MORE	CHECK CONNECTIONS & POINTS FOR EXCESSIVE RESISTANCE

CHANGE TO "POINTS OPEN - IGNITION ON"		
READ AND RECORD BATTERY VOLTAGE		
1	BATTERY VOLTAGE	O. K.
	LESS THAN BATTERY VOLTAGE	CURRENT FLOWING IN CIRCUIT, CHECK #3 & #4
2	BATTERY VOLTAGE	O. K.
	LESS THAN VOLTAGE IN #1	DEFECTIVE AMPLIFIER OR SHORT IN DISTRIBUTOR WIRING, CHECK #4
3	NO VOLTS	O. K.
	ANY VOLTAGE	DEFECTIVE AMPLIFIER OR SHORT IN DISTRIBUTOR WIRING, CHECK #4
4	BATTERY VOLTAGE	O. K.
	0 TO 1 VOLT	SHORTED DISTRIBUTOR WIRING - TEST WIRING & POINTS

system voltage checks.

343

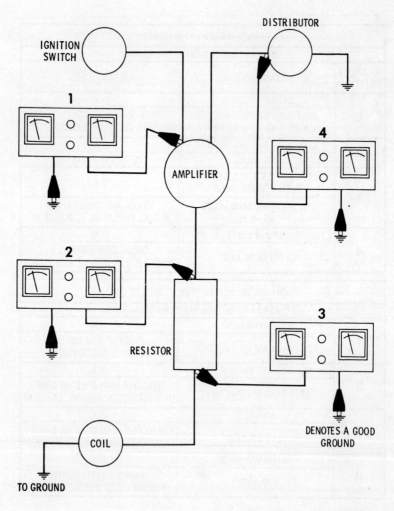

IGNITION SWITCH

DISTRIBUTOR

1

AMPLIFIER

4

2

RESISTOR

3

COIL

TO GROUND

DENOTES A GOOD GROUND

Fig. 26.   Transistor ignition

TYPE TESTING "POINTS CLOSED - IGNITION ON"		
READ AND RECORD BATTERY VOLTAGE		
VOLTMETER POSITION	VOLTAGE READING	TEST RESULTS
1	BATTERY VOLTAGE	O.K.
	LESS THAN BATTERY VOLTAGE (MORE THAN 1/2 VOLT DROP)	CHECK WIRING—SWITCH TO BATTERY IGNITION SWITCH, ALL CONNECTIONS
2	.5 TO 2 VOLTS LESS THAN VOLTAGE IN #1	O.K.
	NO VOLTS OR BATTERY VOLTAGE	DEFECTIVE AMPLIFIER
3	LESS THAN VOLTAGE IN #2	O.K.
	NO VOLTS	DEFECTIVE RESISTOR
4	0 TO .2 VOLTS	O.K.
	.2 VOLTS OR MORE	CHECK CONNECTIONS & POINTS FOR EXCESSIVE RESISTANCE

CHANGE TO "POINTS OPEN - IGNITION ON"		
READ AND RECORD BATTERY VOLTAGE		
1	BATTERY VOLTAGE	O.K.
	LESS THAN BATTERY VOLTAGE	CURRENT FLOWING IN CIRCUIT CHECK #2
2	BATTERY VOLTAGE	O.K.
	NO VOLTS OR LESS THAN BATTERY VOLTAGE	DEFECTIVE AMPLIFIER OR SHORT IN DISTRIBUTOR WIRING
3	BATTERY VOLTAGE	O.K.
	LESS THAN BATTERY VOLTAGE	SAME AS #2
	NO VOLTS	DEFECTIVE RESISTOR
4	BATTERY VOLTAGE	O.K.
	0 TO 1 VOLT	TEST WIRING AND POINTS

system voltage checks.

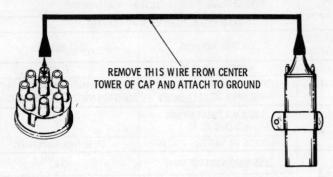

REMOVE THIS WIRE FROM CENTER
TOWER OF CAP AND ATTACH TO GROUND

Fig. 27.   Grounding high-tension wire.

of the readings. Not more than a 10% variation in the reading for all cylinders should exist for maximum performance. Refer to the specifications for normal pressure. There is no material advantage in operating more than five compression strokes per cylinder in making this test because, in too many instances, the battery voltage will have dropped sufficiently to decrease the revolutions per minute, thereby giving a false compression reading.

A low reading in one or more cylinders is interpreted as a condition due to one of the following:

1. Faulty valves.
2. Faulty rings.
3. Faulty head gasket.
4. Faulty piston or wall condition.

To determine if a compression loss is due to bad valves or a bad ring condition, inject a small amount of light engine oil on the top of each piston, taking four complete strokes for a second reading. The light engine oil will temporarily seal the piston rings, and if the compression readings are now considerably higher—

20 lbs. or more—it is a definite indication that the rings are leaking. If no increase is noted, it is an indication that the valves are not seating properly.

When the compression is low between two adjacent cylinders, it is an indication of gasket leakage between the cylinders. Before condemning a low compression reading engine, and to eliminate all possibility of doubt, run the motor for a few minutes and allow a small amount of any good grade tune-up oil to pass through the motor through the air inlet of the carburetor. After the motor has run for 5 or 10 minutes, recheck for compression, and if the reading is now closer to a normal reading, you will find gummy or sticky valves.

VACUUM GAUGE

The vacuum gauge is connected to the windshield wiper fitting at the intake manifold, or by removing a pipe plug from the manifold and inserting the fitting supplied with the instrument. If the car is equipped with a vacuum pump that operates the wiper, the connection should *not* be made at the wiper tubing. The operation of the pump will affect the reading of the gauge. All tests should be made with the motor at operating temperature.

Test No. 1

With engine running at a normal idle speed, the needle of the vacuum gauge should point to 17 for slow-speed engines, 18 or 19 for medium-compression engines, 19 to 21 for high-compression engines. Check the manufacturer's recommendations. *A slow movement* of the needle over about 3 points indicates the carburetor is out of adjustment. A mixture that is *too rich or too lean* will burn slower, and combustion will continue, interrupting the vacuum. The carburetor should be adjusted to smooth out the needle at the highest point of vacuum.

A sudden periodic drop of the needle of 1 or 2 points indicates a burned valve or defective spark plug. A sticky valve will cause the needle to drop 2 to 4 points every engine revolution. *Late ignition* timing will read 1 to 3 points below normal, while advanced timing will cause the needle to jerk irregularly 1 to 2 points above the normal reading. *Unusually low* compression will cause the needle to read 1 or 2 points above the normal reading.

Uneven compression will cause the needle to vibrate slightly. Weak cylinders can be located by shorting out the spark plugs one at a time. The momentary vacuum drop should be equal on all cylinders. A weak cylinder will show less drop in vacuum than cylinders with normal compression. *A very low* reading with the pointer floating from 5 to 10 indicates late valve timing. This condition will cause the motor to overheat and be sluggish.

Test No. 2

Open the throttle quickly, allowing the engine to attain a speed of approximately 2000 rpm. There should be zero to two inches of vacuum while the motor is accelerating. The pointer should jump to 24 or 25 when the throttle is suddenly closed. If these readings are not obtained, it is a good indication that the oil is thin or the rings are in bad condition.

Test No. 3

With the engine operating at a speed of approximately 2,000 rpm, the vacuum should be slightly less than the idle reading. If the needle is not steady, but dances wildly between 10 to 22, it is an indication of weak valve springs or sticky valves. If the needle shows the vacuum gradually going lower you are justified in suspecting a clogged exhaust system. A further test should be made by opening and closing the throttle. If the gauge does not read approximately 25 when the throttle is suddenly closed, this proves that the exhaust system is obstructed, possibly due to a clogged muffler or a dented exhaust pipe.

Do not race the motor excessively—serious damage can result.

Ignition Timing

The vacuum gauge can be used in timing the spark. Short out every other plug on the 6-cylinder engines, or the four center plugs on straight-8 engines. Set the throttle to operate the engine at approximately 1500 rpm. Advance the distributor to the highest steady vacuum reading. Retard the distributor about one scale division.

Centrifugal Spark Advance

Run the engine at idle. Set the distributor to obtain the highest steady vacuum reading. Open the throttle sufficiently to obtain an engine speed of 1500 rpm. If a higher vacuum reading can be obtained by manually advancing the centrifugal spark, the action is not properly advancing the spark. If the spark must be retarded to get a satisfactory vacuum reading, the springs are weak, allowing the spark to advance too far.

Carburetor Adjustment

Single downdraft carburetors are adjusted to the highest steady vacuum. Most downdraft carburetors have a volume-type idle system. Turn the adjusting needle *out* for a richer mixture and *in* for a leaner mixture. Some of the later engines require a slightly rich idle. For such cases, turn the idle adjusting needle *out* until the gauge drops 1/2 to 1 division from the highest steady vacuum, as shown in Fig. 28.

Fig. 28. Adjusting the idle screws with the use of a
vacuum gauge.

Dual Carburetors

Adjust one barrel of the carburetor at a time. Turn the adjusting needle *out* for a richer mixture and *in* for a leaner mixture. When one side is adjusted to the highest steady vacuum, adjust the other side to correspond.

Carburetors with High-Speed Adjustments

Run the motor at approximately 1500 rpm and set the high-speed adjustment for a maximum reading on the gauge. When two carburetors are used with separate manifolds, as on some V-type engines, adjust each carburetor separately, holding the same idling speed.

Fuel Pump Tests

The gauge should be connected in the line between the fuel pump and carburetor. With the engine operating at a very fast idle, the fuel pump pressure should average 2 to 3 pounds, depending on the type of pump being tested. High fuel pump pressure will raise the fuel level in the carburetor, resulting in low gasoline mileage and, in many cases cause the carburetor to flood. Low pressure indicates a worn pump; the fuel level in the carburetor will be low with a resulting leaner mixture and poor performance.

Fuel pump vacuum can be checked by connecting the gauge to the tank side of the pump. With the engine operating at a very fast idle, the vacuum should read 7 or more inches.

Vacuum Tank Test

Drain most of the fuel out of the tank. Connect the gauge to the fuel inlet connection on the vacuum tank cover. With the engine idling, the vacuum should read approximately the same as at the intake manifold. A low reading indicates a leaking valve or gasket in the tank. Vacuum-operated equipment is checked by connecting the gauge to the intake line of the accessory. The reading should be the same as at the intake manifold, otherwise leaks are present in the line leading to the accessory. The above readings are based on an altitude of sea level to approximately 1000 feet. For every additional 100 feet of altitude, deduct 1″ or one scale division from the vacuum readings.

TIMING LIGHTS

Three types of timing lights are in use today. The least expensive of these is the series-connected light. This type is inserted in the high-voltage circuit by removing the high-voltage lead from the No. 1 spark plug and inserting the light between the spark plug and the spark-plug lead. This type of light does not have as much light output as the power-type timing lights.

351

Power timing lights are either AC or DC powered. The AC power light must be connected to a 110-volt AC outlet and can be used on any voltage ignition system. The DC powered light derives its power from the automobile battery. Most DC powered lights can be directly connected to 6- or 12-volt batteries, as they are automatically operated by relays. A light of this type cannot be used on any voltage ignition system other than that for which it has been designed.

With any timing light, especially a metal-cased unit, it is important that the battery connections be made before the high-voltage connections. When removing a timing light, it is important that the spark-plug connection be broken first before the battery connections are broken.

Connecting Timing Lights

In all timing operations, the timing light is connected to the No. 1 spark plug. The illustrations in Fig. 29 show the location of the No. 1 plug and the firing order of various engines.

NOTE: On some *Chrysler* engines, the timing light can be connected to the No. 1 tower on the distributor cap. This tower is usually fitted with a red or light-colored cover, as shown in Fig. 30.

Locating Timing Marks and Pointers

With the engine idling, the spark is timed to reach the spark plug when the piston reaches approximately top dead center (TDC). To indicate the position of the No. 1 piston, timing marks are placed on parts rigidly connected to the crankshaft. In order to be made readily visible, they may be placed on:

1. The flywheel, at the rear of the engine.
2. The vibration damper or front crankshaft pulley.
3. Behind the fan belts, at the front of the engine.

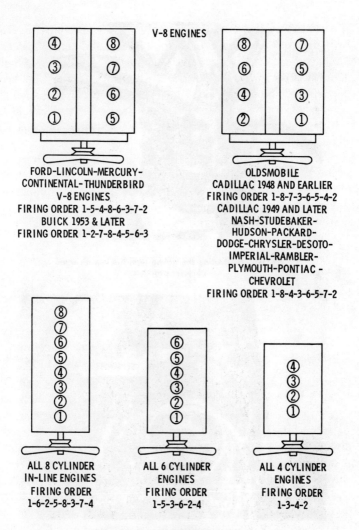

V-8 ENGINES

FORD-LINCOLN-MERCURY-
CONTINENTAL-THUNDERBIRD
V-8 ENGINES
FIRING ORDER 1-5-4-8-6-3-7-2
BUICK 1953 & LATER
FIRING ORDER 1-2-7-8-4-5-6-3

OLDSMOBILE
CADILLAC 1948 AND EARLIER
FIRING ORDER 1-8-7-3-6-5-4-2
CADILLAC 1949 AND LATER
NASH-STUDEBAKER-
HUDSON-PACKARD-
DODGE-CHRYSLER-DESOTO-
IMPERIAL-RAMBLER-
PLYMOUTH-PONTIAC -
CHEVROLET
FIRING ORDER 1-8-4-3-6-5-7-2

ALL 8 CYLINDER
IN-LINE ENGINES
FIRING ORDER
1-6-2-5-8-3-7-4

ALL 6 CYLINDER
ENGINES
FIRING ORDER
1-5-3-6-2-4

ALL 4 CYLINDER
ENGINES
FIRING ORDER
1-3-4-2

Fig. 29. Typical cylinder firing order.

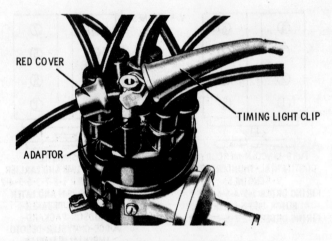

Fig. 30. Illustrating the timing light hookup on some *Chrysler* products.

Fig. 31. A typical timing mark on a *General Motors* product.

Flywheel Type

On some *General Motors* vehicles with 6-cylinder and straight-8 engines, the timing mark is located at the rear of the engine, as shown in Fig. 31. The majority of cars have marks on the right side of the motor. Some cars use small dust covers which must be removed before the timing marks are visible. The marks are either scribed lines or a shiny steel ball embedded in the flywheel.

Vibration Damper Type

Timing marks on all V-8 engines, and all engines made by *Ford Motor Co.* and *Chrysler Corp.,* are located on the front crankshaft pully or vibration damper, as illustrated in Fig. 32. The pointer position varies (between 10:00 and 2:00 o'clock) depending on the car manufacturer. Because of road grime and dirt, the marks may not be readily visible. Alternately jog the engine with the starter and wipe the damper clean until the marks are located. Highlight the appropriate mark with chalk for better visibility when using the timing light. Various timing marks are shown in Fig. 32.

Checking Timing Advance

The engine must be at normal operating temperature. While the engine is *warming up*, some mechanics prefer to use a crankcase additive or top-cylinder oil to free the valves, rings, etc. Run the engine at idle speed with the timing light focused on the timing marks and pointer. The timing marks are more visible if all outside light, other than the flash of the timing light, is kept to a minimum. Slowly accelerate the engine to medium speed and watch the timing degree marks in relation to the pointer. The marks should move smoothly in the opposite direction to the rotation of the engine. All engines rotate clockwise as viewed from

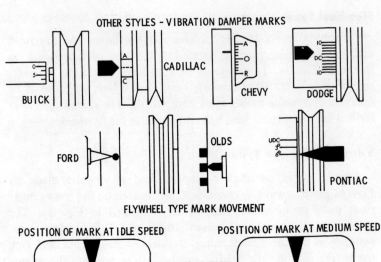

OTHER STYLES - VIBRATION DAMPER MARKS

BUICK

CADILLAC

CHEVY

DODGE

FORD

OLDS

PONTIAC

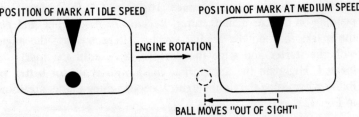

FLYWHEEL TYPE MARK MOVEMENT

POSITION OF MARK AT IDLE SPEED   POSITION OF MARK AT MEDIUM SPEED

ENGINE ROTATION

BALL MOVES "OUT OF SIGHT"

MARK MOVES IN OPPOSITE DIRECTION TO ROTATION OF ENGINE

VIBRATION DAMPER TYPE MOVEMENT

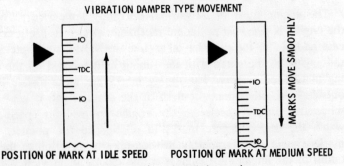

IO

TDC

IO

IO

TDC

IO

MARKS MOVE SMOOTHLY

POSITION OF MARK AT IDLE SPEED   POSITION OF MARK AT MEDIUM SPEED

Fig. 32. Illustrating various timing marks.

the front. On flywheel-type timing marks, the *ball* or marks should move *out of sight*.

Checking Vacuum Advance

Set the engine speed fast enough to move the timing marks from their slow-speed position, as shown in Fig. 33. While watch-

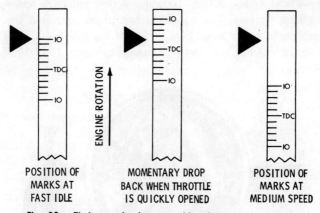

POSITION OF MARKS AT FAST IDLE   ENGINE ROTATION   MOMENTARY DROP BACK WHEN THROTTLE IS QUICKLY OPENED   POSITION OF MARKS AT MEDIUM SPEED

Fig. 33. Timing marks change position due to engine speed.

ing the timing mark, quickly open the throttle and then permit it to return to its closed position. If the vacuum advance control is functioning, the timing mark will rotate in a clockwise direction with each opening of the throttle. Actually, what is happening in this instance is that, with sudden acceleration, the vacuum in the engine falls off which, in turn, should allow the vacuum chamber to retard the spark.

Checking Centrifugal Weights

Disconnect the vacuum line to the distributor and then note the position of the timing mark with the engine at normal idle. Increase the engine speed gradually. If the centrifugal weights are in satisfactory working condition, the timing mark will move steadily in a counterclockwise direction as the engine speed is increased. When engine speed is reduced, the timing mark will move back to its original position at normal idling speed. This action, if followed with the timing light, should be a steady advance and retard without erratic action. Irregular action indicates bad springs or sticking weights. The condition has to be corrected for satisfactory performance upon completion of the tune-up. *CAUTION: Ford*-built V-8 engines, 1949-56, and 6 cylinder, 1949-58, do not

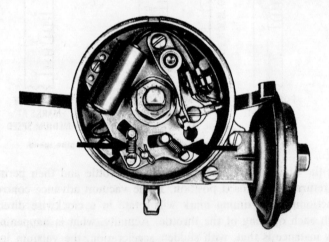

Fig. 34. The two springs indicate a distributor which does not have a centrifugal advance mechanism.

have centrifugal advance mechanisms. When the vacuum line is disconnected, the marks should not move. These distributors can be identified by the two springs above the distributor plate, as shown in Fig. 34.

TACHOMETER

Hook up the tachometer instrument as per the manufacturer's instructions for all tests. A typical hookup is shown in Fig. 35.

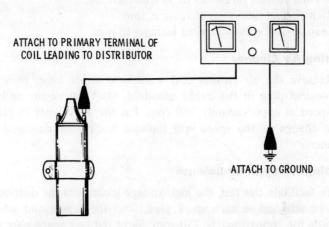

ATTACH TO PRIMARY TERMINAL OF
COIL LEADING TO DISTRIBUTOR

ATTACH TO GROUND

Fig. 35.   Illustrating the hookup procedure of a tachometer.

Adjusting Carburetor for Idle Speed

Start the engine and allow it to warm up thoroughly—the tachometer will read the engine rpm. For a more accurate reading at low speeds, turn the selector switch to *low* scale, if this scale is available. With the fast idle cam in the slow position, and the choke off, adjust the idling screw to specifications (450-525 rpm). Adjust the idle mixture screw or screws for the highest engine rpm obtainable. Re-adjust the idling speed if necessary.

Testing Air-Fuel Ratio

Remove the air cleaner and start the engine. Set the speed at approximately 750 rpm. Slide a flat plate or your hand slowly over the air horn on the carburetor to partially shut off the intake of air, and note the meter reading. The following indications will show:

Normal air-fuel ratio—25 to 50 rpm increase.
Rich air-fuel ratio—no increase in rpm.
Lean air-fuel ratio—marked increase in rpm.

Testing Air Cleaner

Remove the air cleaner and windshield wiper hose, or some convenient plug in the intake manifold. Start the engine and set its speed at approximately 750 rpm. Put the air cleaner in place. Any change in the speed will indicate a dirty or damaged air cleaner.

Testing for Cylinder Balance

To facilitate this test, the high-voltage leads from the distributor can be attached to each spark plug. Start the engine and set the throttle for approximately 750 rpm. Short out one spark plug at a time, noting the change in engine rpm that occurs while the plug is shorted. There will be a decrease in rpm, and this decrease should be approximately the same for all cylinders. A cylinder which is not operating at the same efficiency as the others will not show as great a decrease in rpm when the plug is shorted out.

Checking Distributor Automatic Advance Operation

Place the scale selector switch in the *low* position, and operate the engine at approximately 500 rpm. Advance the distributor until the maximum reading is obtained on the tachometer. With the distributor in this position, place the scale selector in the *high* position, increase the engine speed to approximately 1500 rpm, and then try to increase the speed still further by advancing or retarding the distributor, but without changing the throttle opening.

If the engine speed can be increased more than 100 rpm by advancing or retarding the distributor, then the centrifugal advance mechanism is not operating correctly and the distributor should be removed for repair. Re-time the ignition with the timing light and re-check the idle speed carburetor adjustment.

TUNE-UP PROCEDURES

Following a definite step-by-step procedure when tuning an engine, and using the same procedure on every tune-up job is very important to consistent quality tune-ups. Without a definite procedure, a tune-up man is apt to use a different approach or procedure on every engine. This leads to critical services being overlooked from time to time. It also leads to imperfect results after the tune-up is completed, necessitating rework and wasted time.

If the tune-up specialist uses the same procedure repeatedly, the operation becomes *second nature* and the jobs proceed smoothly and quickly. The trouble is found the first time around, which is the tune-up man's major objective.

The following items should be checked before your tune-up operation. If their service has been neglected during normal lubrication and service intervals, their condition will undesirably influence your tune-up.

Drive Belts

Inspect the condition and check the tension of the generator (alternator) drive belt. A slipping belt will result in an undercharged battery, even though the charging system is otherwise functioning normally. Poor water circulation will also result which may overheat the engine.

Manifold Heat Control Valve

Check the manifold heat control valve action. A valve stuck in the open position will cause poor cold-engine operation and prolonged engine warm-up with extended use of the choke. A valve stuck in the closed position will result in loss of performance when the normal operating temperature is reached. It can also result in burned engine valves due to an excessively lean carburetor fuel mixture.

Carburetor Air Cleaner

Service or replace dirty air cleaners. A dirty carburetor air cleaner acts as a partial choke, upsetting the carburetor air-fuel ratio, making a fine carburetor adjustment impossible.

Fuel Filter

A partially clogged fuel filter will restrict the fuel supply at high speed, resulting in a performance complaint. A clogged fuel filter has the same effect on engine operation as a defective fuel pump.

Positive Crankcase Ventilation Valve

Most PCV-equipped engines are calibrated or adjusted to accommodate the additional air drawn from the crankcase. A clogged PCV valve upsets the carburetor mixture, causing a rough idle and making a first-class tune-up impossible.

Valve Clearance

Loose tappets are noisy. Tight tappets hold valves off their seats, causing engine roughness and resulting in burned-out valves. Valves should be adjusted when the need is indicated.

Procedure

1. *Diagnosis*
   Talk to the car owner and obtain an accurate description, if possible, of any problems that have been encountered. An overall systems check can be made to isolate problem areas.
2. *Visual Inspection*
   Inspect the entire vehicle with the engine running and with the engine stopped, paying particular attention to hose clamps, seals, and loose or frayed wires.
3. Clean and inspect the battery.
4. Test the battery.
5. Test the cranking voltage.
6. Test the compression.
7. Inspect the coil.
8. Inspect the distributor cap and rotor.
9. Inspect the primary wiring and secondary cables.
10. Replace the breaker points.
11. Replace the condenser.
12. Inspect and lubricate the distributor.
13. Check the centrifugal weight action.
14. Check the vacuum advance action.
15. Set the breaker point dwell angle.
16. Replace or service the spark plugs.
17. Set the ignition timing.
18. Lubricate the generator, where used.
19. Test the charging system.
20. Test the fuel pump.
21. Adjust the carburetor.
22. Road test the vehicle.

IGNITION TROUBLESHOOTING

Symptoms	Possible Cause	Possible Remedy
1. Engine is cranked by starting motor but will not start (not getting spark.)	**1-1 Points**	**1-1 Points**
	a. Burned points	a. Replace points
	b. Points not opening	b. Adjust point gap
	c. Loose connection	c. Tighten wire and check points
	d. Worn cam rubbing block (point gap too close)	d. Replace points
	e. Weak point spring tension	e. Replace points
	1-2 Distributor Cap	**1-2 Distributor Cap**
	a. Cracked distributor cap	a. Replace distributor cap
	b. Corroded secondary wire terminals	b. Clean terminal contacts or replace cap
	c. Temporary trouble caused by moisture	c. Thoroughly clean and dry distributor cap
	d. Excessive resistance in the built-in cap resistors	d. Replace distributor cap
	e. Carbon tracks in cap	e. Replace cap
	1-3 Distributor Rotor	**1-3 Distributor Rotor**
	a. Broken or cracked rotor	a. Replace rotor
	b. Burned and excessively worn rotor bar	b. Replace rotor
	c. Missing rotor contact	c. Replace rotor
	d. Carbon track on rotor	d. Replace rotor
	e. Rotor or shaft not turning	e. Replace broken part
	1-4 Coil	**1-4 Coil**
	a. Coil burned out or broken primary coil wire winding	a. Check coil continuity and replace coil when found unsatisfactory
	b. Loose primary wire connections	b. Tighten connections, making sure lock washers are used under nuts
	c. Burned resistor	c. Replace resistor

Symptoms	Possible Cause	Possible Remedy
	d. Wet or corroded high-tension (secondary) wire contacts in coil tower	d. Thoroughly clean and dry contacts. Replace high-tension wire or rubber boot if necessary
	e. Broken high-tension wire	e. Replace wire
	f. Cracked coil tower	f. Replace coil
	1-5 Condenser	**1-5 Condenser**
	a. Weak condenser	a. Replace condenser and distributor points
	b. Loose connection at distributor points	b. Tighten connections or solder loose connector
	c. Leaky condenser	c. Test condenser. If leaky, replace
	d. Condenser has high internal resistance	d. Test condenser. If resistance is high, replace
	e. Shorted condenser	e. Replace condenser
	1-6 Ignition Switch	**1-6 Ignition Switch**
	a. Worn ignition contact points in switch	a. Replace ignition switch
	b. Loose wire connections	b. Tighten connections and solder terminals if necessary
	c. High resistance in ignition switch	c. Replace ignition switch
	1-7 Wires	**1-7 Wires**
	a. Loose primary ignition wire connections	a. Trace wires. Tighten or solder all connections
	b. Broken primary ignition wire	b. Trace wire and replace as necessary
2. Engine misses at high speed	**2-1 Points**	**2-1 Points**
	a. Same causes as in 1-1	a. Same correction as in 1-1
	b. Dwell too high or too low	b. Adjust dwell to specifications

Engine Tune-Up Equipment and Procedures

Symptoms	Possible Cause	Possible Remedy
	2-2 Spark Plugs	**2-2 Spark Plugs**
	a. Worn out spark plugs	a. Replace spark plugs
	b. Improper spark-plug gap setting	b. Regap spark plugs
	c. Cracked spark-plug porcelain	c. Replace spark plug
	d. Dirty or fouled spark plug	d. Clean, regap and find cause of fouling
	e. Improper heat range	e. Install proper type
	2-3 Coil	**2-3 Coil**
	a. Weak coil	a. Test and replace if necessary
	b. Same causes as in 1-4 (b and e)	b. Same corrections as in 1-4 (b and e)
	2-4 Condenser	**2-4 Condenser**
	a. Same causes as in 1-5 (a, b, and c)	a. Same corrections as in 1-5 (a, b, and c)
	2-5 Distributor Cap	**2-5 Distributor Cap**
	a. Same causes as in 1-2 (a and b)	a. Same corrections as in 1-2 (a and b)
	2-6 Distributor	**2-6 Distributor**
	a. Worn distributor shaft bearings, causing improper point gap setting	a. Replace distributor assembly
	b. Poor distributor ground to engine block	b. Tighten distributor mounting bolts
3. Engine will not turn over properly. CAUTION: When using a booster battery for start-	**3-1 Battery**	**3-1 Battery**
	a. Battery has low capacity	a. Check battery condition; charge battery or replace if necessary
	b. Battery under charged	b. Check generating circuit

Symptoms	Possible Cause	Possible Remedy
ing cars equipped with alternators, connect the negative (—) booster cable to the negative (—) vehicle battery post and the positive (+) booster cable to the positive (+) vehicle battery post. This is important to prevent serious damage to the alternator rectifiers.	c. Loose or corroded battery or engine-to-frame cables and connections (high resistance)	c. Check battery cable size and condition; repair or replace cables
	d. Defective starting motor or loose mounting bolts	d. Check cause and repair or replace as necessary
	e. Defective starter solenoid or remote switch circuit	e. Clean and tighten all connections. Replace switch if necessary
	f. Drain or short circuit	f. Check with test equipment and correct. NOTE: Check glove box, trunk, underhood, and stoplight switches
	g. Transmission not in neutral, or neutral circuit defective	g. Put in neutral or repair circuit as necessary
	h. Starter drive gear and flywheel ring gear locked	h. Loosen starter and break gears loose. Check cause and recommend necessary repairs
	i. Engine locked	i. Check oil level and investigate cause. Recommend necessary repairs
	j. Engine turns hard	j. Investigate possible upper cylinder gum condition or antifreeze contamination in engine oil
4. Engine idles rough	4-1 Spark Plugs a. Same as in 2-2 b. Cross-fire in plug cables	4-1 Spark Plugs a. Same as in 2-2 b. Reroute cables
	4-2 Points a. Same as in 1-1 (a and c)	4-2 Points a. Same as in 1-1 (a and c)

Symptoms	Possible Cause	Possible Remedy
	4-3 Distributor Cap	4-3 Distributor Cap
	a. Same as in 1-2 (a, b, and c)	a. Same as in 1-2 (a, b, and c)
	b. Improper engine firing order (secondary wires in wrong tower in distributor cap or crossed at plugs)	b. Check engine firing order in distributor cap to spark plugs
	4-4 Ignition Timing	4-4 Ignition Timing
	a. Advanced too far (early)	a. Set to specifications

CHARGING SYSTEMS TROUBLESHOOTING

Symptoms	Possible Cause	Possible Remedy
1. Alternator or generator fails to charge.	1-1 Fan Belt	1-1 Fan Belt
	a. Loose, broken or slipping belt	a. Tighten or replace belt
	1-2 Alternator or Generator	1-2 Alternator or Generator
	a. Loose connection, poor wiring, or poor brush contact	a. Clean and tighten all connections. Replace wiring or brushes
	1-3 Regulator	1-3 Regulator
	a. Defective regulator	a. Replace regulator
	b. Blown fusible wires	b. Replace regulator
2. Charging rate too low, too high, or unsteady.	2-1 Alternator or Regulator	2-1 Alternator or Regulator
	a. High circuit resistance	a. Locate resistance. Clean, tighten, or replace wires and connections
	b. Open windings	b. Replace unit
	2-2 Regulator	2-2 Regulator
	a. High or low regulator setting	a. Adjust regulator

Symptoms	Possible Cause	Possible Remedy
	b. Defective regulator *Caution: Do not attempt to adjust any voltage regulator unless equipped and qualified to do so.*	b. Replace unit

FUEL SYSTEMS TROUBLESHOOTING

Symptoms	Possible Cause	Possible Remedy
1. Engine fails to start (spark plugs getting sufficient current)	1-1 Carburetor a. No gasoline reaching carburetor	1-1 Carburetor a. Check operation of fuel pump and quantity of gasoline in fuel tank
	b. Automatic choke sticking shut	b. Remove air cleaner and hold choke valve open until engine starts. Correct cause of sticking
	c. Clogged fuel line or screen from fuel pump to carburetor	c. Remove fuel line and clean
	d. Carburetor float stuck in raised position	d. Remove top of carburetor. Check and correct cause of float sticking
	e. Carburetor float remains in down position (engine flooding with fuel)	e. Check float level. Check for dirt under valve seat, or heavy float
	1-2 Fuel Pump a. Fuel pump defective	1-2 Fuel Pump a. Replace fuel pump
	b. Sediment bowl not seated against gasket	b. Replace sediment bowl gasket
	c. Plugged fuel line from fuel tank to fuel pump. NOTE: Some Cars have fuel strainer mounted inside gas tank.	c. Disconnect fuel line from pump inlet side, remove gas tank cap and blow out line using compressed air

Symptoms	Possible Cause	Possible Remedy
	d. Defective flexible fuel line at fuel pump	d. Replace flexible line
	e. Air leak in fuel lines caused by broken or damaged line	e. Check fuel lines, and make necessary repairs. Replace as necessary
2. Engine difficult to start (spark plugs getting sufficient current)	2-1 Carburetor a. Same as in 1-1 (b and c)	2-1 Carburetor a. Same as in 1-1 (b and c)
	2-2 Compression a. Same as 4-2 (a - d)	2-2 Compression a. Same as 4-2 (a-d) NOTE: Condition usually worse when engine "hot"
	2-3 Fuel Pump a. Same as in 1-2 (a through e) b. Fuel pump pressure weak	2-3 Fuel Pump a. Same as in 1-2 (a through e) b. Replace fuel pump
3. Engine cuts out and misses at high speed (spark plugs correct heat range and getting sufficient current)	3-1 Fuel Pump a. Fuel pump weak b. Restriction in fuel system c. Same as in 1-2 (b) d. Clogged fuel filter	3-1 Fuel Pump a. Replace fuel pump b. Blow out fuel lines with compressed air and check strainers c. Same as in 1-2 (b) d. Replace filter
	3-2 Carburetor a. Carburetor power valve sticking open b. Automatic choke not correctly adjusted	3-2 Carburetor a. Replace power valve b. Adjust choke and check heat tube for carbon deposits
	3-3 Gas Tank a. Restricted vent pipe or gas tank cap	3-3 Gas Tank a. Correct restriction

Symptoms	Possible Cause	Possible Remedy
4. Engine will not idle smoothly (spark plugs getting sufficient current)	4-1 Heat Riser a. Heat riser valve stuck open	4-1 Heat Riser a. Free-up or replace valve assembly. Check thermostatic spring
	4-2 Carburetor a. Carburetor idle not correctly adjusted	4-2 Carburetor a. Adjust idle speed and fuel mixture
	b. Loose carburetor base or manifold (air entry manifold)	b. Tighten carburetor base or replace gasket
	c. Dirty carburetor	c. Clean or replace carburetor
	d. Damaged idle mixture adjusting screws (turned in too tight)	d. Replace screws
	4-3 Compression a. Low compression on one or more cylinders	4-3 Compression a. Check engine compression and recommend repairs
	b. Blown head gasket between two adjoining cylinders	b. Replace head gasket
	c. Worn piston rings	c. Recommend necessary repairs
	d. Burned or sticking valves	d. Recommend necessary repairs
	e. Improperly functioning hydraulic valve lifters	e. Recommend necessary repairs
	f. Tappets too tight	f. Adjust to specifications
	4-4 Manifold a. Intake manifold loose or gasket blown	4-4 Manifold a. Replace gasket or tighten manifold bolts
	b. Sand hole in manifold casting, or warped manifold	b. Plug hole or replace intake manifold. Surface grind to remove warp

Symptoms	Possible Cause	Possible Remedy
	c. Vacuum leak in intake system	c. Check manifold and carburetor gaskets. Check windshield wiper hose connections at vacuum pump and power brake unit, if so equipped
5. Engine has flat spot on acceleration (engine at operating temperature)	5-1 Carburetor a. Carburetor accelerating circuit not functioning correctly	5-1 Carburetor a. Check cause, clean, repair or replace carburetor
6. Engine has flat spot on acceleration (engine "cold")	6-1 Carburetor a. Choke valve sticking or "too lean" b. Heat riser valve stuck open, or defective thermostatic spring c. Same as 5-1 (a)	6-1 Carburetor a. Free up and adjust choke b. Free up or replace valve assembly or spring as necessary c. Same as 5-1 (a)

SUMMARY

To do good tune-up work a service man must equip himself with proper testing instruments. They need not be expensive but any instrument should be reliable and accurate. Testers eliminate the guesswork and make the service man's job easier and quicker, especially with today's high-powered complicated motors.

Generally there are three factors that constitutes a tune-up—ignition, compression, and carburetion. Each factor plays a very important part in the performance of the car. It must be realized, however, that even a good tune-up job will not correct mechanical defects which may have considerable effect on the operation of the engine. If compression in all cylinders is not somewhat near uniform it is useless to go ahead with the tune-up until the cause for the irregular compression has been eliminated.

REVIEW QUESTIONS

1. What would cause an engine to crank slowly?

2. What causes an engine to be hard to start?

3. What would cause an engine to miss?

4. What would cause an engine to overheat?

5. What would cause an engine to hesitate on acceleration?

CHAPTER 14

Ignition Scope Testing

The ignition scope displays a graph-like picture of all phases of the ignition cycle as it occurs in the engine. This creates a convenient means of observing the ignition system's performance. The picture displayed permits the mechanic to see the results of many factors affecting the system operation. Such factors as firing voltage requirements, spark duration, coil action, condenser action, point set action and maximum system voltage output can be easily and quickly observed.

The scope still requires additional test equipment as previously described if complete testing and tune-up work is to be performed. Although there are slight variations in hookup, the pattern displays are all similar. The illustrations and information used in this book were provided thru the courtesy of the *Sun Electric Company*. Since each part of the pattern represents certain events as they occur in various parts of the ignition circuit, any deviation from normal patterns are easily observed. Many scopes are designed to display the patterns of all cylinders side by side in the engine's firing order or each cylinder's pattern individually.

The display or trace visible on the scope screen is usually referred to as a pattern, and are really graphs with one horizontal

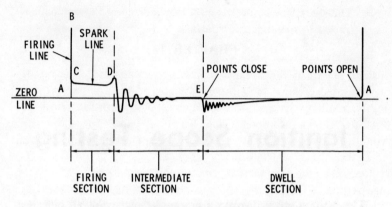

Fig. 1. Illustrating the basic primary waveform.

dimension representing time and the vertical dimension being secondary or primary voltage. Since the secondary pattern is the most informative, the screens are usually divided into 1000-volt (one kilovolt) divisions to permit accurate voltage measurements. Each part of the pattern represents a specific time element of the ignition system, and is divided into three main sections;

1. The firing section.
2. The intermediate section.
3. The dwell section.

THE FIRING SECTION

It is during the firing section that the actual firing of the spark plug takes place and the pattern is composed of only two lines.

1. The firing line is a vertical line indicating the voltage required to break down the plug and rotor gaps.

2. The spark line is a horizontal line indicating the voltage required to maintain the spark.

Point "A" in the pattern illustrated in Fig. 1 represents the instant at which the breaker points have separated, permitting a very rapid collapse of the magnetic field in the coil. The resulting high voltage so produced is indicated by the vertical rise from "A" to "B" in the pattern. The height at point "B" shows the voltage required to fire the plug and rotor gap; sometimes referred to as the "firing" or "ionization" voltage.

Once the plug fires there is a noticeable drop in secondary voltage at point "C." As the spark continues to bridge the gap, the spark voltage remains at a fairly constant low value until the spark extinguishes at point "D".

THE INTERMEDIATE SECTION

The section immediately following the firing and spark line is usually referred to as the *intermediate section*. This is a series of gradually diminishing oscillations which nearly disappear by the time the points open again. Beginning at point "D" (Fig. 1.), the remaining coil energy dissipates itself as an oscillating current, which gradually dies out as it approaches point "E". This oscillation results from the combined effects of the coil and the condenser in dissipating this energy. Whether the remaining energy is or is not completely dissipated by the time the breaker points close at point "E" will depend largely on the speed of the engine and the dwell angle.

THE DWELL SECTION

This section represents the period of time during the ignition cycle in which the breaker points are closed. The dwell period begins at point "E" when the breaker points close. Closing the points causes a short downward line followed by a series of small rapidly diminishing oscillations. The dwell period continues until the points open at the beginning of the next waveform (the next point "A"). During this period ("E" to "A"), the primary current is building up (saturating) the coil's magnetic field in preparation for the next ignition cycle.

NORMAL PATTERNS

Fig. 2 illustrates a scope display of the ignition system of an eight-cylinder engine that contains no suppression and is functioning normally. Fig. 3 illustrates the scope pattern of one of the cylinders displayed in Fig. 2. The patterns illustrated in Fig. 4 rep-

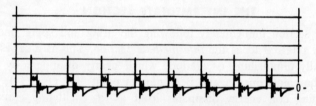

Fig. 2.   Illustrating the normal function of an 8-cylinder ignition system.

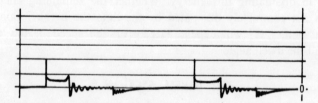

Fig. 3.   Illustrating one section of the scope pattern shown in Fig. 2.

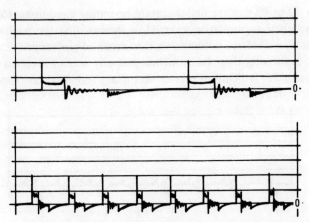

Fig. 4.   Illustrating a scope pattern of a normal functioning
8-cylinder engine.

resent a normal functioning eight-cylinder ignition system that in-
corporates secondary suppression.

Note the slight difference in the length and shape of the spark
lines when comparing the patterns. It will be observed that the
spark lines of the suppressor-equipped system begin at a slightly
higher voltage than that of the other system and that they slant
downward slightly as they approach the intermediate section and
appear to have slightly more oscillations.

COIL POLARITY

Proper coil polarity, as discussed in Chapter 9, is of prime
importance to efficient ignition system operation. Should secondary polarity be reversed, due to improper installation of the coil
or battery, or installation of a coil not designed for a particular
system, the firing voltage requirements of the vehicle may increase

from 20 to 40 percent under certain operating conditions. Coil polarity, whether proper or reversed, is indicated by the position the seconday waveform assumes on the screen of the scope.

With the scope's polarity switch properly set, an inverted waveform would indicate reversed secondary polarity, as shown in

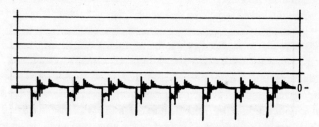

Fig. 5. The scope polarity switch adjusted to invert waveform which would indicate reversed secondary polarity.

Fig. 5. Reversed secondary polarity can be caused by reversed connections to the coil's primary terminals, reversed connection of the vehicle's battery, or the application of an ignition coil not designed for the particular system in which it is being used.

FIRING VOLTAGE

Firing voltage or *required voltage* as the terms imply, is the amount of voltage required to establish a spark across the electrodes of a spark plug. In a running engine, the actual amount of voltage required to fire a particular plug at a particular instant depends on the net results of many factors. Some of the factors which can influence this firing voltage are:

1. Rotor gap.
2. Breaks in the secondary wires.

3. Spark plug gap.
4. Spark plug electrode shape.
5. Improperly connected wire terminals.
6. Temperature.
7. Compression pressure.
8. Air-fuel mixture.
9. Engine speed and load.

Actual *firing voltages* can easily be measured at any reasonable engine speed by observing the height of the firing line on each cylinder's secondary pattern as it is displayed on the scope screen. At any given engine speed, the firing voltage of all of the cylinders of an engine should be fairly uniform and within a normal range for that particular engine. The normal range for most vehicles, at an engine speed of 1500 rpm, is 3 to 7 KV (3000 to 7000 volts). If all firing voltages are fairly uniform but measure higher than normal for the particular engine under test (Fig. 6), it can usually

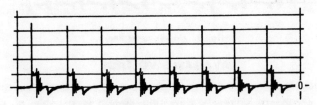

Fig. 6. **Illustrating uniform firing with excessive high voltage.**

be traced to worn spark-plug electrodes, late ignition timing, lean air-fuel mixtures, excessive rotor gap or a break in the coil wire. Usually it is a rise in the level of the spark line and reduction in spark duration.

Uneven firing voltages, as indicated in Fig. 7, can generally be caused by worn spark-plug electrodes, unbalanced air-fuel mix-

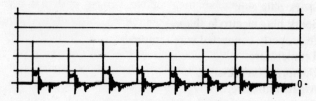

Fig. 7.   Uneven firing voltage.

tures, breaks in spark-plug wires, or a cocked or worn distributor cap. Fig. 8 indicates the increased height of firing and spark lines, and the decrease in spark duration caused by a broken spark-plug wire. Note the increase of oscillation on the spark line.

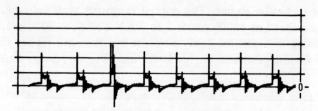

Fig. 8.   Uneven spark line.

AVAILABLE VOLTAGE

Available voltage is a term or phrase used to indicate the maximum secondary voltage an ignition system is capable of producing under a given operating condition. Due to its operating characteristics, an ignition coil will produce its maximum secondary voltage whenever it attempts to fire an impossible gap, such as when a spark-plug wire is removed from a spark plug and held at a distance from ground (open circuit). Ignition system design is such that available voltage is always greater than the ignition requirements generally encountered under most operating conditions. The difference in available voltage and that actually required to fire the spark plugs is commonly referred to as *ignition reserve.*

The maximum secondary voltage available from any given ignition system depends on the combined effect of coil design, coil condition, applied primary voltage, primary-circuit resistance, distributor contact condition, dwell angle and engine speed. When in good working order, most ignition systems are capable of producing well over 20,000 volts; in fact, some systems may even produce as much as 30,000 volts or more. However, should any of the factors involved in the operation of the ignition system deteriorate from their normal condition or adjustment, it will usually result in a change in available voltage values. Therefore, measuring the avail-

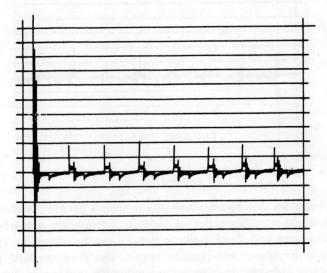

Fig. 9. Illustrating the rise in secondary voltage when a spark-plug wire is removed.

able voltage provides a quick means of determining the overall efficiency of any particular system.

Secondary voltage will rise to its maximum when a spark-plug wire is removed from the spark plug. The normal available voltage for a particular system is indicated by the upward extent of the #1 cylinder's pattern as illustrated in Fig. 9. As represented in Fig. 10, low available voltage for a particular system would be

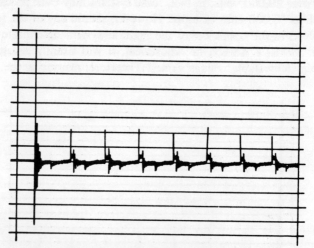

Fig. 10. Illustrating low secondary voltage when a spark-plug wire is removed.

indicated by the upward extent of a cylinder's pattern not reaching the height normally expected for this system when a spark-plug wire is removed. Low available voltage can be caused by excessive resistance in the primary circuit, less than specified point dwell, a defective coil, secondary insulation leakage or low primary input voltage.

SECONDARY INSULATION

When an ignition coil produces a surge of high voltage, this voltage is transmitted from the coil tower through the coil wire, distributor cap, rotor and a secondary wire and delivered to a spark plug to create the spark across its electrodes. It must be realized that the insulation of all parts of the secondary circuit must be of high quality and in good condition to ensure reliable ignition system function under all operating conditions. Should the insulation of one or more of these secondary components be defective or have deteriorated to some degree, it may have little or no effect on ignition system operation when the firing voltage requirements of the vehicle are moderate. However, when firing voltage requirements are high, this defective insulation may leak or breakdown, allowing much of the voltage surge to be lost to ground resulting in misfire of one or more plugs.

When a spark-plug wire is removed from the plug to measure the available voltage of a system, the insulation of the secondary components transmitting the coil's high-voltage surge are also being stressed to the maximum, and any leakage of this voltage, whether intermittent or otherwise, will readily be indicated by the shape of the pattern observed on the scope screen. Caution must be exercised before performing this test on many transistor ignition systems. Always check the manufacturer's recommendations before running a transistor system open circuited or the heat sink may be permanently damaged.

Normal secondary insulation in the circuit supplying the #1 spark plug is indicated in Fig. 11 by the fact that the lower extent of this cylinder's pattern is consistent and its size is equal to at least 1/2 of the pattern's upward extent. Insulation breakdown is indicated by a pattern's lower extent being shorter than normal, intermittant, or completely absent when the cylinder's spark-plug wire

Ignition Scope Testing

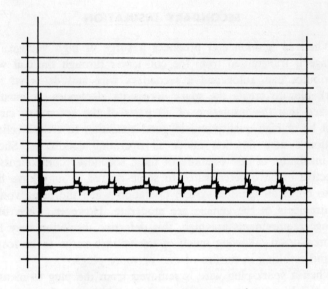

Fig. 11. Illustrating a normal secondary insulation in the #1 spark-plug wire.

is disconnected as pictured in Fig. 12. Insulation leakage or breakdown can occur within the coil, at the coil tower, rotor, coil wire, distributor cap, or spark-plug wire. If insulation leakage or breakdown is indicated on all cylinders when each is tested in turn, the trouble will be located in a component or portion of the circuit common to all cylinders. On the other hand if an insulation leakage is indicated for only one or a few cylinders, the fault is probably at the distributor cap or in those particular spark-plug wires.

SECONDARY RESISTANCE

Resistance is a factor present to some degree in every portion of all electrical circuits, and it has a hindering effect on the flow

386

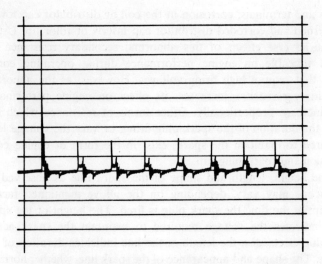

Fig. 12. Insulation break down is illustrated by the lower
extent being shorter than normal.

of electrical current. In ignition system design, some manufacturers specifically build a reasonable amount of resistance into the secondary circuit for the purpose of controlling secondary current flow in an effort to extend spark-plug electrode life. This is also done for the purpose of minimizing any possible interference with radio and television reception. Resistance of this nature is generally referred to as *suppression,* and may be located in any one or a number of places such as in the rotor, the distributor cap, the secondary wires or the spark plug. Suppression resistance, provided it does not exceed the values specified by the ignition system or vehicle manufacturer, has no adverse effects on ignition system performance.

Occasionally suppressors will deteriorate or additional resistance will develop in the secondary circuit due to improperly connected wires and terminals, corrosion in the coil or distributor cap towers or burned and corroded distributor cap inserts or rotor tip. Usually the adverse effects of this abnormal secondary resistance are most noticable on engine performance during operating conditions that require high firing voltages. However, as the abnormal secondary resistance increases, its effect on engine performance will increase proportionally. Other forms of resistance which can vary the duration of the spark plug firing, or vary the voltage level required to maintain the spark, exist in the form of engine compression and spark-plug gap.

The height, length and shape of the spark line as observed on the scope may vary, depending on the above mentioned factors present at the time the spark plug is fired. The height of the spark line indicates the voltage required to maintain the spark across the plug electrodes; the length of the line indicates duration of the spark. The shape and appearance of the spark line, whether horizontal or slanted, smooth or irregular, depend on how much resistance is encountered and how much the resistance value changes during the firing. Fig. 13 represents a scope display of a system which has developed excessive secondary resistance in a portion of the circuit which is common to all cylinders; while Fig. 14 indicates the presence of excessive secondary resistance only in a portion of the system supplying one particular cylinder.

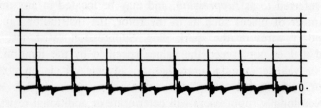

Fig. 13. Illustrating excessive secondary resistance.

The scope display shown in Fig. 15 readily shows the excessive oscillations on the spark lines of all cylinders that are caused by a poor contact between the rotor and the center button of the distributor cap. Note that the spark lines are not extremely high nor do they have a tendency to slant excessively. A similar scope in-

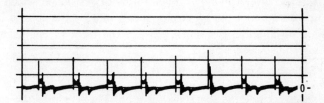

Fig. 14. Illustrating excessive secondary resistance in only a portion of the circuit.

dication can also be attributed to an accumulation of deposits on spark plugs. Fig. 16 shows how the patterns appear when displayed individually.

FOULED SPARK PLUGS

The pattern caused by a fouled spark plug will appear on the scope screen in a manner somewhat similar to that of a pattern

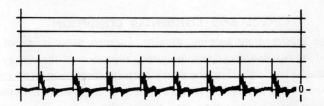

Fig. 15. Illustrating poor contact between distributor tower button and rotor.

indicating excessive resistance. It should be particularly noted that when a fouled plug condition exists, the firing line will usually be slightly lower than the others, and the spark line begins at the top of the firing line and slants downward to the intermediate section. Fig. 17 illustrates how the pattern of a fouled spark plug would appear as viewed in an all-cylinder display or as viewed individually.

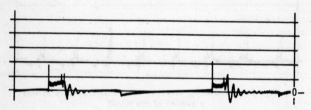

Fig. 16. Illustrating one section of the scope pattern shown in Fig. 15.

GROUNDED SPARK-PLUG WIRE

The pattern illustrated in Fig. 18 denotes a grounded spark-plug wire. Immediately evident are the extremely low firing and spark lines and the extended spark duration. The *firing section* of a pattern indicating a grounded plug wire remains visible because a spark does exist across the rotor gap, even though no spark is established across the electrode gap of the spark plug.

COIL AND CONDENSER CONDITION

The *intermediate section,* usually observed as a series of diminishing oscillations representing the dissipation of the energy remaining in the coil after the spark plug has fired, can very easily be examined when each cylinder's pattern is displayed individually. The number of oscillations that can be observed in the intermediate section depends on a number of factors such as; dwell angle,

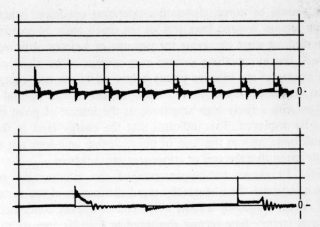

Fig. 17. Illustrating fouled spark plugs.

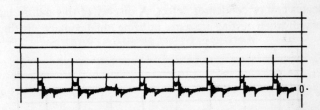

Fig. 18. Illustrating a grounded spark-plug wire.

engine speed, duration of spark, degree of coil saturation, and coil and condenser condition. The *intermediate section* can be analyzed for ignition trouble by noting the rate at which these oscillations diminish. Normally, these oscillations, will diminish gradually; but should the system contain a shorted coil or leaky condenser, these oscillations will diminish to zero rapidly. In such a case, probably only one or two oscillations will be seen at an engine speed of 1500 *rpm* providing the dwell angle and firing section length are normal.

It should be noted, that under operating conditions where the firing section is quite long and/or the dwell angle is greater than specified, or when observing the patterns of a system utilizing dual points, the intermediate section may appear to be shortened by the closing of the breaker points before all of the coil energy has been dissipated. Under these conditions, fewer than normal oscillations with a fairly high amplitude at the instant of point closing may be displayed. This indicates that the energy level in the coil is still quite high at the time of point closing and does not necessarily mean that the coil or condenser are defective.

Fig. 19 shows the appearance of the intermediate section which indicates the abnormally rapid dissipation of the remaining coil energy caused by a short in the coil or a leaky condenser. The normal *intermediate section* displayed in Fig. 20 appears to have fewer than the expected number of oscillations, but by no means indicates coil or condenser defect. A display of this nature may be observed when testing systems utilizing dual-contact distributors,

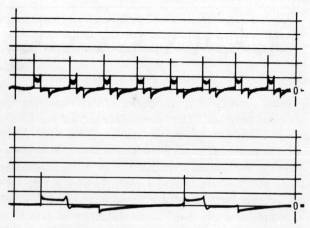

Fig. 19. The intermediate section which indicates a shorted coil or leaky condenser.

when testing at speeds considerably higher than 1500 *rpm,* or when the distributor point dwell setting is much greater than auto manufacturer's specifications.

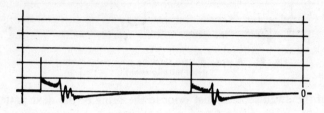

Fig. 20. A typical waveform observed when testing dual ignition systems.

BREAKER POINT ACTION

The *dwell section* begins when the distributor contacts close, and extends to the instant at which the contacts open to fire the next cylinder. In analyzing this section of the pattern, the point-close and the point-open portions should be carefully observed. Normally when the points close, this action is seen as a short downward line followed by a series of diminishing oscillations. Note particularly that the first line's downward extent should be greater than any of the oscillations following. Should it be observed that the first downward line is not as long as one or more of those following, it indicates the condition of poor breaker point contact. On the other hand, should any of the oscillations following the point-close signal rise above the zero line, it can usually be attributed to a point bounce condition.

When the breaker points open, the end of the dwell section should appear as a clean right angle formed by the horizontal dwell line and the vertical firing line of the next pattern. Point arcing upon opening of the breaker points will be seen at the right

393

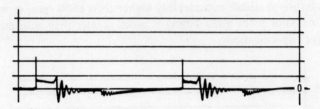

Fig. 21. A scope pattern showing poor point contact or
point misalignment.

end of the dwell section, just prior to the firing of the next pattern. This will appear as a false start to firing, followed a short interval later by the actual firing line. In observing the scope patterns, if a display such as shown in Fig. 21 is observed at the beginning of the *dwell section,* it is an indication of poor point contact or point misalignment. Oscillations extending above the zero line shortly after the points have initially closed, such as shown in Fig. 22, indicate a breaker-point bounce condition, which could be caused by a weak spring.

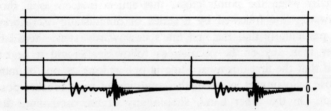

Fig. 22. Indicating contact-point bounce.

Any unusual display noticed at the instant of point opening can be attributed to point arcing caused by dirty or burned points or high condenser series resistance. Fig. 23 is a common scope pattern which indicates breaker-point arcing.

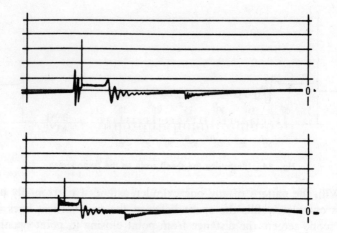

Fig. 23. Indicating contact points arcing.

BREAKER POINT DWELL

Proper distributor point dwell is important to the overall operation and efficiency of the ignition system, in that it should be set to a specific value to assure adequate coil saturation to meet the firing requirements at all engine speeds. Dwell angle can accurately be measured by utilizing the dwell scale located near the bottom of the scope screen. Expanding any one cylinder's pattern until it completely fills the space between the two vertical lines on the screen, then lowering the pattern until it rests on the dwell scale, makes the dwell angle measurable directly from the scale. The dwell scale actually consists of two sets of graduations; the upper one for eight-cylinder engines and the lower one for six-cylinder engines. The dwell angle of four-cylinder engines may also be measured with equal ease by doubling the dwell reading obtained from the eight-cylinder scale.

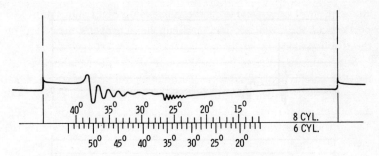

Fig. 24. Illustrating the dwell scale on the scope screen.

With the pattern of any one cylinder extended horizontally until it completely fills the space between the two vertical lines on the scope screen, the distance from point closing to point opening can be measured on the dwell scale. Fig. 24 represents one cylinder's pattern of an eight-cylinder engine indicating a dwell period of 26-1/2 degrees.

DISTRIBUTOR CAM LOBE

The accuracy of the distributor cam determines the ignition timing relationship of all cylinders. Should one or more lobes of the distributor cam become worn or should the distributor shaft be bent, uneven timing of the various cylinders would result. Cam lobe accuracy can be measured on the scope screen by superimposing the patterns of all of the cylinders. This is accomplished by connecting both the trigger and pattern pickups in series between the coil tower and the coil secondary wire with the aid of adaptors. With the pattern shift control in its full clockwise position, the superimposed display is expanded until it completely fills the space between the two vertical lines on the screen and then is lowered to rest on the dwell scale. Any inaccuracies of the cam or distrib-

wear in most cases become more noticeable evident on the scope display when an engine is momentarily loaded by snap acceleration. Under momentary load, the firing voltage of all cylinders should increase in a consistent manner. One type of exception is shown in Fig. 26. The firing voltage of the third pattern in the display has climbed considerably higher than the others, indicating a wide plug gap or badly deteriorated electrodes. The example

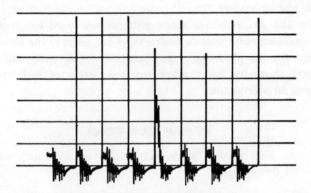

Fig. 27. Scope pattern showing the effect of a fouled plug, flashover, or cracked insulator.

shown in Fig. 27 indicates that the fourth plug in the firing order is failing to fire due to partial fouling or flashover.

It must be kept in mind that the examples of scope indications shown here were selected to best serve the purpose of explaining and understanding scope patterns of secondary waveforms. In scope testing, minor variations of these examples may be observed. Scope patterns indicating certain defects, troubles or malfunctions will vary according to the severity of the trouble present, the speed at which the engine is operating and the specific scope used.

SUMMARY

An oscilloscope provides a convenient means of observing the performance of an ignition system. A scope does this by displaying an easily interpreted graph-like picture of all phases of the ignition cycle at the instant at which they occur in an operating engine. The display picture permits the observer actually to see in detail the results of the many factors which affect the performance of the ignition system.

The test and resultant scope patterns are listed for your general guidance only. Specific instructions are given in the instruction manual for the particular engine analyzer being used. The scope patterns shown in this chapter are those expected to be seen in the general over-all use.

REVIEW QUESTIONS

1. On what portion of the screen do you accurately measure the dwell angle?

2. If the scope display indicates a high firing voltage on one or more cylinders, where would the trouble most likely be?

3. If oscillations are not present in the intermediate section of the waveform, the cause may be where?

4. If the firing lines are uneven, what would you check first?

5. If the scope has an inverted pattern, what would be the cause?

Index

Index

Index

AUDEL BOOKS *practical reading for profit*

Automobile Guide   (60015)

Practical reference for auto mechanics, servicemen, trainees & owners. Explains theory, construction and servicing of modern domestic motor cars. FEATURES: All parts of an automobile—engines—pistons—rings—connecting rods—crankshafts—valves—cams—timing—cooling systems—fuel-feed systems—carburetors—automatic choke—transmissions—clutches—universals—propeller shafts—differentials—rear axles—running gear—brakes—wheel alignment—steering gear—tires—lubrication—ignition systems—generators—starters—lighting systems—storage batteries.

Home Appliance Servicing   (60016)

A practical "How To Do It" book for electric & gas servicemen, mechanics & dealers. Covers principles, servicing and repairing of home appliances. Tells how to locate troubles, make repairs, reassemble and connect, wiring diagrams and testing methods. Tells how to fix electric refrigerators, washers, ranges, toasters, ironers, broilers, dryers, vacuums, fans, and other appliances.

Radiomans Guide   (60017)

A key to the practical understanding of radio. For radio engineers, servicemen, amateurs. FEATURES: Radio fundamentals and Ohm's law—physics of sound as related to radio—radio-wave transmission—electrical measuring instruments—power supply units—resistors, inductors and capacitors—radio transformers—vacuum tubes—radio receivers—speakers—antenna systems—radio testing.

Television Service Manual   (60018)

Now completely updated and revised to include the latest designs and information. Thoroughly covers television with transmitter theory, antenna designs, receiver circuit operation and the picture tube. Provides the practical information necessary for accurate diagnosis and repair of both black-and-white and color television receivers. A MUST BOOK FOR ANYONE IN TELEVISION.

Handy Book of Practical Electricity   (60019)

For maintenance engineers, electricians and all electrical workers. A ready reference book, giving complete instruction and practical information on the rules and laws of electricity—maintenance of electrical machinery—AC and DC motors—wiring diagrams—house lighting—power wiring—meter and instrument connections—bells and signal wiring—motor wiring—transformer connections—fractional-horsepower motors—circuit breakers—relay protection—switchgear—power stations—automatic substations. THE KEY TO A PRACTICAL UNDERSTANDING OF ELECTRICITY.

Truck & Tractor Guide   (60020)

A shop companion for truck mechanics and drivers—shop foremen—garagemen—maintenance men—helpers—owners—troubleshooters—fleet maintenance men—bus mechanics and drivers—farm tractor operators and mechanics. Covers gas and diesel motor principles—construction—operation—maintenance—repair—service operations—troubleshooting—engine tune-up—carburetor adjusting—ignition tuning—brakes—service of all parts.—1001 FACTS AT YOUR FINGER TIPS.

Plumbers and Pipe Fitters Library—3 Vols.   (60021)

New revised edition. A practical illustrated trade assistant and reference for master plumbers, journeyman and apprentice pipe fitters, gas fitters and helpers, builders, contractors, and engineers. Explains in simple language, illustrations, diagrams, charts, graphs and pictures, the principles of modern plumbing and pipe-fitting practices.

Vol. 1—(60064)—Materials, tools, calculations.
Vol. 2—(60065)—Drainage, fittings, fixtures.
Vol. 3—(60066)—Installation, heating, welding.

Painting & Decorating Manual   (60022)

A reliable guide for painters, journeymen, apprentices, contractors, home owners, and all paint users. The book is divided into two sections. Section I contains information on: basic tools and equipment; selection of paint; guide to color; techniques of applying paint with brush, roller and spray gun; wood and floor finishing. Section II provides information about: cost estimate; glossary of terms; a review of the mathematics and information about running a paint business. Profusely illustrated.

Carpenters & Builders Guides—4 Vols.   (60023)

A practical illustrated trade assistant on modern construction for carpenters, builders, and all woodworkers. Explains in practical, concise language and illustrations all the principles, advances and short cuts based on modern practice. How to calculate various jobs.
Vol. 1—(60068)—Tools, steel square, saw filing, joinery, cabinets.
Vol. 2—(60069)—Mathematics, plans, specifications, estimates.
Vol. 3—(60070)—House and roof framing, laying out, foundations.
Vol. 4—(60071)—Doors, windows, stairs, millwork, painting.

Diesel Engine Manual   (60024)

A practical treatise on the theory, operation and maintenance of modern Diesel engines. Explains Diesel principles—valves—timing—fuel pumps—pistons and rings—cylinders—lubrication—cooling system—fuel oil—engine indicator—governors—engine reversing—answers on operation—calculations. AN IMPORTANT GUIDE FOR ENGINEERS, OPERATORS, STUDENTS.

Welders Guide   (60025)

A concise, practical text on operation and maintenance of all welding machines, for all mechanics. Covers electric, oxyacetylene, thermit, unionmelt welding for sheet metal; spot and pipe welds; pressure vessels; aluminum, copper, brass, bronze and other metals; airplane work; surface hardening and hard facing; cutting; brazing; eye protection. EVERY WELDER SHOULD OWN THIS GUIDE.

Mathematics & Calculations for Mechanics   (60026)

Mathematics for home study or shop reference. This work has been arranged as a progressive study, starting with the first principles of arithmetic and advancing step-by-step, through the various phases of mathematics. Thousands of mathematical calculations and tables. New, easy, correct methods covering a complete review of practical arithmetic. Illustrated with examples. A REAL HELP TO ALL MECHANICS.

Wiring Diagrams for Light & Power   (60028)

Brand-new updated edition. Electricians, wiremen, linemen, plant superintendents, construction engineers, electrical contractors and students will find these diagrams a valuable source of practical help. Each diagram is complete and self-explaining. A PRACTICAL HANDY BOOK OF ELECTRICAL HOOK-UPS.

New Electric Library—10 Vols.   (60030)

For engineers, electricians, electrical workers, mechanics and students. Presenting in simple, concise form the fundamental principles, rules and applications of applied electricity. Fully illustrated with diagrams and sketches, also calculations and tables for ready reference. Based on the best knowledge and experience of applied electricity.
Vol. 1—(60031)—Electricity, magnetism, armature winding, repairs.
Vol. 2—(60032)—Dynamos, DC motors, construction, installation, maintenance, troubleshooting.
Vol. 3—(60033)—Electrical testing instruments, storage battery construction and repairs.
Vol. 4—(60034)—Alternating current principles and diagrams, power factor, alternators, transformers.
Vol. 5—(60035)—AC motors, converters, switches, fuses, circuit breakers.
Vol. 6—(60036)—Relays, capacitors, regulators, rectifiers, meters, switchboards, power-station practice.
Vol. 7—(60037)—Wiring, high-tension transmission, plans, calculations.
Vol. 8—(60038)—Railways, signals, elevators.
Vol. 9—(60039)—Radio, telephone, telegraph, television, motion pictures.
Vol. 10—(60040)—Refrigeration, illumination, welding, X-ray, modern electrical appliances.

Answers on Blueprint Reading   (60041)

Covers all types of blueprint reading for mechanics and builders. The man who can read blueprints is in line for a better job. This book gives you this secret language, step by step in easy stages. NO OTHER TRADE BOOK LIKE IT.

Masons & Builders Guides—4 Vols.   (60042)

A practical illustrated trade assistant on modern construction for bricklayers, stone masons, cement workers, plasterers, and tile setters. Explains in clear language and with detailed illustrations all the principles, advances and short cuts based on modern practice—including how to figure and calculate various jobs.

Vol. 1—(60072)—Brick work, bricklaying, bonding, designs.
Vol. 2—(60073)—Brick foundations, arches, tile setting, estimates.
Vol. 3—(60074)—Concrete mixing, placing forms, reinforced stucco.
Vol. 4—(60075)—Plastering, stone masonry, steel construction, blueprints.

Oil Burner Guide   (60044)

A practical, concise treatise explaining in detail both domestic and industrial oil burners, including electrical hook-ups and wiring diagrams. Fully covering the theory, construction, installation, operation, testing, servicing and repair of all oil-burner equipment. Fully indexed for quick reference.

Sheet Metal Pattern Layouts   (60045)

A practical illustrated encyclopedia covering all phases of sheet-metal work including pattern cutting, pattern development and shop procedure. Developed by experts for sheet-metal workers, layout men, mechanics and artisans, apprentices, and students. A MASTER BOOK FOR ALL THE SHEET METAL TRADES.

Sheet Metal Workers Handy Book   (60046)

Containing practical information and important facts and figures. Easy to understand. Fundamentals of sheet metal layout work. Clearly written in everyday language. Ready reference index.

Questions & Answers for Electricians Examinations   (60049)

A practical book to help you prepare for all grades of electricians' license examinations. A helpful review of all the fundamental principles underlying each question and answer needed to prepare you to solve any new or similar problem. Covers the National Electrical Code; questions and answers for license tests; Ohm's law with applied examples; hook-ups for motors; lighting and instruments. A COMPLETE REVIEW FOR ALL ELECTRICAL WORKERS.

Electrical Power Calculations   (60050)

275 TYPICAL PROBLEMS WORKED OUT. Presents and explains the mathematical formulas and the fundamental electrical laws for all the everday, practical problems in both AC and DC electricity. EVERY ELECTRICAL WORKER AND STUDENT NEEDS THIS MODERN MATHEMATICAL TOOL.

New Electric Science Dictionary   (60051)

For every worker who has anything to do with electricity. The language of your profession in convenient, alphabetical order so you can instantly locate any word, phrase or term. To be an expert in any line you must talk the language. This new dictionary enables you to understand and explain electrical problems so you can be thoroughly understood. AN ABSOLUTE NECESSITY TO EVERY ELECTRICAL WORKER AND STUDENT.

Power Plant Engineers Guide   (60052)

A complete steam-engineer's library in one book, with questions and answers. For all Engineers, Firemen, Water Tenders, Oilers, Operators, Repairmen and Applicants for Engineers' License Examinations. 1001 FACTS AND FIGURES AT YOUR FINGER TIPS.

Questions & Answers for Engineers and Firemans Examinations (60053)

An aid for stationary, marine, Diesel & hoisting engineers' examinations for all grades of licenses. A new concise review explaining in detail the principles, facts and figures of practical engineering. Questions & answers.

Pumps, Hydraulics, Air Compressors (60054)

A comprehensive guide for engineers, operators, mechanics, students. Question and answer form. Practical information covering: power & air pumps—condensers—calculations—cooling ponds and towers—water supply—hydraulic rams—dredges—hydraulic drives—machine-tool power—accumulators—elevators—airplane control—presses—turbines—compressor classification —inter and after coolers—regulating devices—installation—lubrication—operation—maintenance—pneumatic hand tools.

House Heating Guide (60055)

For heating, ventilating and air-conditioning engineers, plumbers, maintenance men, contractors, building superintendents and mechanics seeking practical, authentic information on heating, ventilating, air conditioning. This comprehensive reference book gives answers to 1001 questions.

Millwrights & Mechanics Guide (60056)

Practical information on plant installation, operation, and maintenance. For millwrights, mechanics, erecting maintenance men, riggers, shopmen, servicemen, foremen, inspectors, superintendents.

Do-It-Yourself Encyclopedia—2 Vols. (60057)

An all-in-one home repair and project guide for all do-it-yourselfers. Packed with step-by-step plans, thousands of photos, helpful charts. A really authentic, truly monumental, home-repair and home-project guide.

Water Supply & Sewage Disposal Guide (60059)

Fully illustrated with detailed data on every phase of rural water-supply, septic-tank, and sewage systems. A MUST BOOK for plumbers, well drillers, home owners and farmers located outside of municipal water and sanitary service areas.

Gas Engine Manual (60061)

A completely practical book covering the construction, operation and repair of all types of modern gas engines. Part I covers gas-engine principles; engine parts; auxiliaries; timing methods; ignition systems. Part II covers troubleshooting, adjustment and repairs.

Outboard Motor & Boating Guide (60062)

An essential tool for every outboard boating operator. Provides all the information needed to maintain, adjust and repair all types of outboard motors. Gives exploded views of the various parts assemblies, with relative position of each component.

Foreign Auto Repair Manual (60078)

Contains complete, service and repair data for the most popular imported makes, including Fiat, Hillman Minx, M.G., Opel, Peugot, Renault, SAAB, Simca, Volkswagen, and Volvo. Introductory chapters provide complete data on operation and maintenance of fuel and ignition systems.

Home Workshop & Tool Handy Book (60087)

The most modern, up-to-date manual ever designed for home craftsmen and do-it-yourselfers. Tells how to set up your own home workshop (basement, garage, or spare room), all about the various hand and power tools (when, where, and how to use them, etc.). Covers both wood-and metal-working principles and practices. An all-in-one workshop guide for handymen, professionals and students.

Home Modernizing & Repair Guide   (60097)

FOR THE "DO-IT-YOURSELFER" WHO LIKES TO DO MOST OF HIS HOME UPKEEP JOBS HIMSELF. Here is a practical guide that presents step-by-step instructions, photos, drawings, and other details for many typical home handyman jobs. Explains what tools are needed, how to use them, and includes tips for doing a really professional job.

Practical Guide to Mechanics   (60102)

A convenient reference book valuable for its practical and concise explanations of the applicable laws of physics. Presents all the basics of mechanics in everyday language, illustrated with practical examples of their applications in various fields.

Auto Engine Tune-Up   (60103)

A practical guide to the adjustment of modern autos. Comprehensive and fully illustrated instructions on how to keep your car in top-notch running condition. Covers ignition, valve, cooling, carburetion, and electrical systems on modern auto engines. Includes the use of tune-up test equipment.

Gas Appliances and Heating   (60104)

A reliable guide to acquaint repairmen and home owners with the construction, operation, and servicing of modern gas-fired appliances such as may be found in the average home.

Architects & Builders Guide   (60105)

A valuable reference for the architect, builder, and home owner. Explains the effects of natural phenomena such as wind, fire, sound, water, and lightning on all types of buildings. Tells how to minimize their destructive effects and take advantage of their beneficial effects.

Machinists Library   (60109)

Covers modern machine-shop practice. Tells how to set up and operate lathes, screw and milling machines, shapers, drill presses and all other machine tools. A complete reference library. A SHOP COMPANION THAT ANSWERS YOUR QUESTIONS.
Vol. 1—(60106)—Basic Machine Shop Practices.
Vol. 2—(60107)—Machine Shop.
Vol. 3—(60108)—Toolmakers Handy Book.

Practical Mathematics for Everyone— 2 Vols.   (60112)

A concise and reliable guide to the understanding of practical mathematics. People from all walks of life, young and old alike, will find the information contained in these two books just what they have been looking for. The mathematics discussed is for the everyday problems that arise in every household and business.
Vol. 1—(60110)—Basic Mathematics.
Vol. 2—(60111)—Financial Mathematics.

Handbook of Commercial Sound Installations   (60126)

A practical complete guide to planning commercial systems, selecting the most suitable equipment, and following through with the most proficient servicing methods. For technicians and the professional and businessman interested in installing a sound system.

Practical Guide to Tape Recorders   (60127)

Comprehensive guide to tape recorders, covering the history, operation, construction, and maintenance. Service technicians, hobbyists, and even professional recordists can perform their job or pursue their hobby better if they understand the principles of tape recorders.

Practical Guide to Citizens Band Radio   (60130)

Covers how to select, install, operate, maintain, and adjust all types of CB equipment. Also describes the latest equipment and FCC regulations. For everyone who now uses or plans to use a CB unit, as well as those who install and service such gear.

Practical Electronics Projects for the Beginner   (60131)

This book can be your first venture in electronics. Clear, concise text plus hundreds of illustrations tell you all you need to know to build numerous functioning projects. HAVE FUN WHILE LEARNING ELECTRONICS FUNDAMENTALS—no previous knowledge necessary.

Practical Guide to Servicing Electronic Organs   (60132)

Detailed, illustrated discussions of the operation and servicing of electronic organs. Including models by Allen, Baldwin, Conn, Hammond, Kinsman, Lowrey, Magnavox, Thomas, and Wurlitzer.

Home Refrigeration and Air Conditioning   (60133)

NEW AND UP-TO-DATE. Covers basic principles, servicing, operation, and repair of modern household refrigerators and air conditioners. Automobile air conditioners are also included. Troubleshooting charts aid in trouble diagnosis. **A gold mine of essential facts for engineers, servicemen, and users.**

Practical Guide to Fluid Power   (60136)

An essential book for the owner, operator, supervisor, or maintenance man concerned with hydraulic or pneumatic equipment. A complete coverage of modern design, application, and repair of fluid power devices. Fully illustrated.

Building Maintenance   (60140)

A comprehensive book on the practical aspects of building maintenance. Chapters are included on: painting and decorating; plumbing and pipe fitting; carpentry; calking and glazing; concrete and masonry; roofing; sheet metal; electrical maintenance; air conditioning and refrigeration; insect and rodent control; heating; maintenance management; custodial practices: A MUST BOOK FOR BUILDING OWNERS, MANAGERS, AND MAINTENANCE PERSONNEL.

Practical Science Projects in Electricity/Electronics   (60141)

An ideal collection of projects in electricity and electronics for the beginner. Practical projects constructed on pegboard with simple easily obtained parts make basic electronic principles fun to learn. Young and old alike will find this book the answer to their search for knowledge.

Carpentry and Building   (60142)

Answers to the problems encountered in today's building trades. The actual questions asked of an architect by carpenters and builders are answered in this book. No apprentice or journeyman carpenter should be without the help this book can offer.

Commercial Refrigeration   (60145)

Installation, operation, and repair of commercial refrigeration systems. Included are ice-making plants, locker plants, grocery and supermarket refrigerated display cases, etc. Trouble charts aid in the diagnosis and repair of defective systems.

Guide to the National Electrical Code   (60149)

An interpretation and simplification of the rulings contained in the National Electrical Code. Electrical contractors, wiremen, and electricians will find this book invaluable for a more complete understanding of the National Electrical Code. Illustrated.

Electric Motors   (60150)

New revised edition. Covers the construction, theory of operation, connection, control, maintenance, and troubleshooting of all types of electric motors. A handy guide for electricians and all electrical workers.

TO ORDER AUDEL BOOKS mail this handy form to
Theo. Audel & Co., 4300 W. 62nd
Indianapolis, Indiana 46206

Please send me for FREE EXAMINATION books marked (x) below. If I decide to keep them I agree to mail $3 in 7 days on each book or set ordered and further mail $3 monthly on each book or set until I have paid price plus shipping charges. Otherwise, I will return them.

☐ (60041) Answers on Blueprint Reading........$ 5.25	☐ (60030) New Electric Library (10 Vols.).......$35.00
☐ (60105) Architects and Builders Guide........ 4.95	☐———Single volumes sold separately..ea. 4.00
☐ (60103) Auto Engine Tune-Up................ 5.95	☐ (60051) New Electric Science Dictionary....... 3.50
☐ (60015) Automobile Guide 7.95	☐ (60044) Oil Burner Guide.................... 4.50
☐ (60140) Building Maintenance............... 5.50	☐ (60062) Outboard Motor & Boating Guide...... 4.95
☐ (60023) Carpenters & Builders Guides (4 Vols.) 16.95	☐ (60022) Painting & Decorating Manual........ 5.50
☐———Single volumes sold separately..ea. 4.95	☐ (60021) Plumbers & Pipe Fitters Library (3 Vols.) 12.50
☐ (60142) Carpentry and Building.............. 5.95	☐———Single volumes sold separately..ea. 4.50
☐ (60145) Commercial Refrigeration........... 5.95	☐ (60052) Power Plant Engineers Guide.......... 7.50
☐ (60024) Diesel Engine Manual................ 6.95	☐ (60098) Practical Chemistry for Everyone..... 5.95
☐ (60057) Do-It-Yourself Encyclopedia (2 Vols.).. 8.95	☐ (60131) Practical Electronics Projects
☐ (60077) Domestic Compact Auto Repair Manual 5.95	for the Beginner........................ 4.95
☐ (60050) Electrical Power Calculations........ 4.50	☐ (60130) Practical Guide to Citizens Band Radio. 4.95
☐ (60150) Electric Motors..................... 5.95	☐ (60136) Practical Guide to Fluid Power........ 6.95
☐ (60063) Encyclopedia of Space Science (4 Vols.) 19.95	☐ (60102) Practical Guide to Mechanics........ 4.95
☐ (60078) Foreign Auto Repair Manual.......... 5.95	☐ (60132) Practical Guide to Servicing
☐ (60104) Gas Appliances and Heating.......... 4.25	Electronic Organs 4.95
☐ (60061) Gas Engine Manual.................. 4.50	☐ (60127) Practical Guide to Tape Recorders.... 4.95
☐ (60149) Guide to the National Electrical Code.. 6.95	☐ (60112) Practical Mathematics for Everyone
☐ (60126) Handbook of Commercial Sound	(2 Vols.) 8.95
Installations 5.95	☐———Single volumes sold separately..ea. 4.95
☐ (60019) Handy Book of Practical Electricity.... 6.95	☐ (60141) Practical Science Projects in
☐ (60016) Home Appliance Servicing........... 6.95	Electricity/Electronics 4.95
☐ (60097) Home Modernizing & Repair Guide..... 3.95	☐ (60086) Programmed Basic Electricity Course... 4.95
☐ (60133) Home Refrigeration and Air	☐ (60054) Pumps, Hydraulics, Air Compressors... 7.95
Conditioning 6.95	☐ (60049) Questions & Answers for Electricians
☐ (60087) Home Workshop & Tool Handy Book.... 5.00	Examinations 3.95
☐ (60055) House Heating Guide................. 6.95	☐ (60053) Questions & Answers for Engineers &
☐ (60019) Machinist Library (3 Vols.)............ 15.50	Firemans Examinations 4.95
☐———Volume 1 sold separately......ea. 5.50	☐ (60017) Radiomans Guide 5.50
☐———Volume 2 sold separately......ea. 5.95	☐ (60045) Sheet Metal Pattern Layouts.......... 11.95
☐———Volume 3 sold separately......ea. 5.50	☐ (60046) Sheet Metal Workers Handy Book...... 4.50
☐ (60042) Masons & Builders Guides (4 Vols.).... 14.95	☐ (60018) Television Service Manual............ 5.95
☐———Single volumes sold separately..ea. 4.00	☐ (60020) Truck & Tractor Guide............... 6.95
☐ (60026) Mathematics & Calculations for	☐ (60059) Water Supply & Sewage Disposal Guide 4.50
Mechanics 5.50	☐ (60025) Welders Guide 5.50
☐ (60056) Millwrights & Mechanics Guide....... 7.95	☐ (60028) Wiring Diagrams for Light & Power.... 4.50

Name_____

Address_____

City_____State_____Zip_____

Occupation_____Employed by_____

☐ **SAVE SHIPPING CHARGES! Enclose Full Payment With Coupon and We Pay Shipping Charges.**

PRINTED IN USA